Reading Essentials *for* New York Science

An Interactive Student Textbook

Grade 8

Mc
Graw
Hill
Education

Glencoe Science

To the Student

In today's world, knowing science is important for thinking critically, solving problems, and making decisions. But understanding science sometimes can be a challenge.

Reading Essentials takes the stress out of reading, learning, and understanding science. This book covers important concepts in science, offers ideas for how to learn the information, and helps you review what you have learned.

In each chapter:

- **Before You Read** sparks your interest in what you'll learn and relates it to your world.
- **Read to Learn** describes important science concepts with words and graphics. Next to the text you can find a variety of study tips and ideas for organizing and learning information:
  - The **Study Coach** offers tips for getting the main ideas out of the text.
  - **Foldables™ Study Organizers** help you divide the information into smaller, easier-to-remember concepts.
  - **Reading Checks** ask questions about key concepts. The questions are placed so you know whether you understand the material.
  - **Think It Over** elements help you consider the material in-depth, giving you an opportunity to use your critical-thinking skills.
  - **Picture This** questions specifically relate to the art and graphics used with the text. You'll find questions to get you actively involved in illustrating the concepts you read about.
  - **Applying Math** reinforces the connection between math and science.
- Use **After You Read** to review key terms and answer questions about what you have learned. The **Mini Glossary** can assist you with science vocabulary. Review questions focus on the key concepts to help you evaluate your learning.

See for yourself. *Reading Essentials* makes science easy to understand and enjoyable.

MHEonline.com

Cover: (t)Songquan Deng/iStock/360/Getty Images, (bl)DK Limited/Corbis, (bl)Larry West/Photo Researchers, (br)James Randklev/Corbis

Mc Graw Hill Education

Send all inquiries to:
McGraw-Hill Education
8787 Orion Place
Columbus, OH 43240

ISBN: 978-0-07-877883-4
MHID: 0-07-877883-2

Printed in the United States of America.

9 10 11 12 13 14 QVS 19 18 17 16 15

Table of Contents

chapter 1

The Nature of Science

section ❶ What is science?

 AID M3.1a: Use appropriate scientific tools to solve problems about the natural world. **ED T1.1a:** Identify a scientific or human need that is subject to a technological solution which applies scientific principles. **Also covered:** AID S1.1a, S1.3, S2.1d, IPS 1.1

● Before You Read

How do you find answers to questions about what is happening around you?

_____

_____

_____

_____

What You'll Learn

■ how science is part of everyday life
■ skills and tools used in science

● Read to Learn

Science in Society

What do you think of when you hear the word *science*? Do you think only about your science class or your science book? Is there any connection between what you learn in science class and the rest of your life? Perhaps you have problems to solve or questions to answer. <u>Science</u> is a way or a process used to investigate what is happening around you. It can give you possible answers to your questions.

When did people first use science?

People have always tried to find answers to questions about what was happening around them. Early scientists tried to explain things based on what they observed using their senses—sight, touch, smell, taste, and hearing. But, using only your senses can be misleading. How heavy is heavy? What is cold or hot?

Today, scientists use numbers to describe observations. Tools, such as thermometers, add numbers to descriptions. Like scientists, you can observe, investigate, and experiment to find answers.

Study Coach

Ask Questions Read each subhead. Then work with a partner to write questions about the information in each subhead. Take turns asking and answering the questions. Use the questions as a study guide.

FOLDABLES™

Ⓐ **Describe** Make a two-tab book, as shown below. Use the Foldable to describe tools scientists use and skills they develop.

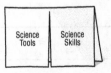

Science Tools | Science Skills

Using Science Every Day

You use science in different ways. When you are doing research for your history class, for example, you are using science. In fact, you can use scientific thinking every day to make decisions. Think about the decisions that the people in the photos below have to make. How are these similar to the types of decisions that you have to make?

KS Studios   Stephen Webster

What clues do scientists use?

When you have a project to do for history class, you have a problem to solve. You look for clues to find the answers to the questions in your history project. You use several skills and tools to find the clues.

Using Prior Knowledge

Scientists use prior experience to predict what will occur in investigations. They test their predictions. Scientists then form theories when their predictions have been well tested. A theory is an explanation that is supported by facts. Scientists also form laws. These are rules that describe a pattern in nature, like gravity. ☑

Using Science and Technology

To get information, you need a variety of resource materials. You can use the computer to find books, magazines, newspapers, videos, and web pages that have the necessary information.

1. Identify three decisions you have made in the past 24 hours.

_____

_____

_____

2. Explain What is a theory?

_____

_____

_____

What is technology?

Modern scientists use the computer to find and analyze data. The computer is a kind of technology. **Technology** is the application of science to make products or tools that people can use. ☑

What skills do scientists use?

Scientists use skills such as observing, classifying, and interpreting data. You use these skills when you solve problems or run experiments.

Why are observation and measurement skills important?

Observing and measuring are important skills, particularly for scientists. Observation sometimes does not give a complete picture of what is happening. In addition to observation, it is important to take accurate measurements to be sure that your data are useful.

Communication in Science

After scientists get the results of their observations, experiments, and investigations, they use several methods to share their observations with others. Results and conclusions of experiments often are reported in the many scientific journals or magazines that are published each year.

What is the purpose of a science journal?

Keeping a science journal is another way of communicating scientific data and results. A journal can be used to record observations and the step-by-step procedures that were followed. The journal can be used to list the materials and equipment that were used. It can include the results of an investigation.

Your journal, like the one to the right, should include mathematical measurements or formulas that were used to analyze the data. Include any problems that happened during the investigation. You might summarize the data in a paragraph or by using tables, charts, or graphs.

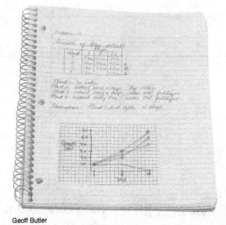
Geoff Butler

Reading Check

3. Describe How do scientists use computers in their work?

_____

_____

_____

Picture This

4. Explain one way you might use a science journal.

_____

_____

_____

● After You Read
Mini Glossary

science: a way or a process used to investigate what is happening around you

technology: the application of science to make products or tools that people can use

1. Review the terms and their definitions in the Mini Glossary. Write a sentence that describes a way scientists use technology in their work.

_____

_____

_____

2. Complete the diagram by listing the skills that scientists need to do their work.

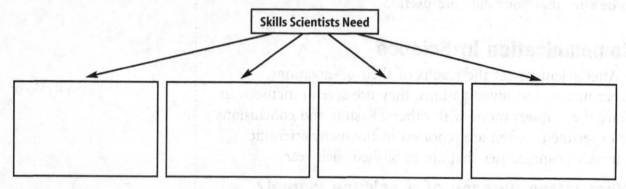

Skills Scientists Need

3. How did asking and answering questions help you remember what you have learned about science?

_____

_____

_____

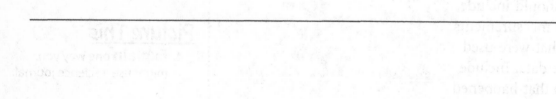
Science Online Visit **glencoe.com** to access your textbook, interactive games, and projects to help you learn more about what science is.

section ② Doing Science

AID S1.2b Propose a model of a natural phenomenon. **S2.2b** Design scientific investigations. **ICT 2.2** Use models to study processes that cannot be studied directly. **Also covered:** AID S1.1c, S2.1d, S2.2a, S2.2b, S2.2c, S2.2d, S2.2e, S2.3c, S3.1a, S3.2a, S3.2b, S3.2d

● Before You Read

You need your science book to complete an assignment that is due tomorrow, but you left your book at school. How would you solve this problem?

_____

_____

_____

What You'll Learn

- the steps used to solve a problem in a scientific way
- how a well-designed investigation is developed

● Read to Learn

Solving Problems

You know there is more than one way to solve a problem. This also is true of scientific problems. Every day, scientists work to solve scientific problems. The types of problems are different and require different kinds of investigations. However, scientists use some steps in all investigations.

What is the first step in an investigation?

The first thing scientists do is identify the problem. They have to make sure that everyone working to solve the problem has a clear understanding of the problem. Sometimes one problem must be solved before another one can be addressed. For example, a scientist cannot find a cure for a disease until the source of the disease is known. The first problem, finding the source of the disease, must be answered before the second problem can be investigated.

How can the problem be solved?

Scientific problems can be solved in different ways. Two ways are descriptive research and experimental research design. **Descriptive research** answers scientific questions through observation.

▸ **Mark the Text**

Identify the Main Idea
Underline the main idea in each paragraph. Review these ideas when you have finished reading the section.

FOLDABLES

B Define Make a vocabulary book as shown below. Use the Foldable to record the vocabulary words in this section and their definitions.

Experimental research design is used to answer scientific questions by testing a hypothesis through the use of a series of carefully controlled steps. Scientific methods are ways, or steps to follow, to try to solve problems. Different problems will require different scientific methods to solve them. The figure below shows one way to use scientific methods.

1. List What steps must be completed before a scientist draws a conclusion?

_____

_____

_____

_____

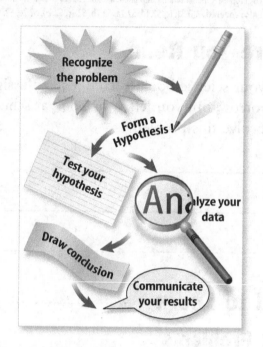

Recognize the problem

Form a Hypothesis !

Test your hypothesis

Analyze your data

Draw conclusion

Communicate your results

Descriptive Research

Scientists solve some problems by using descriptive research. Descriptive research is based mostly on observations. Scientists use this method when it would be impossible to run experiments. Descriptive research involves several steps.

Research objective The first step in descriptive research is stating the research objective. A research objective is what you want to find out.

Research design A research design does several things. It tells how the investigation will be carried out. It tells what steps will be used and how the data will be recorded and analyzed. An important part of any research design is safety.

Bias When scientists expect a certain result in an investigation, this is known as bias. A good investigation avoids bias. One way to avoid bias is by using careful numerical measurements for all data. Bias also can happen in surveys or groups that are chosen for investigation. To get an accurate result, you need to use a random sample. ☑

✔ **Reading Check**

2. Explain one way that an experiment can be biased.

_____

_____

_____

Equipment, Materials, and Models

When you use descriptive research, the equipment and materials you use are important.

How do scientists select their materials?

Scientists try to use the most up-to-date materials. You should use equipment such as balances, spring scales, microscopes, and metric measurements when performing investigations. Calculators and computers can be used to evaluate and display data. You do not need the latest or most expensive material to run successful investigations.

Your investigations can be completed successfully and the data displayed with materials found in your home or classroom. Items such as paper, colored pencils, and markers can be used to create effective displays. Good organization of information, such as the display below, is important.

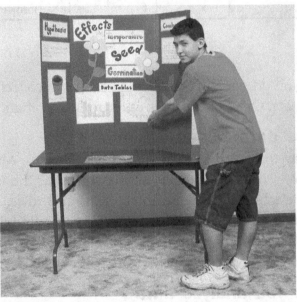

Aaron Haupt

Why do scientists use models?

Sometimes models are used to carry out investigations. In science, a **model** represents things that happen too slowly, too quickly, or are too big or too small to observe directly. Models are also used when direct observation would be too dangerous or too expensive. Tables, graphs, and spreadsheets are examples of models. Computers can make three-dimensional models of things such as a bacterium. Models save time and money because they test ideas that might otherwise be too small, too large, or take too long to build. ✔

Copyright © Glencoe/McGraw-Hill, a division of The McGraw-Hill Companies, Inc.

💡 **Think it Over**

3. Draw Conclusions
Why is up-to-date material important to scientists?

_____

_____

_____

✔ **Reading Check**

4. Identify two reasons scientists use models.

_____

_____

_____

_____

C **Identify** Make a three-tab concept map book on notebook paper, as shown below. Write descriptions of three forms of scientific measurements.

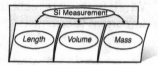

5. **Calculate** Use the table at the right to calculate the number of milligrams in three kilograms.

_____

_____

_____

What is scientific measurement?

Scientists around the world use a system of measurement called the International System of Units, or SI, to make observations. By using the same system, they can understand each other's research and compare results. The table below shows some common SI measurements.

Common SI Measurements			
Measurement	**Unit**	**Symbol**	**Equal to**
Length	1 millimeter	mm	0.001 (1/1,000) m
	1 centimeter	cm	0.01 (1/100) m
	1 meter	m	100 cm
	1 kilometer	km	1,000 m
Liquid volume	1 milliliter	mL	0.001 L
	1 liter	L	1,000 mL
Mass	1 milligram	mg	0.001 g
	1 gram	g	1,000 mg
	1 kilogram	kg	1,000 g
	1 tonne	t	1,000 kg = 1 metric ton

Data

When you do scientific research, you have to collect and organize data. Organized data is easier to interpret and analyze.

How are data tables designed?

One way to record results is to use data tables. Most tables have a title that quickly shows you what the table is about. The table is divided into columns and rows. These are usually trials or characteristics to be compared. You can set up your data tables before beginning the experiment. Then you will have a place to record your data.

How do you analyze data?

Once you finish your investigation, you have to determine what your results mean. You have to review all of the recorded observations and measurements. Charts and graphs are excellent ways to organize data.

Draw Conclusions

After your data is organized, you are ready to draw a conclusion. You have to decide if the data answered your question and if your prediction was correct. Your experiment can still be successful even if it does not come out the way you originally predicted.

How are results communicated?

Analyzing data and drawing conclusions make up the end of an investigation. However, most scientists do not stop there. They usually share their results. They might share with other scientists, government agencies, or the public. They write reports that show how their experiments were run, the data they obtained, and the conclusions they drew. Scientists usually publish their most important findings.

You also have the chance to communicate the data you obtain from your investigations to members of your class. You can give an oral presentation, display the results on a bulletin board, or make a poster. You can share charts, tables, and graphs that show your data. Analyzing and sharing data are important parts of descriptive and experimental research. ☑

Experimental Research Design

Another way to solve scientific problems is through experimentation. Experimental research design answers scientific questions by observing a controlled situation. The design includes several steps.

How do you form a hypothesis?

A **hypothesis** (hi PAH thuh sus) is a prediction, or statement, that can be tested. To form a hypothesis, you use your prior knowledge, new information, and any previous observations.

What are variables?

In a planned experiment, one factor, or variable, is changed at a time. This means that the variable is controlled. The variable that is changed is called the **independent variable.** Suppose an experiment is testing the effect of two different antibiotics on the growth of bacteria. The type of antibiotic is the independent variable. A **dependent variable** is the factor being measured. In this experiment, the dependent variable is the growth of bacteria. ☑

To test which antibiotic works best, you have to make sure that every variable is the same except for the type of antibiotic. The variables that stay the same are called **constants.** For example, you should not run the experiments at two different temperatures, for different lengths of time, or with different amounts of antibiotics.

✔ **Reading Check**

6. Conclude How can you share the results of your investigations with your classmates?

_____

_____

_____

_____

✔ **Reading Check**

7. Explain What is the dependent variable in an experiment?

_____

_____

_____

To have a valid experiment, you have to use controls. A **control** is a sample that is treated like the other experimental groups except that the independent variable is not applied to it. In the experiment with antibiotics, the control is a sample of bacteria that is not treated with either antibiotic. The control shows how bacteria grow when they are not treated by an antibiotic. ☑

After you have formed your hypothesis and planned your experiment, you must give a copy of it to your teacher. This is a good way to find out if there are any problems with the setup of your experiment.

Once you start the experiment, you have to carry it out as planned. If you change or skip steps in the middle of the experiment, you will have to start the experiment again. You should record your observations and finish your data tables in a timely manner to ensure accuracy.

Should experiments be repeated?

To make sure that the results of the experiment are valid, you have to do the experiment several times. The more trials you do using the same methods, the more likely it is that your results will be reliable. How many trials you do will depend on how much time, space, and material you have to complete the experiment.

How are results analyzed?

After you complete your experiment and get your data, you should analyze the results. You should see if your data support your hypothesis. Even if your data do not support your hypothesis, the experiment can still provide useful information. Maybe your hypothesis needs to be revised. Or maybe the experiment needs to be run in a different way.

After you analyze the results, you can communicate them to your teacher, as shown here, and your class. By sharing your results, you might get new ideas from other students for improving your research. Your results may contain information that will help other students.

John Evans

---

8. Identify What is a control?

_____

_____

_____

💡 **Think it Over**

9. Draw Conclusions Why do you think that an experiment that is run several times is more reliable than one that is run only once?

_____

_____

_____

● After You Read

Mini Glossary

constant: variable that stays the same in an experiment

control: a sample that is treated like the other experimental groups except that the independent variable is not applied to it

dependent variable: the factor being measured in an experiment

descriptive research: type of research design that answers scientific questions through observation

experimental research design: type of research design used to answer scientific questions by testing a hypothesis through the use of a series of carefully controlled steps

hypothesis: a prediction, or statement, that can be tested

independent variable: the variable that is changed in an experiment

model: a representation of things that happen too slowly, too quickly, or are too big or too small to observe directly

scientific methods: steps to follow to try to solve problems

1. Review the terms and their definitions in the Mini Glossary. Write a sentence that compares descriptive research and experimental research design.

   _____

   _____

   _____

2. Imagine that you want to find out whether plants grow better in red or blue light. Decide how you will set up the experiment. Identify the constants. Identify the dependent variable, the independent variable, and the control. Present the information in a summary paragraph.

   _____

   _____

   _____

   _____

   _____

 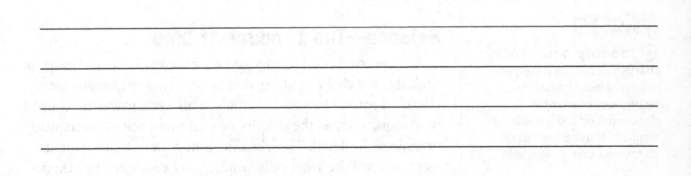 Visit **glencoe.com** to access your textbook, interactive games, and projects to help you learn more about doing scientific research.

 End of Section

The Nature of Science

section ❸ Science and Technology

 IS 3.2 Describe applications of information technology in mathematics, science, and other technologies that address needs and solve problems in the community.
Also covered: AID M3.1a, IPS 1.3

What You'll Learn

- how science and technology influence your life
- how modern technology allows scientific discoveries to be communicated worldwide

---

Study Coach

Create an Outline On a separate sheet of paper, write an outline that includes the main headings and supporting details about the headings.

FOLDABLES

ⓓ Identify Make a folded chart on notebook paper, as shown below. List advances in technology or scientific discoveries on the left side and results of those advances or discoveries on the right side.

● Before You Read

Name three scientific discoveries that affect your life every day.

_____

_____

_____

● Read to Learn

Scientific Discoveries

Science influences your life in many ways. For example, new discoveries have led to new technologies such as DVDs.

How are technological advances helpful?

Technology helps to make your life more convenient. Foods can be prepared quickly in microwave ovens. A satellite tracking system in a car can give you directions to places in an unfamiliar city.

Science—The Product of Many

As new scientific knowledge becomes available, old ways of thinking are challenged. At one time, living organisms were classified into plants and animals. This system was used until new tools, such as the microscope, allowed scientists to study organisms in detail. The classification system that scientists use today will be used only until a new discovery lets them look at information in a different way.

Who practices science?

Scientific discoveries have been made by both men and women and by people of all races, cultures, and time periods. In fact, even students have made scientific discoveries.

How is scientific information used?

People use new information that science provides to make decisions. A new drug can help cure a disease. A new way might be developed to make electricity. However, science cannot decide whether the new information is good or bad. People have to decide whether the new information is used to help or harm the world and its people. With the use of the Internet, new information and technology can be shared quickly by people in all countries. However, any information received from the Internet must be checked for accuracy.

Looking to the Future

Today, scientists use cellular phones and computers to communicate with one another. This **information technology** has led to information being distributed worldwide. ☑

©Klaus Tiedge/Blend Images LLC

💡 Think it Over

1. **Explain** Name one way that science can be used to help people and one way it can be used to harm people.

_____

_____

_____

_____

☑ Reading Check

2. **Identify** two information technology tools that scientists use to communicate with one another.

_____

_____

_____

● After You Read

Mini Glossary

information technology: technology such as computers used for communication

1. Review the term and its definition in the Mini Glossary. Write a sentence explaining how you use information technology.

_____

_____

_____

2. Choose one of the question headings in the Read to Learn section. Write the question in the space below. Then write your answer to that question on the lines that follow.

Write your question here.

_____

_____

_____

3. Describe a problem in the world today that science could help solve.

_____

_____

_____

End of Section

Science online Visit **glencoe.com** to access your textbook, interactive games, and projects to help you learn more about science and technology.

Cell Reproduction

section ❶ Cell Division and Mitosis

 **LE 2.1d** In asexual reproduction, all the genes come from a single parent. Asexually produced offspring are genetically identical to the parent.
Also covered: LE 1.1b, 4.1b, 4.4b

● Before You Read

List five living things on the lines below. Then write one thing that these items have in common with each other and with you.

_____

_____

_____

What You'll Learn

- why mitosis is important
- the steps of mitosis
- the similarities and differences between mitosis in plant and animal cells
- examples of asexual reproduction

● Read to Learn

Why is cell division important?

All living things are made up of cells. Many organisms start as one cell. The cell divides and becomes two cells, two cells become four, four become eight, and so on. Through the process of cell division, the organism grows.

Cell division is still important after an organism stops growing. For example, every day billions of your red blood cells wear out and are replaced through cell division. During the time it takes you to read this sentence, your bone marrow produced about six million red blood cells.

Cell division is the way a one-celled organism makes another organism of its kind. When a one-celled organism reaches a certain size, it reproduces by dividing into two cells.

The Cell Cycle

Every living organism has a life cycle. A life cycle has three parts. First, the organism forms. Next, it grows and develops. Finally, the life cycle ends when the organism dies. Right now, you are in a part of your life cycle called adolescence (a doh LEH sence), which is a time of active growth and development.

Mark the Text

Identify Details Highlight each question head. Then use another color to highlight the answer to that question.

FOLDABLES

A **Describe** Use quarter sheets of notebook paper, as shown below, to describe cell growth and development and cell division.

Cell Growth and Development | Cell Division

How long is the life cycle of a cell?

Every cell has a life cycle. A cell's life cycle is called a cell cycle, as shown in the figure below. A cell cycle is not completed in the same amount of time in all cells. For example, the cell cycle of some human cells takes about 16 hours. The cell cycle of some plant cells takes about 19 hours. A cell cycle has three parts—interphase, mitosis, and cytoplasm division.

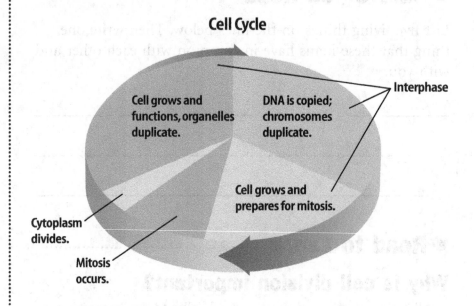

Cell Cycle

Cell grows and functions, organelles duplicate.

DNA is copied; chromosomes duplicate.

Interphase

Cell grows and prepares for mitosis.

Cytoplasm divides.

Mitosis occurs.

What is the longest part of the cell cycle?

For cells that have a nucleus, the longest part of the cell cycle is a period of growth and development called **interphase**. Cells in your body that no longer divide, such as nerve and muscle cells, are always in interphase.

During interphase, an actively dividing cell, such as a skin cell, copies its DNA and prepares for cell division. DNA is the chemical code that controls an organism's growth and operation. A copy of a cell's DNA must be made before dividing so that each of the two new cells will get a complete copy. Each cell needs a complete set of hereditary material to carry out life functions.

Mitosis

After interphase, cell division begins. Mitosis is the first step in cell division. **Mitosis** (mi TOH sus) is the process in which the cell's nucleus divides to form two nuclei. Each new nucleus is identical to the original nucleus. The steps of mitosis are called prophase, metaphase, anaphase, and telophase.

Picture This

1. Identify Draw an outline around the interphase part of the cell cycle to the right. Approximately how much of the cell cycle is interphase?

_____

FOLDABLES

B Sequence Make a four-tab book, as shown below. Use the Foldable to identify facts about the four steps of mitosis.

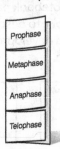

Prophase

Metaphase

Anaphase

Telophase

What happens to chromosomes during cell division?

A chromosome (KROH muh sohm) is a structure in the nucleus that contains DNA. During interphase, each chromosome is copied. When the nucleus is ready to divide, the two copies of each chromosome coil tightly into two thickened, identical DNA strands called chromatids (KROH muh tidz). In the figure to the right, the chromatids are held together at a place called the centromere.

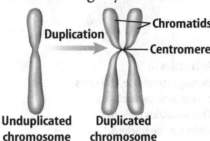

Duplication

Chromatids

Centromere

Unduplicated chromosome

Duplicated chromosome

Picture This

2. Identify Circle the place where the chromatids are held together.

Prophase During prophase, the chromatid pairs can be seen. The nuclear membrane breaks apart. Two small structures called centrioles (SEN tree olz) move to opposite ends of the cell. Between the centrioles, threadlike spindle fibers stretch across the cell. Animal cells have centrioles, but plant cells do not. ☑

Metaphase In metaphase, the chromatid pairs line up across the center of the cell. The centromere of each pair usually becomes attached to two spindle fibers—one from each side of the cell.

Anaphase In anaphase, each centromere divides. The spindle fibers become shorter, and each chromatid separates from its partner. The separated chromatids begin to move to opposite ends of the cell. They are now called chromosomes.

Telophase The final step of mitosis is telophase. During telophase, the spindle fibers start to disappear. The chromosomes start to uncoil, and a new nucleus forms.

How does the cytoplasm divide?

For most cells, after the nucleus divides, the cytoplasm separates and two new cells are formed. Each new cell contains one of the new nuclei. In animal cells, the cell membrane pinches in the middle, like a balloon with a string tightened around it. The cell divides at the pinched area to form two new cells. Each new cell contains half the cytoplasm from the old cell.

After the division of the cytoplasm, most new cells begin interphase again. Use the figure on the next page to review the cell division of an animal cell.

☑ **Reading Check**

3. Explain what happens to the centrioles during prophase.

_____

_____

_____

Picture This

4. Describe Highlight the chromosomes in each phase of mitosis. As you highlight the step, explain to a partner what is happening to the chromosome.

Cell Division for an Animal Cell

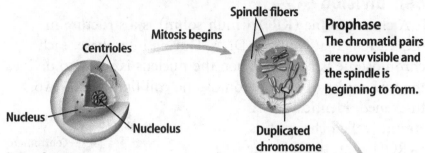

Centrioles

Nucleus

Nucleolus

Mitosis begins

Spindle fibers

Prophase
The chromatid pairs are now visible and the spindle is beginning to form.

Duplicated chromosome (2 chromatids)

Interphase
During interphase, the cell's chromosomes duplicate. The nucleolus is clearly visible in the nucleus.

Metaphase
Chromatid pairs are lined up in the center of the cell.

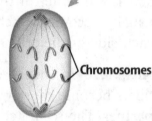

The two new cells enter interphase and cell division usually begins again.

Anaphase
The chromosomes have separated.

Telophase
In the final step, the cytoplasm is beginning to separate.

Mitosis ends

Chromosomes

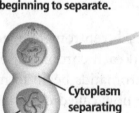

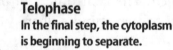

Cytoplasm separating

New nucleus

✔ Reading Check

5. Explain In plant cells, what divides the cytoplasm into two parts?

_____

How do plant cells divide after mitosis?

In plant cells, a cell plate forms in the middle of the cell. The cell plate divides the cytoplasm into two parts. New cell walls form along the cell plate, and new cell membranes develop inside the cell walls. ✔

What are the results of mitosis?

You should remember two important things about mitosis. First, mitosis is the division of a cell's nucleus. Second, it produces two new nuclei that are identical to each other and to the original nucleus. Every cell in your body, except sex cells, has a nucleus with 46 chromosomes—23 pairs. This is because you began as one cell with 46 chromosomes in its nucleus. Skin cells, produced to replace or repair your skin, have the same 46 chromosomes as the original single cell you developed from.

The 46 chromosomes of a human cell are shown below. Notice that the last pair is labeled XY. This is the chromosome pair that determines sex. The XY label indicates a male. Females have XX chromosome pairs.

Chromosomes of a human cell

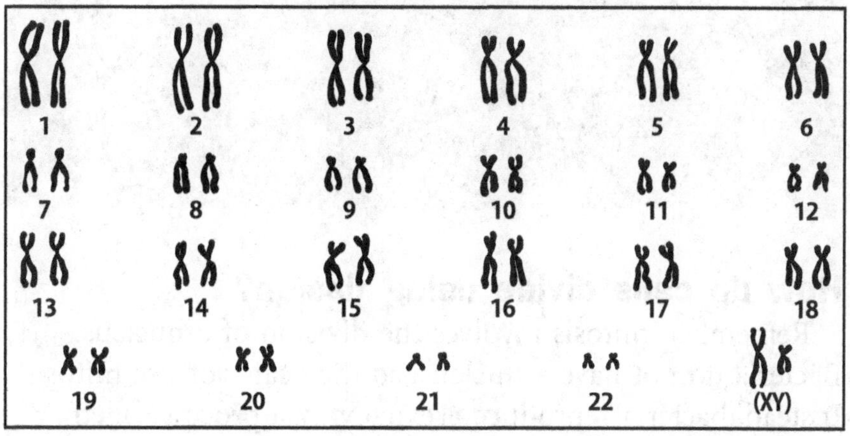

_____ (No. of chromosome pairs) × 2 = _____ (No. of chromosomes)

Picture This

6. Solve Complete the equation at the bottom of the figure using the information in the figure.

Each of the trillions of cells in your body, except sex cells, has a copy of the same DNA. All of your cells, however, use different parts of the DNA to become different types of cells. Skin cells and blood cells contain a copy of the same DNA. They use different parts of the DNA to perform their different functions.

Cell division allows growth and replaces worn out or damaged cells. You are much larger than you were when you were a baby. This is possible because of cell division. If you cut yourself, the wound heals because cell division replaces damaged cells. ✔

✔ Reading Check

7. Explain What is the purpose of cell division?

_____

_____

_____

Asexual Reproduction

The way an organism produces others of its kind is called reproduction. Among living organisms, there are two types of reproduction—sexual and asexual. Sexual reproduction usually involves two parent organisms. In **asexual reproduction,** a new organism (sometimes more than one) is produced from only one parent organism. The new organism has the same DNA as the parent. New strawberry plants can be reproduced asexually from horizontal stems called runners. The figure below shows the asexual reproduction of a strawberry plant.

Copyright © Glencoe/McGraw-Hill, a division of The McGraw-Hill Companies, Inc.

How do cells divide using fission?

Remember, mitosis involves the division of a nucleus. Bacteria do not have a nucleus, so they can not use mitosis. Instead, bacteria reproduce asexually by a process called fission. During fission, a bacteria cell's DNA is copied. The cell then divides into two identical organisms. Each new organism has a complete copy of the parent organism's DNA.

How do organisms reproduce using budding?

Budding is a type of asexual reproduction in which a new organism grows from the body of the parent. When the bud on the adult becomes large enough, it breaks away to live on its own. ☑

How do some organisms regrow body parts?

Some organisms, such as sponges and sea stars, can regrow damaged or lost body parts. The process that uses cell division to regrow body parts is called regeneration. If a sea star breaks into pieces, a whole new organism can grow from each piece.

Picture This

8. Identify How many organisms were needed to produce the strawberry runner?

_____

_____

✔ **Reading Check**

9. Explain budding, which is a form of asexual reproduction.

_____

_____

_____

● After You Read

Mini Glossary

asexual reproduction: the way a new organism is produced from one organism

chromosome (KROH muh sohm): a structure in the nucleus that contains hereditary material

mitosis (mi TOH sus): the process in which the nucleus divides to form two identical nuclei; the four steps include prophase, metaphase, anaphase, telophase

1. Review the terms and their definitions in the Mini Glossary. Write a sentence to explain mitosis using a skin cell as an example.

_____

_____

2. Complete the Venn diagram below to help you compare mitosis in plant and animal cells. Write one similarity at each phase in the overlapping area.

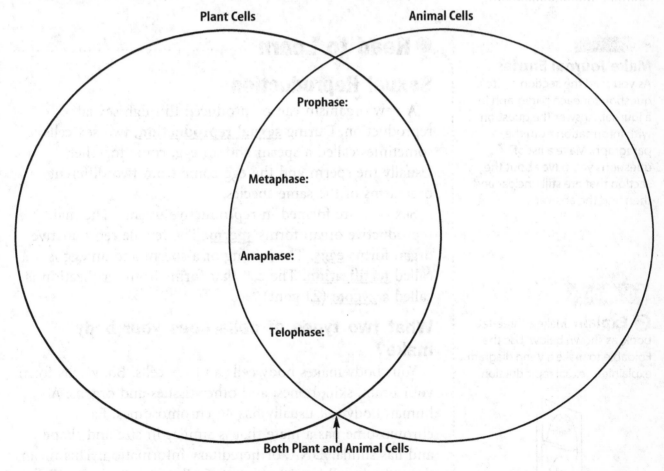

Plant Cells   **Animal Cells**

Prophase:

Metaphase:

Anaphase:

Telophase:

Both Plant and Animal Cells

ScienceOnline   Visit **glencoe.com** to access your textbook, interactive games, and projects to help you learn more about cell division and mitosis.

End of Section

Cell Reproduction

section ❷ Sexual Reproduction and Meiosis

 LE 4.2a The fertilization of an egg by a sperm results in a fertilized egg. **4.3a** Multicellular organisms exhibit complex changes in development, which begin after fertilization. **Also covered:** LE 2.1e, 4.1c, 4.2b, 4.4c

What You'll Learn

- the stages of meiosis
- how sex cells are produced
- why meiosis is needed for sexual reproduction
- the names of the cells involved in fertilization
- how fertilization occurs in sexual reproduction

◄ Study Coach

Make Journal Entries
As you read the section, write a question for each paragraph in a journal. Answer the question with information from the paragraph. Make a list of questions you have about the section that are still unclear and then find the answers.

FOLDABLES

❻ Explain Make a three-tab book, as shown below. Use the Foldable to make a Venn diagram explaining sexual reproduction.

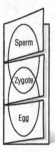

● Before You Read

On the lines below, explain what makes you different from anyone else in your class.

_____

_____

_____

● Read to Learn

Sexual Reproduction

A new organism can be produced through sexual reproduction. During **sexual reproduction,** two sex cells, sometimes called a sperm and an egg, come together. Usually the sperm and the egg come from two different organisms of the same species.

Sex cells are formed in reproductive organs. The male reproductive organ forms **sperm.** The female reproductive organ forms **eggs.** The joining of a sperm and an egg is called **fertilization.** The cell that forms from fertilization is called a **zygote** (ZI goht).

What two types of cells does your body make?

Your body makes body cells and sex cells. Body cells form your brain, skin, bones, and other tissues and organs. A human body cell usually has 46 chromosomes. Each chromosome has a mate that is similar in size and shape and has similar DNA, or hereditary information. This means that a body cell has 23 pairs of similar chromosomes. Cells that have pairs of similar chromosomes are called **diploid** (DIH ployd) cells.

What are haploid cells?

A sex cell has half the number of chromosomes found in a body cell, or 23 chromosomes. A sex cell has only one chromosome from each pair. A cell that does not have pairs of chromosomes is called a **haploid** (HA ployd) cell.

Meiosis and Sex Cells

A process called **meiosis** (mi OH sus) produces haploid sex cells. During meiosis, two divisions of the nucleus occur. These divisions are called meiosis I and meiosis II. The steps of each division of meiosis are named like the steps in mitosis—prophase, metaphase, anaphase, and telophase. The figure below shows what happens during meiosis I.

Meiosis I

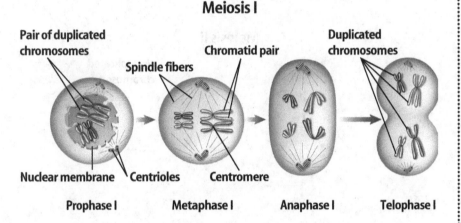

Pair of duplicated chromosomes | Chromatid pair | Duplicated chromosomes
Spindle fibers
Nuclear membrane | Centrioles | Centromere

Prophase I | Metaphase I | Anaphase I | Telophase I

What happens to a cell during meiosis I?

Before meiosis begins, each chromosome is copied. When the cell is ready for meiosis, the two copies of each chromosome can be seen under a microscope as two chromatids. Follow the steps in meiosis I in the figure above. Notice that in prophase I, each pair of duplicated chromosomes comes together. ☑

In metaphase I, the pairs of duplicated chromosomes line up in the center of the cell. As you can see, the centromere of each chromatid pair attaches to one spindle fiber.

In anaphase I, the two copies of the same chromosome, the chromatids, move away from each other to opposite ends of the cell. Notice that each duplicated chromosome still has two chromatids.

In telophase I, the cytoplasm divides and two new cells form. Each new cell has one duplicated chromosome from each similar pair.

Copyright © Glencoe/McGraw-Hill, a division of The McGraw-Hill Companies, Inc.

<u>Picture This</u>
1. Identify How many cells form in meiosis I?

_____

▸ **Reading Check**

2. Explain What happens in a cell before meiosis I begins?

_____

_____

_____

What happens in meiosis II?

The two cells that formed in meiosis I now begin meiosis II. Follow the steps in meiosis II in the figure below. As you can see in prophase II, the duplicated chromosomes and spindle fibers reappear in each new cell.

In metaphase II, the duplicated chromosomes move to the center of each cell. The centromere of each chromatid pair attaches to two spindle fibers.

In anaphase II, the centromere in each cell divides. Then the chromatids separate and move to opposite ends of each cell. Each chromatid becomes an individual chromosome.

In telophase II, the spindle fibers disappear, and a nuclear membrane forms around the chromosomes at each end of the cell. When meiosis II is finished, the cytoplasm of each cell divides.

Meiosis II

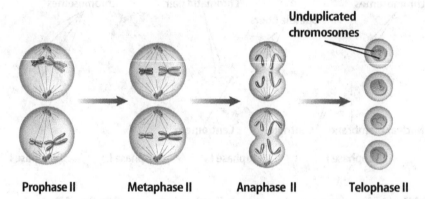

Prophase II   Metaphase II   Anaphase II   Telophase II

Unduplicated chromosomes

What is the final result of meiosis?

During meiosis I, one cell divides into two cells. During meiosis II, those two cells divide. When meiosis II ends, there are four sex cells. Each sex cell has 23 unpaired chromosomes. This is one-half the number of chromosomes that were in the original nucleus—46 chromosomes.

What can go wrong in meiosis?

Mistakes sometimes occur during meiosis. These mistakes can produce sex cells with too many or too few chromosomes. Zygotes, cells that form from fertilized eggs, produced from these sex cells sometimes die. If the zygote lives, every cell that grows from the zygote will have the wrong number of chromosomes. Organisms with the wrong number of chromosomes usually do not grow normally. ☑

Copyright © Glencoe/McGraw-Hill, a division of The McGraw-Hill Companies, Inc.

💡 Think it Over

3. Explain how metaphase I and metaphase II differ.

_____

_____

_____

_____

_____

✔ Reading Check

4. Explain What is the usual result of too many or too few chromosomes?

_____

_____

_____

● After You Read

Mini Glossary

diploid (DIH ployd): cells that have pairs of similar chromosomes

egg: sex cell formed in the female reproductive organs

fertilization: the joining of a sperm and an egg

haploid (HA ployd): cells that do not have pairs of chromosomes, such as sex cells

meiosis (mi OH sis): a process that produces haploid sex cells

sexual reproduction: two sex cells come together to produce a new organism

sperm: sex cell formed in the male reproductive organs

zygote (ZI goht): the cell that forms from fertilization

1. Review the terms and their definitions in the Mini Glossary. Choose the terms that explain the process of sexual reproduction and write one or two sentences explaining how the process works.

_____

_____

_____

2. Complete the graphic organizer below to label the steps that occur during meiosis I and meiosis II.

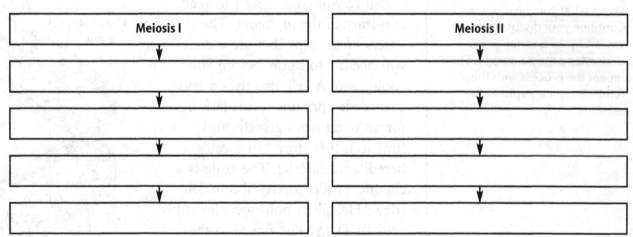

Meiosis I	Meiosis II

3. How do your journal entries help you understand sexual reproduction and meiosis?

_____

_____

 Science Online Visit **glencoe.com** to access your textbook, interactive games, and projects to help you learn more about sexual reproduction and meiosis.

End of Section

Cell Reproduction

section ❸ DNA

LE 2.1b Each gene carries a single unit of information. A single inherited trait of an individual can be determined by one pair or by many pairs of genes. A human cell contains thousands of different genes. **Also covered:** LE 2.1a, 2.1c, 2.2a, 3.1a

What You'll Learn

- the parts of a DNA molecule and its structure
- how DNA copies itself
- the structure and role of each kind of RNA

● Before You Read

Write on the lines below how police departments use DNA to solve crimes.

_____

_____

_____

Study Coach

Discuss Read a paragraph to yourself, then take turns with your partner saying something about what you have learned. Continue your discussion until you and your partner understand the paragraph. Then repeat the process with the remaining paragraphs in the section.

● Read to Learn

What is DNA?

Before you could learn to read, you learned the alphabet. The letters of the alphabet are a code you needed to know before you could read. A cell also uses a code. That code contains information for an organism's growth and function. It is stored in a cell's hereditary material. The code is a chemical called deoxyribonucleic (dee AHK sih ri boh noo klay ihk) acid, or **DNA**. The figure to the right shows the spiral-shaped structure of DNA.

When a cell divides, the DNA code is copied and passed to the new cells. New cells get the same DNA code that was in the original cell. Every cell that has ever been formed in your body or in any organism has DNA.

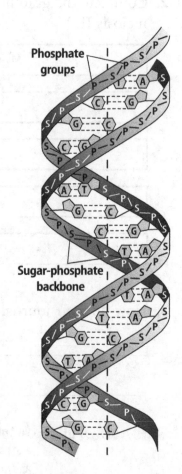

Phosphate groups

Sugar-phosphate backbone

Picture This

1. Infer Examine the DNA strand in the figure. What do the letters "P" and "S" represent?

_____

_____

What does DNA look like?

In 1952, scientist Rosalind Franklin discovered that DNA is two chains of molecules. As you can see in the figure on the previous page, DNA looks like a twisted ladder. Each side of the ladder is made up of sugar-phosphate molecules. The sugar in each molecule is called deoxyribose (dee AHK sih ri bohs). In 1953, scientists James Watson and Francis Crick made a model of a DNA molecule. ☑

What are the four nitrogen molecules that make up DNA?

The rungs, or steps, of the DNA ladder are made up of molecules called nitrogen bases. The four kinds of nitrogen bases found in DNA are adenine (A duh neen), guanine (GWAH neen), cytosine (SI tuh seen), and thymine (THI meen). In the DNA model on the previous page, the first letters of the name of each base, A, G, C, and T, are used to stand for the bases. Also notice that adenine (A) always pairs with thymine (T), and guanine (G) always pairs with cytosine (C).

How is DNA copied?

When chromosomes are copied before mitosis or meiosis, the amount of DNA in the nucleus is doubled. The figure below shows how the DNA copies itself. The two sides of DNA unwind and separate. Each side then becomes a pattern on which a new side can form. The new DNA pattern is exactly the same as the original DNA pattern.

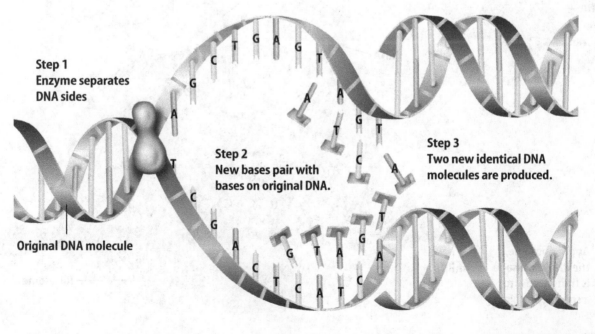

Step 1
Enzyme separates DNA sides

Step 2
New bases pair with bases on original DNA.

Step 3
Two new identical DNA molecules are produced.

Original DNA molecule

Reading Check

2. Identify What did Rosalind Franklin discover?

_____

_____

_____

[handwritten] pairs
Adenine — Thymine
Guanine — Cytosine
G G A T

Picture This

3. Determine Write one quiz question in the space below based on one of the steps in this figure.

_____

_____

_____

Genes

What color are your eyes? How tall are you? The answers to questions like these depend on the kinds of proteins your cells make. Proteins build cells and tissues or work as enzymes. The instructions for making certain proteins are found in genes. A **gene** is a section of DNA on a chromosome. Each chromosome has hundreds of genes. ☑

What are proteins?

Proteins build cells and tissues. Proteins are made of chains of many amino acids. The gene decides the order of amino acids in a protein. Changing the order of the amino acids makes a different protein. Genes are found in the nucleus, but proteins are made on ribosomes in cytoplasm.

What is RNA?

The codes for making proteins are carried from the nucleus to the ribosomes by ribonucleic acid, or **RNA**. RNA is made in the nucleus on a DNA pattern, but it is different from DNA. Look at the model of an RNA molecule below. Notice that RNA is like a ladder with its rungs sawed in half. Like DNA, RNA has the bases A, G, and C. But it has the base uracil (U) instead of thymine (T). The sugar-phosphate molecules in RNA contain the sugar ribose.

✔ **Reading Check**

4. **Explain** where the instructions for making certain proteins are found.

_____

_____

_____

Picture This

5. **Apply** Fill in the two circles in the figure with the correct letter.

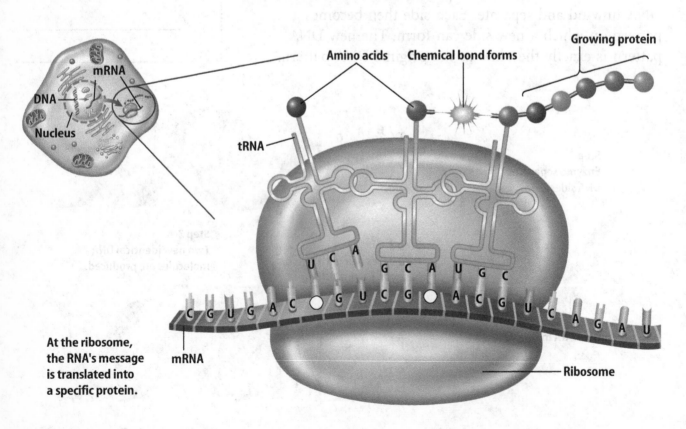

At the ribosome, the RNA's message is translated into a specific protein.

What does RNA do?

There are three main kinds of RNA made from DNA in a cell's nucleus. They are messenger RNA (mRNA), ribosomal RNA (rRNA), and transfer RNA (tRNA). Protein is made when mRNA moves into the cytoplasm. In the cytoplasm, ribosomes, which are made of rRNA, attach to the mRNA. The ribosomes get amino acids from tRNA molecules that are already in the cytoplasm. Inside the ribosomes, three nitrogen bases on the mRNA temporarily match with three nitrogen bases on the tRNA. The same thing happens for the mRNA and another tRNA molecule. The amino acids that are attached to the two tRNA molecules connect. This is the beginning of a protein.

How do cells control genes?

Even though most cells in an organism have exactly the same genes, they do not make the same proteins. Each cell uses only the genes that make the proteins that it needs. For example, muscle proteins are made in muscle cells but not in nerve cells.

Cells control genes by turning some genes off and turning other genes on. Sometimes the DNA is twisted so tightly that no RNA can be made. Other times, chemicals attach to DNA so that it cannot be used.

Mutations

If DNA is not copied exactly, proteins may not be made correctly. These mistakes, called **mutations,** are permanent changes in the DNA sequence of a gene or chromosome. ☑

What are the results of a mutation?

An organism with a mutation may not be able to grow, repair, or maintain itself. A mutation in a body cell may or may not cause problems for the organism. A mutation in a sex cell, however, makes changes to the species when the organism reproduces. Many mutations are harmful to organisms, often causing their death. Some mutations have no effect on an organism. Other mutations can be helpful to an organism.

FOLDABLES

D Identify Make a three-tab book, as shown below. Use the Foldable to write facts about the three types of RNA.

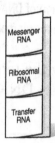

Messenger RNA

Ribosomal RNA

Transfer RNA

☑ **Reading Check**

6. Explain What is a mutation?

_____

_____

_____

⬤ After You Read

Mini Glossary

DNA: a chemical in a cell that contains information for an organism's growth and function

gene: a section of DNA on a chromosome that contains the instructions for making a specific protein

mutations: any permanent change in the DNA sequence of a gene or chromosome of a cell

RNA: a nucleic acid that carries the codes for making proteins from the nucleus to the ribosomes

1. Review the terms and their definitions in the Mini Glossary. Write a short paragraph that contrasts DNA and RNA.

_____

_____

_____

_____

_____

2. Moving from left to right, write the letters (A, T, C, or G) in the empty circles of the bases that will pair with the bases on the top strand to this DNA molecule. The first three pairs have been created for you.

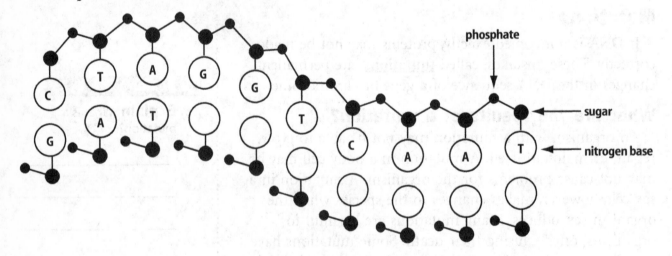

Science⬤nline Visit **glencoe.com** to access your textbook, interactive games, and projects to help you learn more about DNA.

Plant Reproduction

section ① Introduction to Plant Reproduction

 LE 4.1b There are many methods of asexual reproduction, including division of a cell into two cells, or separation of part of an animal or plant from the parent, resulting in the growth of another individual. **4.1c** Methods of sexual reproduction depend upon the species. In many species, including plants and humans, eggs and sperm are produced. **Also covered:** LE 4.1a, 4.3e

● Before You Read

List four things you need to survive. Then circle the items on your list that you think plants also need to survive.

_____

_____

_____

What You'll Learn

■ the differences between the two types of plant reproduction
■ the two stages in a plant's life cycle

● Read to Learn

Types of Reproduction

What do humans and plants have in common? Both need water, oxygen, energy, and food to grow. Like humans, plants reproduce and make similar copies of themselves. Most plants can reproduce in two different ways—by sexual reproduction and by asexual reproduction.

What happens in asexual plant reproduction?

Asexual reproduction does not require the production of sex cells. Instead, one organism produces a new organism that is genetically identical to it. Under the right conditions, an entire plant can grow from one leaf or part of a stem or root. When growers use these methods to start new plants, they must make sure that the plant part has plenty of water and anything else it needs to survive. The stems of lawn grasses grow underground and produce new grass plants asexually along the length of the stem.

What is sexual plant reproduction?

Sexual reproduction in plants requires the production of sex cells—usually called sperm and eggs—in reproductive organs. The organism produced by sexual reproduction is genetically different from either parent organism.

Mark the Text

Identify Main Ideas Underline the important ideas in this section. Review these ideas as you study the section.

💡 Think it Over

1. **Analyze** A cutting from a plant can be placed in water and roots grow. Is this an example of asexual or sexual reproduction? Explain your answer.

_____

_____

_____

Copyright © Glencoe/McGraw-Hill, a division of The McGraw-Hill Companies, Inc.

Fertilization An important part of sexual reproduction is fertilization. Fertilization happens when a sperm and egg combine to produce the first cell of the new organism, the zygote. In plants, water, wind, or animals help bring the sperm and the egg together.

What reproductive organs do plants have?

A plant's female reproductive organs produce eggs. The male reproductive organs produce sperm. Some plants have both reproductive organs. A plant with both reproductive organs can usually reproduce by itself. Other plants have either female or male reproductive organs. For fertilization to happen, the male and female plants must be near each other.

Plant Life Cycles

A plant has a life cycle with two stages—the gametophyte (guh MEE tuh fite) stage and the sporophyte (SPOHR uh fite) stage. The figure below shows the two stages.

Gametophyte Stage When reproductive cells undergo meiosis and produce haploid cells called <u>spores</u>, the <u>gametophyte stage</u> begins. Spores divide by cell division to form plant structures or an entire new plant. The cells in these structures or plants are haploid and have half a set of chromosomes. Some of these cells undergo cell division and form sex cells.

Sporophyte Stage Fertilization—the joining of haploid sex cells—begins the <u>sporophyte stage</u>. Cells formed in this stage are diploid and have the full number of chromosomes. Meiosis in some of these cells forms spores, and the cycle repeats.

FOLDABLES™

A Explain Make a shutterfold book, as shown below. Explain the two stages of the plant life cycle.

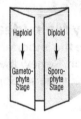

Picture This

2. Identify Write the name of the stage that begins with meiosis below the word *Meiosis*. Write the name of the stage that begins with fertilization above the word *Fertilization*.

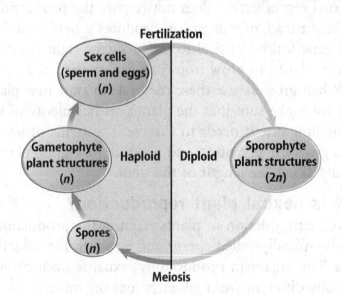

● After You Read

Mini Glossary

gametophyte (guh MEE tuh fite) stage: the stage in plant reproduction when reproductive cells undergo meiosis

spores: haploid cells produced in the gametophyte stage

sporophyte (SPOHR uh fite) stage: the stage in plant reproduction when fertilization begins

1. Review the terms and their definitions in the Mini Glossary. Write a sentence that explains the difference between the gametophyte stage and the sporophyte stage.

_____

_____

_____

2. Choose one of the question headings in the Read to Learn section. Write the question in the space below. Then write your answer to that question on the lines that follow.

> **Write your question here.**

_____

_____

_____

3. Fill in the table below with either "yes" or "no" to compare asexual and sexual reproduction in plants.

	Asexual Reproduction	Sexual Reproduction
a. Requires production of sex cells?		
b. Produces organism that is genetically identical to parent?		
c. Requires fertilization?		

ScienceOnline Visit **glencoe.com** to access your textbook, interactive games, and projects to help you learn more about the basics of plant reproduction.

End of Section

Plant Reproduction

section ❷ Seedless Reproduction

 LE 4.1d Fertilization and/or development in organisms may be internal or external. **Also covered:** LE 4.1a, 4.3e

What You'll Learn

- the life cycles of a moss and a fern
- why spores are important to seedless plants
- the structures ferns use for reproduction

Study Coach

Read and Discuss the main topics of the section with a partner. Read a paragraph and then take turns saying something about what you have learned. Continue until you both understand the main ideas.

FOLDABLES™

B Compare Make a two-tab concept map Foldable. Write the facts related to all nonvascular plants and some vascular plants.

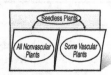

● Before You Read

Describe what happens when you suddenly open a bag of candy or a bag of chips.

_____

_____

● Read to Learn

The Importance of Spores

If you want to grow ferns and moss plants, you can't go to a garden store and buy a package of seeds. Ferns and moss plants don't produce seeds. They reproduce by forming spores. The sporophyte stage of these plants produces haploid spores in structures called spore cases.

If you break open a bag of candy, the candy may spill out. In the same way when a spore cases break open, the spores spill out and are spread by wind or water. The spores can grow into plants that will produce sex cells. Seedless plants include all nonvascular plants and some vascular plants.

Nonvascular Seedless Plants

A nonvascular plant does not have structures that transport water and materials throughout the plant. Instead, water and materials move from cell to cell. Mosses, liverworts, and hornworts are all nonvascular plants. They cover the ground or grow on fallen logs in damp, shaded forests.

The sporophyte stage of most nonvascular plants is very small. Moss plants have a life cycle typical of how sexual reproduction occurs in this plant group.

How do nonvascular plants reproduce sexually?

A moss is a green, low-growing plant when in the gametophyte stage. When brownish stalks grow up from the tip of the plant, moss is in the sporophyte stage. The sporophyte stage does not carry on photosynthesis. It depends on the gametophyte for nutrients and water. On the tip of the stalk is a tiny spore case where millions of spores have been produced. Under the right environmental conditions, the spore case opens and the spores are released.

New moss gametophytes can grow from each spore and the cycle repeats. This process is shown in the figure below.

Picture This

1. **Explain** Highlight each of the following words in the captions of the figure: *meiosis, gametophyte, fertilization, sporophyte.* Use each of these words as you explain to a partner the life cycle of a moss.

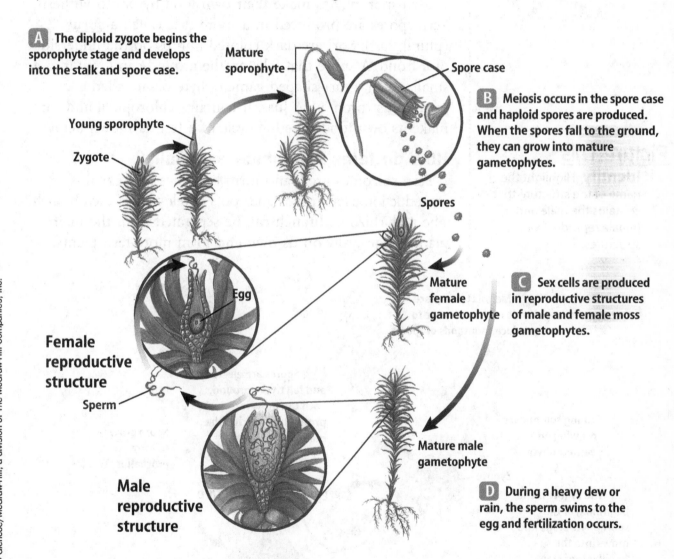

A The diploid zygote begins the sporophyte stage and develops into the stalk and spore case.

Mature sporophyte

Spore case

B Meiosis occurs in the spore case and haploid spores are produced. When the spores fall to the ground, they can grow into mature gametophytes.

Young sporophyte

Zygote

Spores

Mature female gametophyte

C Sex cells are produced in reproductive structures of male and female moss gametophytes.

Egg

Female reproductive structure

Sperm

Male reproductive structure

Mature male gametophyte

D During a heavy dew or rain, the sperm swims to the egg and fertilization occurs.

How do nonvascular plants reproduce asexually?

If a piece of moss gametophyte plant breaks off, it can grow into a new plant. Liverworts can form small balls of cells on the surface of the gametophyte plant. These can be carried away by water and grow into new gametophyte plants.

Vascular Seedless Plants

Vascular plants have tubelike cells that transport water and materials throughout the plant. Most vascular seedless plants are ferns. Horsetails and club mosses are other vascular seedless plants. Unlike nonvascular plants, the gametophyte of a vascular seedless plant is the part that is small.

How do ferns reproduce sexually?

A fern leaf is called a **frond** and grows from an underground stem called a **rhizome**. Roots grow from the rhizome. Roots anchor the plant and absorb water and nutrients.

Fern sporophytes make their own food by photosynthesis. Fern spores are produced in a spore case called a **sorus** (plural, *sori*). Sori are dark colored bumps on the underside of a frond. A spore that falls on the ground can grow into a small, green, heart-shaped gametophyte plant called a **prothallus** (proh THA lus). It contains chlorophyll and can make its own food. The life cycle of a fern is shown below.

How do ferns reproduce asexually?

Fern rhizomes grow and form branches in asexual reproduction. New fronds and roots develop from each branch. The new rhizome branch can be separated from the main plant. It can grow on its own and form more fern plants.

Picture This

2. **Identify** Highlight the name of the structure that contains the male and female reproductive structures.

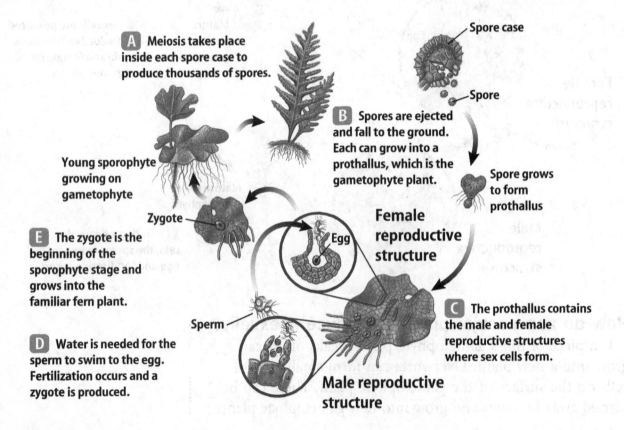

A Meiosis takes place inside each spore case to produce thousands of spores.

Spore case

Spore

B Spores are ejected and fall to the ground. Each can grow into a prothallus, which is the gametophyte plant.

Spore grows to form prothallus

Young sporophyte growing on gametophyte

Zygote

Egg

Female reproductive structure

E The zygote is the beginning of the sporophyte stage and grows into the familiar fern plant.

Sperm

C The prothallus contains the male and female reproductive structures where sex cells form.

D Water is needed for the sperm to swim to the egg. Fertilization occurs and a zygote is produced.

Male reproductive structure

⦿ After You Read

Mini Glossary

frond: a fern leaf

prothallus (proh THA lus): a small, green, heart-shaped gametophyte fern plant

rhizome: underground stem of a fern

sorus: a spore case where fern spores are produced

1. Review the terms and their definitions in the Mini Glossary. Write a sentence that explains the relationship between a frond and a sorus.

_____

_____

2. Complete the flow chart below to show the life cycle of a moss.

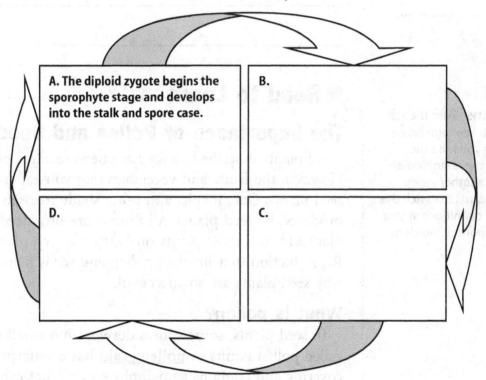

A. The diploid zygote begins the sporophyte stage and develops into the stalk and spore case.

B.

C.

D.

3. How does discussing what you have read help you remember the important ideas?

_____

_____

 Visit **glencoe.com** to access your textbook, interactive games, and projects to help you learn more about seedless reproduction in plants.

End of Section

Plant Reproduction

section **3** Seed Reproduction

LE 4.1c Methods of sexual reproduction depend upon the species. All methods involve the merging of sex cells to begin the development of a new individual.
4.3e Patterns of development vary among plants. Their later development into adulthood is characterized by varying patterns of growth from species to species.
Also covered: LE 4.1d

What You'll Learn

- the life cycles of most gymnosperms and angiosperms
- the structure and function of the flower
- the ways seeds are scattered

● Before You Read

On the lines below, write the names of three fruits or vegetables. Next to each name, describe its seed.

_____

_____

_____

Study Coach

Define Terms Skim the text and write each key term on an index card. As you read the section, write the definition of each term on another index card. Use the cards to match the terms to their definitions as you review the important words in this section.

● Read to Learn

The Importance of Pollen and Seeds

All plants described so far have been seedless plants. However, the fruits and vegetables that you eat come from seed plants. Oak, maple, and other shade trees also are produced by seed plants. All flowers are produced by seed plants. In fact, most plants on Earth are seed plants. Reproduction that involves pollen and seeds helps explain why seed plants are so successful.

What is pollen?

In seed plants, some spores develop into small structures called pollen grains. A **pollen grain** has a waterproof covering and contains gametophyte parts that can produce sperm. The waterproof covering of a pollen grain can be used to identify the plant that the pollen grain came from.

The sperm of seed plants are carried as part of the pollen grain by gravity, wind, water, or animals. The transfer of pollen grains to the female part of the plant is called **pollination**. ☑

After the pollen grain reaches the female part of the plant, a pollen tube is produced. The sperm moves through the pollen tube, then fertilization can happen.

✓ Reading Check

1. **Identify** one way a pollen grain reaches the female part of the plant.

_____

What are the three main parts of a seed?

After fertilization, the female part can develop into a seed. As shown in the figure below, a seed has three main parts, an embryo, stored food, and a protective seed coat. The embryo will grow to become the plant's stem, leaves, and roots. The stored food gives the embryo energy when it begins to grow into a plant. Because a seed contains an embryo and stored food, a new plant develops faster from a seed than from a spore.

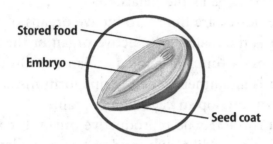

Picture This

2. Infer Circle the part of the seed that will become a plant.

Gymnosperms and Angiosperms Gymnosperms (JIHM nuh spurmz) and angiosperms are the two groups of seed plants. In gymnosperms, seeds usually develop in cones. In angioperms, seeds develop in flowers and fruit.

Gymnosperm Reproduction

Cones are the reproductive structures of gymnosperms. Gymnosperm plants include pines, firs, cedars, cycads, and ginkgoes. Each kind of gymnosperm has a different cone.

A pine tree is a gymnosperm. The way pines produce seeds is typical of most gymnosperms. The pine is a sporophyte plant that produces both male cones and female cones. Male and female gametophyte structures are produced in the cones, but they are very small. A mature female cone is made up of woody scales on a short stem. At the base of each scale are two ovules. The egg is produced in the **ovule**. Pollen grains are produced in the smaller male cones. In the spring, clouds of pollen are released from the male cones.

How are gymnosperm seeds produced?

Pollen is carried from the male cones to the female cones by the wind. The pollen must land between the scales of a female cone to be useful. There it can be trapped in the sticky fluid given off by the ovule. If the pollen grain and the female cone are the same species, fertilization can take place. It can take from two to three years for the seed to develop.

FOLDABLES

C Categorize Make a folded chart, as shown below. Write facts in each block to describe the reproduction of gymnosperms and angiosperms.

Seed Reproduction	Reproductive Organs	Seeds
Gymnosperm Reproduction		
Angiosperm Reproduction		

3. Identify the four main parts of a flower.

_____

_____

_____

_____

Angiosperm Reproduction

Most seed plants are angiosperms. All angiosperms have flowers, which are the reproductive organs. Flowers have gametophyte structures that produce sperm or eggs for sexual reproduction.

Most flowers have four main parts—petals, sepals, stamen, and pistil, as shown in the figure below. The petals usually are the most colorful parts of the flower. Sepals often are small, green, leaflike parts. In some flowers, the sepals are as colorful and as large as the petals. ☑

Inside the flower are the reproductive organs of the plant. The **stamen** is the male reproductive organ of the plant. The stamen has a thin stalk called a filament. On the end of the filament is an anther. Pollen grains form inside the anther. Sperm develop in each pollen grain.

The **pistil** is the female reproductive organ. It consists of a stigma, a long stalklike style, and an ovary. Pollen grains land on the stigma and move down the style to the ovary. The **ovary** is the swollen base of the pistil where the ovules are found. Eggs are produced in the ovules. Not all flowers have both male and female reproductive parts.

Picture This

4. Locate Highlight the male reproductive structure. Circle the female reproductive structure.

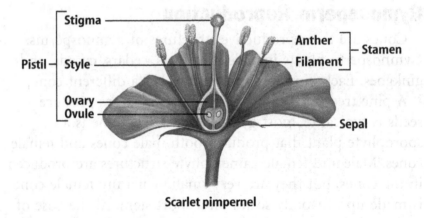

Stigma — Anther — Stamen
Pistil — Style — Filament
Ovary — Ovule — Sepal

Scarlet pimpernel

How is pollen spread?

Insects and other animals eat the flower, its nectar, or pollen. As insects and other animals move about the flower, they get pollen on their body parts. These animals spread the flower's pollen to other plants they visit. Some flowers depend on the wind, rain, or gravity to spread their pollen. Following pollination and fertilization, the ovules of flowers can develop into seeds.

How do angiosperm seeds develop?

A flower is pollinated when pollen grains land on a pistil. A pollen tube grows from the pollen grain. The pollen tube enters the ovary and reaches an ovule. The sperm then travels down the pollen tube and fertilizes the egg in the ovule. A zygote forms and grows into a plant embryo. ☑

Parts of the ovule develop into the stored food and the seed coat that surround the embryo, and a seed is formed. The seeds of some plants, like beans and peanuts, store food in structures called cotyledons. The seeds of other plants, like corn and wheat, store food in a tissue called endosperm.

Seed Dispersal

Some plant seeds are spread by gravity. They fall off the parent plant. Other seeds have attached structures, like wings or sails, which help the wind carry them.

Some seeds are eaten by animals and spread after the seeds are digested. Other seeds are stored or buried by animals. Raindrops can knock seeds out of dry fruit. Some fruits and seeds float on flowing water or ocean currents.

What is germination?

A series of events that results in the growth of a plant from a seed is called **germination**. Seeds will not germinate until the environmental conditions are right. Conditions that affect germination include temperature, light, water, and oxygen. Germination begins when seed tissues absorb water. This causes the seed to get larger and the seed coat to break open.

As you can see in the figure below, a root eventually grows from the seed. Then a stem and leaves grow. Once the plant grows above the soil, photosynthesis begins. Photosynthesis provides food as the plant continues to grow.

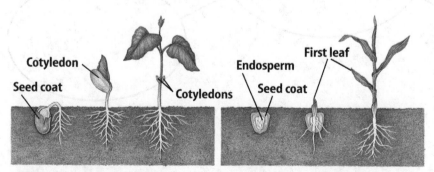

In beans, the cotyledons rise above the soil. As the stored food is used, the cotyledons shrivel and fall off.

In corn, the stored food in the endosperm remains in the soil and is gradually used as the plant grows.

Cotyledon
Seed coat
Cotyledons
Endosperm
First leaf
Seed coat

✔ **Reading Check**

5. Identify Where is the egg fertilized?

_____

_____

Picture This

6. Locate Highlight the structure in each plant that stores food.

● After You Read

Mini Glossary

germination: a series of events that result in the growth of a plant from a seed

ovary: the swollen base of the pistil where ovules are found

ovule: the place where eggs are produced

pistil: the female reproductive organ in the flower of an angiosperm

pollen grain: a small structure in seed plants that has a waterproof covering and that contains gametophyte parts that can produce sperm

pollination: the transfer of pollen grains to the female part of the plant

stamen: the male reproductive organ in the flower of an angiosperm

1. Review the terms and their definitions in the Mini Glossary. Write a sentence that describes either the male or the female reproductive organs of a flower.

_____

_____

_____

2. Complete the concept web below to identify the ways seeds are spread.

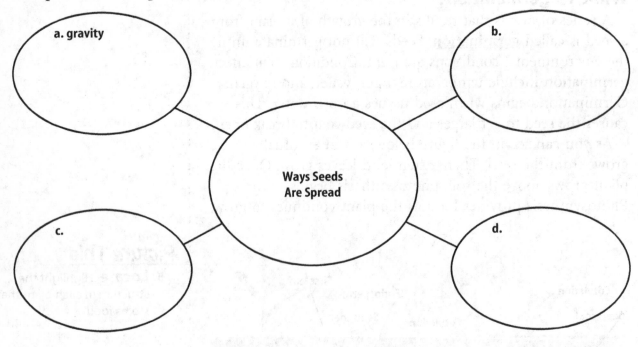

a. gravity

b.

c.

d.

Ways Seeds Are Spread

End of Section

Science⬤nline Visit **glencoe.com** to access your textbook, interactive games, and projects to help you learn more about seed reproduction in plants.

Classifying Animals

section ❶ What is an animal?

LE 1.1h: Living things are classified by shared characteristics on the cellular and organism level. In classifying organisms, biologists consider details of internal and external structures. Biological classification systems are arranged from general (kingdom) to specific (species). **Also covered:** LE 1.1c, 1.1d, 1.1e, 1.1g

● Before You Read

List the names of five animals on the lines below. Then write one thing that these animals have in common.

_____

_____

_____

What You'll Learn
- the characteristics of animals
- the differences between vertebrates and invertebrates

● Read to Learn

Animal Characteristics

If you asked ten people what all animals have in common, you would get many different answers. Animals come in many different shapes and sizes. All animals, however, have five common characteristics.

1. All animals are many-celled organisms that are made of different kinds of cells.
2. Most animal cells have a nucleus and organelles. The nucleus and many of the organelles are surrounded by a membrane. A cell that contains a nucleus and organelles surrounded by membranes is called a eukaryotic (yew ker ee AH tihk) cell.
3. Animals cannot make their own food.
4. Animals digest their food. Large food particles are broken down into substances cells can use.
5. Most animals can move from place to place.

What is symmetry?

As you study different groups of animals, you will look at their symmetry (SIH muh tree). **Symmetry** refers to the way parts of an object are arranged. If the parts are arranged in a way that allows the object to be divided into similar halves, it is symmetrical.

Study Coach

Quiz Yourself As you read the section, write a question for each paragraph. Answer the question with information from the paragraph. Use the questions and answers to study the section.

🔆 Think it Over

1. **Analyze** Name one reason animals need to move from place to place.

_____

_____

_____

What kind of symmetry do most animals have?

Most animals have either radial symmetry or bilateral symmetry. An animal with body parts arranged in a circle around a central point has radial symmetry. As you can see in the figure below, a sea anemone has radial symmetry. An animal with radial symmetry can find food and gather information from all directions. Other animals that have radial symmetry are jellyfish and sea urchins. ☑

An animal with bilateral symmetry has parts that are nearly mirror images of each other. You can draw a line down the center of its body to divide it into two similar parts. The figure below shows that a lobster has bilateral symmetry. A human also has bilateral symmetry.

What is an asymmetrical animal like?

An animal with an uneven shape is called asymmetrical (AY suh meh trih kul). Its body cannot be divided into halves that are similar. Look at the sponge in the figure below. Notice that you cannot draw a line down the center of its body to divide it into two halves that are similar. As you learn more about invertebrates, think about their body symmetry. Notice how body symmetry affects the way they gather food and do other things. Most animals have radial or bilateral symmetry. Only a few animals are asymmetrical.

Copyright © Glencoe/McGraw-Hill, a division of The McGraw-Hill Companies, Inc.

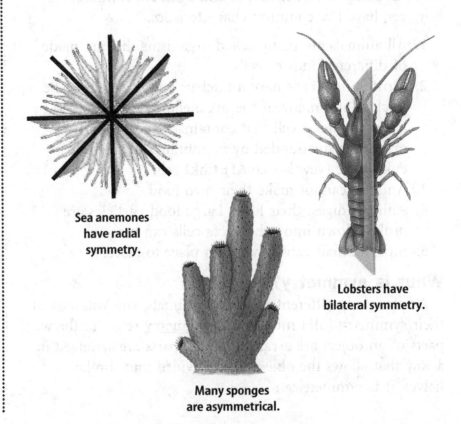

Sea anemones have radial symmetry.

Lobsters have bilateral symmetry.

Many sponges are asymmetrical.

Picture This

3. **Classify** Draw a simple human figure beside the animal with the type of symmetry that humans have.

Animal Classification

Animals have many characteristics in common. But when you think about the variety of animals you can name, you know that there are many different kinds of animals. Some animals have legs, others have wings. Some live on land, others live in water. Scientists use a classification system to place all animals into related groups.

Scientists separate animals into two groups—vertebrates (VUR tuh bruts) and invertebrates (ihn VUR tuh bruts). These two groups are shown in the figure below. **Vertebrates** are animals that have a backbone. **Invertebrates** are animals that do not have a backbone. About 97 percent of all animals are invertebrates.

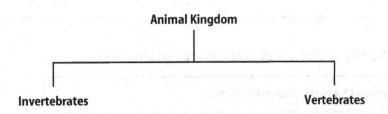

Scientists further classify the invertebrates into smaller groups, as shown in the figure below. The animals in each group share similar characteristics. These characteristics show that the animals within the group may have had a common ancestor.

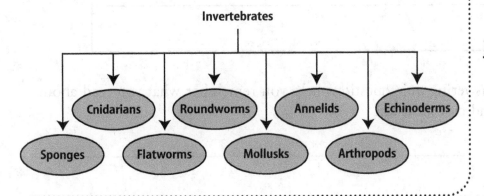

Applying Math

4. Create a Circle Graph
In the circle below, draw a circle graph showing the percent of invertebrates and the percent of vertebrates.

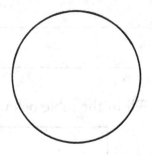

Picture This

5. Identify Circle any words in the diagram that you do not know. When you have finished reading this chapter, review the words you circled and state a characteristic of each one.

● After You Read

Mini Glossary

invertebrates (ihn VUR tuh bruts): animals that do not have a backbone

symmetry (SIH muh tree): the way parts of an object are arranged

vertebrates (VUR tuh bruts): animals that have a backbone

1. Review the terms and their definitions in the Mini Glossary. Write a sentence that explains the difference between an animal that has symmetry and one that is asymmetrical.

_____

_____

_____

2. Fill in the table below to describe the common characteristics of animals.

Common Characteristics of All Animals
1.
2.
3.
4.
5.

3. How did writing and answering quiz questions help you remember what you read about animal characteristics and classification?

_____

_____

_____

 **Science** **online** Visit **glencoe.com** to access your textbook, interactive games, and projects to help you learn more about the characteristics of animals.

chapter 4 Classifying Animals

section ② Invertebrate Animals

 LE 1.1h Living things are classified by shared characteristics on the cellular and organism level. In classifying organisms, biologists consider details of internal and external structures. Biological classification systems are arranged from general (kingdom) to specific (species). **Also covered:** LE 1.1e, 4.1a, 4.3d, 5.1a, 5.1b, 5.1g

● Before You Read

On the lines below, list a difference between the way plants and animals get food.

_____

_____

_____

● Read to Learn

Sponges

Scientist have identified about 15,000 species of sponges. Most sponges live in the ocean, although some live in freshwater. Adult sponges remain attached to one place for their lifetime.

How does a sponge eat?

Sponge bodies are made of two layers of cells. Water containing tiny food particles and oxygen flows through the pores of the sponge. The inner part of a sponge's body is lined with collar cells. Thin, whiplike structures called flagella (flah JEH luh) are attached to the collar cells. The whiplike movements of the flagella keep water moving through the sponge. Other cells digest the food, carry nutrients to all parts of the sponge, and remove wastes from the sponge.

How does a sponge protect itself?

Many sponges have soft bodies that are supported by sharp, glass-like structures called spicules (SPIHK yewlz). Other sponges have a material called spongin. Spongin is like foam rubber. It makes sponges soft and stretchable. Some sponges have both spicules and spongin to protect their soft bodies.

Copyright © Glencoe/McGraw-Hill, a division of The McGraw-Hill Companies, Inc.

What You'll Learn

- how invertebrate animals are identified
- the major systems of invertebrate animals
- how invertebrate animals are alike and different

FOLDABLES

Ⓐ Organize Make a seven-tab Foldable, as shown below. Use the Foldable to take notes about each type of invertebrate.

Sponges
Cnidarians
Flatworms & Roundworms
Mollusks
Segmented Worms
Arthropods
Echinoderms

How do sponges reproduce?

Sponges can reproduce asexually and sexually. A sponge reproduces asexually when a bud on the side of the parent sponge develops into a small sponge. The small sponge breaks off, floats away, and attaches itself to a new surface. New sponges also can grow from pieces of a sponge.

Cnidarians

Jellyfish, sea anemones, hydra, and coral are cnidarians (nih DAR ee unz). Cnidarians are hollowed-bodied animals with two cell layers that are organized into tissues. Cnidarians have tentacles surrounding their mouths. The tentacles shoot out harpoon-like stinging cells to capture prey. Cnidarians have radial symmetry, so they can locate food that floats by from any direction. The inner cell layer digests the food. Nerve cells work together as a nerve net throughout the cnidarian's whole body. ☑

How do cnidarians reproduce?

Cnidarians reproduce both sexually and asexually. Some cnidarians, such as hydras, reproduce asexually by budding. Some can reproduce sexually by releasing eggs or sperm into the water. The eggs from one cnidarian are fertilized by the sperm from another cnidarian.

Flatworms and Roundworms

Unlike sponges and cnidarians, flatworms search for food. Flatworms are invertebrates with long, flattened bodies and bilateral symmetry. A flatworm's body is soft and has three layers of tissue organized into organs and organ systems. Some kinds of flatworms can move around and search for food. These flatworms have a digestive system with one opening. Most flatworms are parasites that live in or on their hosts. A parasite gets its food and shelter from its host. ☑

Roundworms are the most widespread animal on Earth. There are thousands of kinds of roundworms. Billions of roundworms can live in an acre of soil.

A roundworm's body is a tube inside a tube. Between the two tubes is a cavity full of fluid. The fluid-filled cavity separates the digestive tract from the body wall. The digestive tract of a roundworm has two openings. Food enters the roundworm through the mouth, it is digested in a digestive tract, and wastes exit through the anus.

☑ **Reading Check**

1. **Explain** Why does a cnidarian use stinging cells?

_____

_____

☑ **Reading Check**

2. **Identify** What type of symmetry do flatworms have?

_____

_____

Mollusks

A mollusk is a soft-bodied invertebrate that usually has a shell. A mollusk also has a mantle and a large, muscular foot. The mantle is a thin layer of tissue that covers the mollusk's soft body. The foot is used for moving or for holding the animal in one place. Snails, mussels, and octopuses are mollusks.

Mollusks that live in water have gills. Gills are organs in which carbon dioxide from the animal is exchanged for oxygen from the water. Mollusks that live on land have lungs in which carbon dioxide from the animal is exchanged for oxygen from the air.

What body systems does a mollusk have?

A mollusk has a digestive system with two openings. Many mollusks have a scratchy, tonguelike organ called the radula (RA juh luh). The radula has rows of tiny, sharp teeth that the mollusk uses to scrape small bits of food off rocks and other surfaces. ☑

Some mollusks have an **open circulatory system**, which means they do not have blood vessels. Instead, the blood washes over the organs, which are grouped together in a fluid-filled cavity inside the animal's body. Others have a **closed circulatory system** in which blood is carried through blood vessels.

Segmented Worms

Earthworms, leeches, and marine worms are segmented worms. Segmented worms are also called annelids (A nul idz). A segmented worm's body is made up of repeating rings that make the worm flexible. Each ring or segment has nerve cells, blood vessels, part of the digestive tract, and the coelom (SEE lum). The coelom is a body cavity that separates the internal organs from the inside of the body wall. A segmented worm has a closed circulatory system and a complete digestive system with two body openings. ☑

What do earthworms eat?

Earthworms are important in shaping the landscape. They move through soil by eating the soil. The earthworm uses the organic matter in the soil for food. The undigested wastes and soil that leave the earthworm make the soil better. Earthworms add nutrients to the soil and loosen it. This increases the fertility of the soil.

✔ Reading Check

3. Define What is a radula?

_____

_____

✔ Reading Check

4. Identify What is another name for segmented worms?

_____

💡 **Think it Over**

5. Infer Like arthropods, you have appendages. Name two human appendages.

_____

_____

Arthropods

Scientists have discovered more than a million species of arthropods (AR thruh pahdz). An arthropod is an invertebrate animal with jointed appendages (uh PEN dih juz). **Appendages** are structures such as claws, legs, or antennae that grow from the body.

Arthropods have bilateral symmetry and segmented bodies similar to annelids. Most arthropods have fewer and more specialized segments. They have an open circulatory system. Oxygen enters the animal's tissues through spiracles. Fertilization in most arthropods is internal.

How does an arthropod protect itself?

Arthropods have hard body coverings called **exoskeletons**. The exoskeleton protects and supports the animal's body and reduces water loss. As the animal grows, it sheds the exoskeleton, which does not grow with the animal.

What is metamorphosis?

The young of many arthropods don't look anything like the adults. Many arthropods completely change their body form as they grow. This change in body form is called **metamorphosis** (met uh MOR fuh sus).

Butterflies, bees, and beetles are arthropods that go through a complete metamorphosis. Complete metamorphosis has four stages—egg, larva, pupa (PYEW puh), and adult. At each stage, the arthropod looks completely different.

Some insects such as grasshoppers and dragonflies go through incomplete metamorphosis. They have only three stages—egg, nymph, and adult. The nymph looks similar to its parents, only smaller. A nymph sheds its exoskeleton by a process called molting as it grows. The two types of metamorphosis are shown in the figure below.

Picture This

6. Identify Circle the names of the stages that are the same for complete and incomplete metamorphosis.

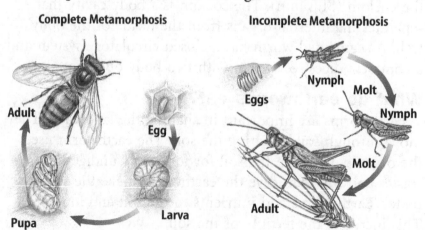

Complete Metamorphosis — Adult, Egg, Larva, Pupa

Incomplete Metamorphosis — Eggs, Nymph, Molt, Nymph, Molt, Adult

Echinoderms

Echinoderms (ih KI nuh durmz) are animals that have radial symmetry. Sea stars and sand dollars are echinoderms. Echinoderms have spines of different lengths that cover the outside of their bodies. Most echinoderms have an internal skeleton made up of bonelike plates that supports and protects the animal. Echinoderms have a simple nervous system, but no head or brain. Some echinoderms are predators, some are filter feeders, and some feed on decaying matter. ☑

What is a water-vascular system?

An echinoderm has a water-vascular system, which is a network of water-filled canals and thousands of tube feet. The tube feet work like suction cups to help the animal move and capture prey. The figure below shows the parts of a sea star. A sea star eats by pushing its stomach out of its mouth and into the opened shell of its prey. After the prey's body is digested, the sea star pulls in its stomach. Like some other invertebrates, sea stars can regrow lost or damaged parts.

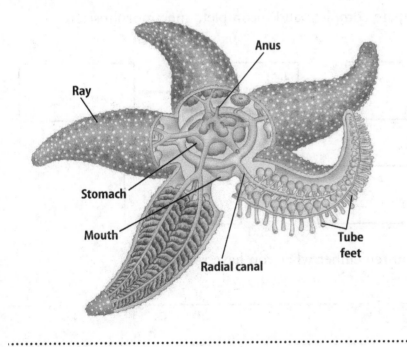

Ray

Anus

Stomach

Mouth

Radial canal

Tube feet

✔ **Reading Check**

7. **List** two examples of echinoderms.

_____

_____

Picture This

8. **Explain** Highlight the name of the body structure a sea star uses to capture prey.

● After You Read

Mini Glossary

appendage (uh PEN dihj): a structure such as a claw, leg, or antennae that grows from the body

closed circulatory system: a circulatory system in which blood is carried through blood vessels

exoskeleton: a hard body covering that protects and supports the body and reduces water loss

metamorphosis (met uh MOR fuh sus): a change in body form

open circulatory system: a circulatory system without blood vessels in which blood washes over the organs

1. Review the terms and their definitions in the Mini Glossary. Write a sentence that describes how an arthropod might use an appendage.

_____

_____

_____

2. Complete the flowcharts to compare complete and incomplete metamorphosis.

Complete Metamorphosis

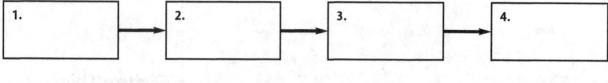

| 1. | → | 2. | → | 3. | → | 4. |

Incomplete Metamorphosis

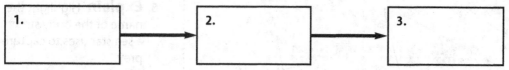

| 1. | → | 2. | → | 3. |

3. How do the sticky-notes help you remember what you have read?

_____

_____

End of Section

Science Online Visit **glencoe.com** to access your textbook, interactive games, and projects to help you learn more about arthropods and echinoderms.

Classifying Animals

section ❸ Vertebrate Animals

 LE 1.1h Living things are classified by shared characteristics on the cellular and organism level. In classifying organisms, biologists consider details of internal and external structures. Biological classification systems are arranged from general (kingdom) to specific (species). **Also covered:** LE 1.1e, 4.1a, 4.1d, 4.3d, 5.1a, 5.1b, 5.1g

● Before You Read

List three animals on the lines below. Then write one thing that all these animals have in common with humans.

_____

_____

_____

● Read to Learn

What is a chordate?

Familiar animals such as birds, fish, cats, and dogs belong to a large group of animals called chordates. **Chordates** (KOR dayts) are animals that have the following three characteristics—a notochord (NOH tuh cord), a nerve cord, and pharyngeal (fur RIN jee uhl) pouches at some time during their development.

The notochord is a flexible rod that runs the length of the developing organism. The nerve cord is made of nerve tissue. In most chordates, one end of the nerve cord develops into the organism's brain.

Pharyngeal pouches are slitlike openings between the inside of the body and the outside of the body. They are present only in the early stages of the organism's development. In some chordates, like the lancelet in the figure below, the pharyngeal pouches develop into gill slits.

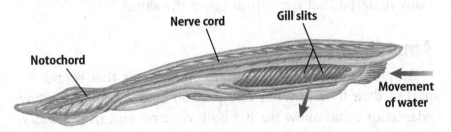

Nerve cord

Gill slits

Notochord

Movement of water

What You'll Learn

- the classification of vertebrate animals
- the systems of vertebrate animals
- the differences between vertebrate animals

 Study Coach

Create a Quiz Write a question about the main idea under each heading. Exchange quizzes with another student. Together, discuss the answers to the quiz questions.

FOLDABLES

❸ Define Use a quarter sheet of notebook paper, as shown below, to define these key words in this section—chordate, ectotherm, and endotherm.

Chordate
Ectotherm
Endotherm

What are the characteristics of vertebrates?

Chordates are classified into several smaller groups. The largest group of chordates is made up of the vertebrates, which include humans. All vertebrates have an internal system of bones called an endoskeleton. The endoskeleton supports and protects the body's internal organs. For example, the skull is the part of the endoskeleton that surrounds and protects the brain.

How do vertebrates control body temperature?

Vertebrates are either ectotherms or endotherms. **Ectotherms** (EK tuh thurmz) are cold-blooded animals. Their body temperature changes as the temperature of their surroundings changes. Fish and reptiles are ectotherms.

Endotherms (EN duh thurmz) are warm-blooded animals. Their body temperature does not change with the surrounding temperature. Humans are endotherms. Your body temperature is usually about 37°C, but can vary by about 1°C, depending on the time of day.

Fish

Fish are the largest group of vertebrates. Scientists classify fish into three groups—bony, jawless, and jawed cartilaginous (kar tuh LA juh nuhs). All fish are ectotherms and live in water. Some species of fish are adapted to live in freshwater and other species are adapted to live in salt water.

Fish have gills. Gills are fleshy filaments where carbon dioxide and oxygen are exchanged. Water that contains oxygen passes over the gills. When blood is pumped into the gills, the oxygen in the water moves into the blood. At the same time, carbon dioxide moves out of the blood in the gills and into the water. ☑

Most fish have pairs of fanlike fins. Fish use fins to steer, balance, and move. The motion of the tail fin pushes the fish through the water.

Most fish have scales. Scales are thin structures made of a bony material that overlap to cover the skin.

Amphibians

Amphibians (am FIH bee unz) are animals that spend part of their lives in water and part on land. They have many adaptations that allow for life both on land and in the water. Amphibians include frogs, toads, salamanders, and newts.

Copyright © Glencoe/McGraw-Hill, a division of The McGraw-Hill Companies, Inc.

FOLDABLES

⊙ Identify Make a two-tab Foldable, as shown below. Identify the characteristics of ectotherms and endotherms.

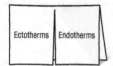

☑ Reading Check

1. **Explain** the purpose of fish gills.

_____

_____

What are characteristics of amphibians?

Amphibians are vertebrates with a strong endoskeleton made of bones. The skeleton helps support their body while on land.

Adult amphibians use lungs instead of gills to exchange oxygen and carbon dioxide. Lungs are an important adaptation for living on land. Amphibians have three-chambered hearts, in which blood carrying oxygen mixes with blood carrying carbon dioxide. This mixing makes less oxygen available to the amphibian. Adult amphibians also exchange oxygen and carbon dioxide through their moist skin, which increases their oxygen supply. Amphibians can live on land, but they must stay moist for the exchange of oxygen and carbon dioxide to occur.

Amphibian hearing and vision also are adapted to life on land. Amphibians have tympanums (TIHM puh nuhmz), or eardrums, that vibrate in response to sound waves. Large eyes help some amphibians catch their prey. Land environments provide many insects as food for adult amphibians. They have long, sticky tongues used to capture the insects.

How do amphibians develop?

Most amphibians go through a series of body changes called metamorphosis (me tuh MOR fuh sus). Eggs are most often laid in water and hatch into larvae. Young larval forms of amphibians live in water. They have no legs and breathe through gills. Over time, they develop the body structures needed for life on land including legs and lungs. The rate of metamorphosis depends on the species, the water temperature, and the amount of available food. The figure below shows the stages of development for one amphibian—the frog.

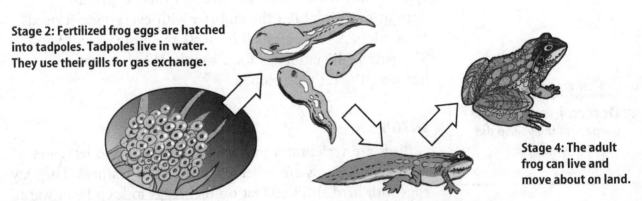

Stage 2: Fertilized frog eggs are hatched into tadpoles. Tadpoles live in water. They use their gills for gas exchange.

Stage 1: Frog eggs are laid and fertilized.

Stage 3: Tadpoles begin to grow into adults. They develop legs and lungs.

Stage 4: The adult frog can live and move about on land.

Think it Over

2. **Describe** two characteristics that allow amphibians to live on land.

_____

_____

_____

Picture This

3. **Compare** Circle the stage of metamorphosis in which frogs are most like fish.

Reptiles

Snakes, lizards, turtles, and crocodilians are reptiles. Reptiles are vertebrates and ectotherms. Most reptiles live their entire lives on land and do not depend on water for reproduction.

What are some types of reptiles?

A turtle is covered with a hard shell. Most turtles can bring their heads and legs into the shell for protection. Alligators and crocodiles are large reptiles that live in or near water. Alligators and crocodiles are predators that live in warmer climates.

Lizards and snakes make up the largest group of reptiles. Snakes and lizards have an organ in the roof of the mouth that senses molecules collected by the tongue. The constant in-and-out motion of the tongue allows a snake or lizard to smell its surroundings. Lizards have movable eyelids and external ears. Most lizards have legs with clawed toes on each foot. Snakes move without legs. They don't have eyelids or ears. Snakes feel vibrations in the ground instead of hearing sounds. ☑

What are some reptile adaptations?

A thick, dry waterproof skin is an adaptation that allows reptiles to live on land. Reptile skin is covered with scales to reduce water loss and help prevent injury. Reptiles breathe with lungs. Reptiles that live in water, like sea turtles, must come to the surface to breathe.

Two adaptations allow reptiles to reproduce on land—internal fertilization and laying shell-covered eggs. Sperm are deposited directly into the female's body. Female reptiles lay fertilized eggs that are covered by tough shells. These eggs are called amniotic (am nee AH tihk) eggs. An **amniotic egg** supplies the embryo with everything it needs to develop. A leathery shell protects the embryo and yolk. The yolk is the embryo's food supply. When a reptile hatches, it is fully developed. ☑

Birds

Birds are vertebrates that have two wings, two legs, and a bill or beak. Birds are covered mostly with feathers. They lay eggs with hard shells and sit on their eggs to keep them warm until they hatch. All birds are endotherms.

☑ **Reading Check**

4. Identify the largest group of reptiles.

_____

_____

_____

☑ **Reading Check**

5. Determine What is the purpose of the yolk in the amniotic egg?

_____

_____

How do bird species differ?

There are more than 8,600 species of birds. Different species have different adaptations. For example, ostriches have strong legs for running. Penguins can't fly, but they are excellent swimmers. Wrens have feet that allow them to perch on branches.

How are birds adapted for flight?

The bodies of most birds are designed for flight. They are streamlined and have light, strong skeletons. The inside of a bird's bones is almost hollow. Special structures make the bones strong, but lightweight. A bird's tail is designed to provide the stiffness, strength, and stability needed for flight. Birds use their tail to steer.

Birds need a lot of energy and oxygen to fly. They eat high-energy foods like nectar, insects, and meat. They have a large, efficient heart. A bird's lungs connect to air sacs that provide a constant supply of oxygen to the blood and make the bird more lightweight.

Birds beat their wings up and down as well as forward and backward. A combination of wing shape, surface area, wind speed, and angle of the wing provide the upward push needed for flight.

What is the function of feathers?

Birds are the only animals with feathers. They have two main types of feathers—contour feathers and down feathers. __Contour feathers__ are strong and lightweight. They give adult birds their streamlined shape and coloring. Contour feathers have parallel strands, called barbs, that extend from the main shaft. Outer contour feathers on the wings and tail help a bird move, steer, and keep from spinning out of control. Feather color and patterns help attract mates. The color patterns also protect birds from predators by helping the birds blend into their surroundings.

Birds have __down feathers__ that trap and keep warm air next to their bodies. In adult birds, down feathers provide a layer of insulation under the contour feathers. Down feathers cover the bodies of some young birds.

Birds care for their feathers by preening. Birds preen, or use their bills, to clean and rearrange their feathers. During preening, birds also spread oil over their bodies and feathers. The oil keeps the bird's skin soft and keeps feathers and scales from becoming brittle.

💡 __Think it Over__

6. __Infer__ What features do airplanes have that are similar to birds?

_____

_____

_____

__FOLDABLES__™

● __Define__ Use a quarter-sheet of notebook paper, as shown below, to define the key words in this section—contour feathers and down feathers.

Contour
feathers

Down
feathers

FOLDABLES™

E Define Use a quarter-sheet of notebook paper, as shown below, to define the key words in this section—herbivore, carnivore, and omnivore.

Herbivore
Carnivore
Omnivore

Mammals

Moles, dogs, bats, and humans are some examples of mammals. Mammals are vertebrates and endotherms. They live in water and in many different climates on land. They burrow through the ground and fly through the air. Mammals have mammary glands in their skin.

A mammal's skin usually is covered with hair that keeps the body from being too hot or too cold. The hair also protects mammals from wind and water. Some mammals, like bears, have thick fur. Other mammals, like humans, have a few patches of thick hair while the rest of the body has little hair. Dolphins have little hair. Porcupines have quills, which are a kind of modified hair.

Why do mammals have mammary glands?

In females, the mammary glands produce and release milk for the young. For the first few weeks or months of life, the milk provides all the nutrients the young mammal needs.

What kinds of teeth do mammals have?

Plant-eating animals are called <u>herbivores</u>. Animals that eat meat are called <u>carnivores</u>. Animals that eat plants and meat are called <u>omnivores</u>.

Mammals have four types of teeth—incisors, canines, premolars, and molars. As the figure below shows, you usually can tell from the kind of teeth a mammal has whether it eats plants, meat, or both.

Picture This

7. Identify Circle the teeth that carnivores use to rip and tear flesh. Highlight the teeth that omnivores and herbivores use to cut vegetables.

Mountain lions are carnivores. They have sharp canines that are used to rip and tear flesh.

Humans are omnivores. They have incisors that cut vegetables, premolars that are sharp enough to chew meat, and molars that grind food.

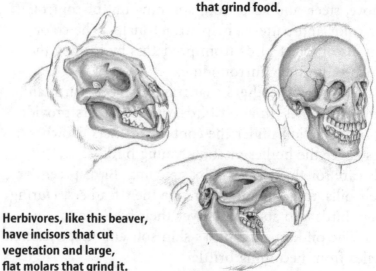

Herbivores, like this beaver, have incisors that cut vegetation and large, flat molars that grind it.

What body systems do mammals have?

Mammals have well-developed lungs made of millions of small sacs called alveoli. Alveoli allow the exchange of carbon dioxide and oxygen during breathing. Mammals also have a complex nervous system that lets them learn and remember more than many other animals. Mammals have larger brains than other animals of similar size.

All mammals have internal fertilization. After an egg is fertilized, the developing mammal is called an embryo. Most mammal embryos develop inside the female in an organ called the uterus. ☑

Monotremes make up the smallest group of mammals. They lay eggs instead of having live births. The female monotreme sits on the eggs for about ten days before they hatch. The mammary glands of monotremes do not have nipples. The milk seeps through the skin onto their fur. The young monotremes lick the milk off the fur. Duck-billed platypuses are an example of monotremes.

How do young marsupials develop?

Most marsupials, such as kangaroos and koalas, live in Australia. The opossum is the only marsupial native to North America. A marsupial embryo develops for only a few weeks within the uterus. When a marsupial is born, it is not fully formed. It has no hair and is blind. The young marsupial uses its sense of smell to find its way to a nipple usually within the mother's pouch. It attaches to the nipple to feed and finishes developing in the pouch.

How do placental embryos develop?

Most mammals belong to a group called placentals. Placentals are named for the placenta, which is a saclike organ that develops from tissues of the embryo in the uterus.

An umbilical cord connects the embryo to the placenta. Food and oxygen are absorbed from the mother's blood. Blood vessels in the umbilical cord carry food and oxygen to the developing young. The blood vessels also take away wastes. In the placenta, the mother's blood absorbs wastes from the developing young. The blood of the mother and the embryo do not mix.

The time of development from fertilization to birth is called the gestation period. Gestation periods vary widely, from about 21 days in rats to about 616 days in elephants. Human gestation lasts about 280 days. ☑

Reading Check

8. **Apply** What kind of fertilization do all mammals have in common?

_____

_____

_____

Reading Check

9. **Define** What is the gestation period?

_____

_____

_____

● After You Read

Mini Glossary

amniotic (am nee AH tihk) egg: the environment for the development of a reptile embryo

carnivore: an animal that eats meat

chordate (KOR dayt): an animal that has, at some time during its development, three characteristics present— a notochord, nerve cord, and pharyngeal pouches

ectotherm (EK tuh thurm): a cold-blooded animal whose body temperature changes as the temperature of its surroundings change

endotherm (EN duh thurm): a warm-blooded animal whose body temperature does not change with the temperature of its surroundings

herbivore: a plant-eating animal

omnivore: an animal that eats plants and meat

1. Review the terms and their definitions in the Mini Glossary. Write one or more sentences to explain how herbivores, carnivores, and omnivores are different.

_____

_____

_____

2. Complete the table below to list the adaptations birds have for flight.

Adaptations for Flight	
1.	4.
2.	5.
3.	6.

3. Complete the diagram below to identify the three types of mammals.

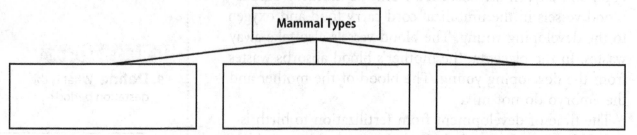

Mammal Types

Copyright © Glencoe/McGraw-Hill, a division of The McGraw-Hill Companies, Inc.

chapter 5 Heredity

section ❶ Genetics

 LE 2.1a Hereditary information is contained in genes. **LE 2.2a** In all organisms, genetic traits are passed on from generation to generation. **LE 2.2c** The probability of traits being expressed can be determined using models of genetic inheritance. **Also covered:** LE 2.1b, 2.2b, 3.1c, 4.4b

● Before You Read

Think of a parent and a child that you know. On the lines below, list four ways the child looks like the parent.

_____

_____

_____

_____

● Read to Learn

Inheriting Traits

Do you look more like one parent or grandparent? Do you have your father's eyes? Eye color, nose shape, and many other physical features are traits. Traits also include things that cannot be seen, such as your blood type. An organism is a collection of traits, all inherited from its parents. <u>Heredity</u> (huh REH duh tee) is the passing of traits from parent to offspring, or children.

What is genetics?

Usually, genes on chromosomes control an organism's shape and function. The different forms of a trait that a gene may have are called <u>alleles</u> (uh LEELZ). When a pair of chromosomes separates during meiosis (mi OH sus), alleles for each trait also separate into different sex cells. As a result, every sex cell has one allele for each trait, as shown in the figure on the next page. The allele in one sex cell may control one form of the trait, such as dimples. The allele in another sex cell may control a different form of the trait, such as no dimples. The study of how traits are inherited through the interactions of alleles is called <u>genetics</u> (juh NE tihks). ☑

What You'll Learn

- how traits are inherited
- Mendel's role in the history of genetics
- how to use a Punnett square
- the difference between genotype and phenotype

Study Coach

Create a Vocabulary Quiz Write a question about each vocabulary word or term in the section. Exchange quizzes with another student. Together discuss the answers to the quizzes.

☑ Reading Check

1. Define the word genetics.

_____

_____

_____

Chromosomes Separate During Meiosis

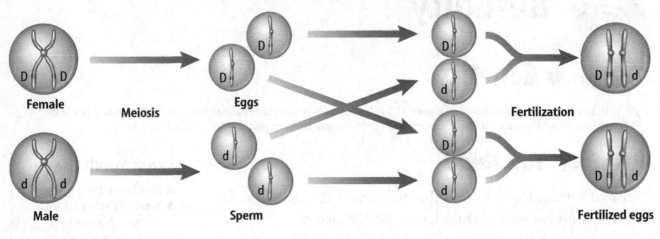

A The alleles that control a trait are located on each duplicated chromosome.

B During meiosis, duplicated chromosomes separate.

C During fertilization, each parent donates one chromosome. This results in two alleles for the trait in the new individual formed.

Copyright © Glencoe/McGraw-Hill, a division of The McGraw-Hill Companies, Inc.

Picture This

2. Identify Circle the sex cells on the diagram.

Think it Over

3. Analyze When Mendel studied traits, how did his methods differ from those of other scientists?

_____

_____

_____

Mendel—The Father of Genetics

Did you know that an experiment with pea plants helped scientists understand why your eyes are the color they are? Gregor Mendel was an Austrian monk who studied mathematics and science. His job at the monastery where he lived was gardening. His interest in plants began as a boy in his father's orchards. He learned to predict the possible types of flowers and fruits that would result from crossbreeding plants.

In 1856, Mendel began experimenting with garden peas. He wanted to know the connection between the color of a pea flower and the type of seed the plant produced. Before Mendel, scientists relied on observation and description. They often studied many traits at one time. This made it hard to develop good hypotheses about how traits are inherited. Mendel used scientific methods in his study. Mendel was the first person to trace one trait through many generations. He was the first person to record the study of how traits pass from one generation to another. He was also the first person to use the mathematics of probability to explain heredity.

In 1900, three plant scientists repeated Mendel's experiments and reached the same conclusions as Mendel. For this reason, Mendel is known as the father of genetics.

Genetics in a Garden

When Mendel studied a trait, he crossed two plants with different forms of the trait. He found that the new plants all looked like one of the two parents. Mendel called each new plant a <u>hybrid</u> (HI brud) because it received different genetic information, or different alleles, for a trait from each parent.

What is a purebred?

Garden peas are easy to breed for pure traits. An organism that always produces the same traits, generation after generation, is called a purebred. For example, plants can be purebred for the trait of tall height. The table below shows the pea plant traits that Mendel studied.

Picture This

4. Identify How many traits did Mendel study?

_____

Traits Compared by Mendel							
Traits	**Shape of Seeds**	**Color of Seeds**	**Color of Pods**	**Shape of Pods**	**Plant Height**	**Position of Flowers**	**Flower Color**
Dominant Trait	Round	Yellow	Green	Full	Tall	At leaf junctions	Purple
Recessive Trait	Wrinkled	Green	Yellow	Flat, constricted	Short	At tips of branches	White

What are dominant and recessive factors?

In nature, insects carry pollen as they move from plant to plant. The pollination by insects is random. In his experiments, Mendel pollinated the plants by hand to control the results. He used pollen from the flowers of purebred tall plants to pollinate the flowers of purebred short plants. This process is called cross-pollination. He found that tall plants crossed with short plants produced seeds that produced all tall plants. Mendel called the tall form the <u>dominant</u> (DAH muh nunt) factor because it dominated, or covered up, the short form. He called the short form the <u>recessive</u> (rih SE sihv) factor because this form seemed to disappear. Today, these factors are called dominant alleles and recessive alleles.

FOLDABLES

A Describe Make a two-tab Foldable, as shown below. Write notes under the tabs to describe dominant and recessive alleles.

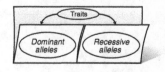

What is probability?

A branch of mathematics that helps you predict the chance that something will happen is called probability. For example, there are two sides to a coin. If you toss the coin in the air, the probability that one side of the coin will land facing up is one out of two, or 50 percent. Mendel used probabilities in his study of genetics. His predictions were very accurate because he studied large numbers of plants over a long period of time. He studied almost 30,000 pea plants over a period of eight years. This increased Mendel's chances of seeing a repeatable pattern. Valid scientific conclusions need to be based on results that can be repeated.

What is a Punnett square?

Scientists use a tool called a Punnett (PUH nut) square to predict results in genetics. A **Punnett square** is used to predict the number of times certain traits will occur. In a Punnett square, letters stand for dominant and recessive alleles. An uppercase letter stands for a dominant allele, and a lowercase letter stands for a recessive allele. The letters are a form of code. They show the **genotype** (JEE nuh tipe), or genetic makeup, of an organism. The way an organism looks and behaves as a result of its genotype is its **phenotype** (FEE nuh tipe). If you have brown hair, the phenotype for your hair color is brown. ✔

How do alleles determine traits?

Most cells in your body have two alleles for every trait. An organism with two alleles that are the same is called **homozygous** (hoh muh ZI gus). In his experiments, Mendel would have written *TT* (homozygous for the tall-dominant trait) or *tt* (homozygous for the short-recessive trait). An organism that has two different alleles for a trait is called **heterozygous** (he tuh roh ZI gus). Mendel would have written *Tt* for plant hybrids that were heterozygous for height.

How do you make a Punnett square?

The letters representing the two alleles from one parent are written in the top row of the Punnett square. The letters representing the two alleles from the other parent are written down the left column. Each square in the grid is then filled in with one allele from each parent. The combinations of letters in the completed Punnett square are the genotypes of the possible offspring those parents could produce.

✔ **Reading Check**

5. **Identify** How is a dominant allele shown in a Punnett square?

_____

_____

💡 **Think it Over**

6. **Contrast** What is the difference between a homozygous organism and a heterozygous organism?

_____

_____

_____

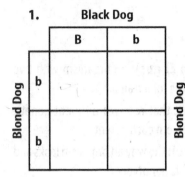

	Black Dog	
1.	B	b
b		
b		

	Black Dog	
2.	B	b
b	B	b
b	B	b

	Black Dog	
3.	B	b
b	Bb	bb
b	Bb	bb

	Black Dog	
4.	B	b
b	Bb	bb
b	Bb	bb

(Blond Dog labels on left side of each square)

How do you use a Punnett square?

You want to know the possible offspring of two dogs. One dog carries heterozygous black-fur traits (*Bb*). The other dog carries homogeneous blond-fur traits (*bb*). How do you complete the Punnett square to find the results? Follow the steps in the figure above.

1. Write the letters representing the alleles from the black dog (Bb) in the top row. Write the letters from the blond dog (bb) in the left column.
2. Write the letter in each column (B or b) in the two squares for that column.
3. Add the letter for each row (b or b) to the squares. You then have two letters in each square.
4. The squares show the possible genotypes of the offspring.

An offspring with a *Bb* genotype will have black fur, and an offspring with a *bb* genotype will have blond fur. In this case, there is one chance in two, or a 50 percent chance, that the offspring will have black fur.

What are the main principles of heredity?

Mendel spent many years repeating his experiments and observing the results. He analyzed the results and reached several conclusions. Mendel's principles of heredity are summarized in the table below.

Mendel's Principles of Heredity
Traits are controlled by alleles on chromosomes.
An allele's effect is dominant or recessive.
When a pair of chromosomes separates during meiosis, the different alleles for a trait move into separate sex cells.

Picture This

7. Identify In step 4, shade the two squares that would result in an offspring with blond fur.

Think it Over

8. Explain What controls traits?

_____

_____

_____

● After You Read

Mini Glossary

alleles (uh LEELZ): the different forms of a trait that a gene may have

dominant (DAH muh nunt): factor that dominates, or covers up, another factor

genetics (juh NE tihks): the study of how traits are inherited through the interactions of alleles

genotype (JEE nuh tipe): genetic makeup of an organism

heredity (huh REH duh tee): passing of traits from parent to offspring

heterozygous (he tuh roh ZI gus): an organism that has two different alleles for a trait

homozygous (hoh muh ZI gus): an organism with two alleles that are the same for a trait

hybrid (HI brud): a plant that receives different genetic information for a trait from each parent

phenotype (FEE nuh tipe): the way an organism looks and behaves as a result of its genotype

Punnett (PUH nut) square: a tool used to predict the number of times certain traits will occur

recessive (rih SE sihv): factor that disappears if a dominant trait is present

1. Review the terms and their definitions in the Mini Glossary. Write a sentence that explains the difference between a dominant allele and a recessive allele.

_____

_____

2. Complete the Punnett square below to show the probability of an offspring having the *DD*, *Dd*, and the *dd* genotypes.

	D	d
D		
d		

3. How can taking a quiz that another student wrote help you prepare for a test?

_____

_____

End of Section

Science Online Visit **glencoe.com** to access your textbook, interactive games, and projects to help you learn more about genetics.

chapter 5

Heredity

section ② Genetics Since Mendel

LE 2.2b Some genes are dominant and some are recessive. Some traits are inherited by mechanisms other than dominance and recessiveness. **3.1a** The processes of sexual reproduction and mutation have given rise to a variety of traits within a species. **3.1b** Changes in environmental conditions can affect the survival of individual organisms with a particular trait. **Also covered:** LE 2.1a, 2.2c

● Before You Read

At dog and cat shows, an animal's owner may be asked to show its pedigree. What do you think a pedigree shows?

_____

_____

_____

● Read to Learn

Incomplete Dominance

A scientist crossed purebred red four-o'clock plants with purebred white four-o'clock plants. He thought the new plants would have all red flowers, but they were pink. Neither allele for flower color was dominant. Next, he crossed the pink-flowered plants with each other. The new plants had red, white, and pink flowers.

He discovered that when the allele for red flowers and the allele for white flowers combined, the result included red flowers, white flowers, and an intermediate, or in-between, phenotype—pink flowers. When the offspring of two homozygous parents show an intermediate phenotype, this inheritance is called **incomplete dominance**.

What are multiple alleles?

A trait that is controlled by more than two alleles is said to be controlled by multiple alleles. A trait controlled by multiple alleles will produce more than three phenotypes of that trait.

What You'll Learn

- how traits are inherited by incomplete dominance
- the difference between multiple alleles and polygenic inheritance
- how sex-linked traits are passed to offspring

Mark the Text

Build Vocabulary Skim the section, circling any words you do not know. After you read the section, review the circled words. Write any words you cannot define on a separate sheet of paper and look up the definitions.

FOLDABLES

Ⓑ Explain Make a layered-look Foldable, as shown below. Write notes under the flaps to explain inheritance patterns.

Inheritance Patterns
Incomplete dominance
Multiple alleles
Polygenic inheritance

What traits are controlled by multiple alleles?

Blood type in humans is an example of a trait controlled by multiple alleles. The alleles for blood type produce six genotypes but only four phenotypes. The alleles for blood type are called A, B, and O. The O allele is recessive to both the A and B alleles. When a person inherits one A allele and one B allele, his or her phenotype is AB. A person with phenotype A blood has the genotype AA or AO. Someone with the phenotype B blood has the genotype BB or BO. A person with phenotype O blood has the genotype OO. ☑

☑ **Reading Check**

1. **Identify** What are the six different blood type genotypes?

_____

_____

_____

Polygenic Inheritance

Eye color is an example of a trait that is produced by a combination of many genes, or polygenic (pah lih JEH nihk) inheritance. **Polygenic inheritance** occurs when a group of gene pairs acts together to produce a trait. Polygenic inheritance results in a wide variety of phenotypes. Examine the eye colors of your classmates. You will likely notice many different shades. For example, you may notice several shades of brown, several shades of green, and so on.

How does the environment affect your genes?

Your environment plays a role in how some of your genes are expressed. Genes can be influenced by an organism's internal or external environment. For example, most male birds are more brightly colored than females. Chemicals in their bodies determine whether or not the gene for brightly colored feathers is expressed.

Your environment plays a role in whether your genes are expressed at all. For example, some people have genes that make them at risk for developing skin cancer. Whether or not they get cancer might depend on external environmental factors. If people who are at risk for skin cancer limit their time in the sun and take care of their skin, they may never develop skin cancer.

💡 **Think it Over**

2. **Draw Conclusions** What environmental factors might affect the size of leaves on a tree?

_____

_____

_____

Human Genes and Mutations

Sometimes genes change. Also, sometimes errors occur in the DNA when it is being copied during cell division. These changes and errors are called mutations. Many mutations are harmful. Some mutations are helpful or have no effect on an organism. Certain chemicals, X rays, and radioactive materials can cause mutations.

What are chromosome disorders?

Problems can happen if the incorrect number of chromosomes is inherited. Mistakes in the process of meiosis can result in an organism with more or fewer chromosomes than normal. Down's syndrome is a disorder in which the person has one more chromosome than normal.

Recessive Genetic Disorders

Many human genetic disorders are caused by recessive genes. Such genetic disorders occur when both parents have a recessive allele responsible for the disorder. Because the parents are heterozygous, they do not show any symptoms of the disorder. However, if each parent passes a recessive allele to the child, the child inherits two recessive alleles and will have the disorder. Cystic fibrosis is a homozygous recessive disorder. It is the most common genetic disorder that can lead to death among Caucasian Americans. People with cystic fibrosis produce thicker mucus than normal. The thick mucus builds up in the lungs and makes it hard to breathe. ☑

Sex Determination

Each egg produced by a female normally contains one X chromosome. Males produce sperm that normally have either one X or one Y chromosome. When a sperm with an X chromosome fertilizes an egg, the offspring is a female, XX. When a sperm with a Y chromosome fertilizes an egg, the offspring is a male, XY. Sometimes chromosomes do not separate during meiosis. When this happens, a person can inherit an unusual number of sex chromosomes.

Sex-Linked Disorders

Some inherited conditions are linked with the X and Y chromosomes. An allele inherited on a sex chromosome is called a __sex-linked gene__. Color blindness is a sex-linked disorder in which people cannot tell the difference between certain colors. The color-blind trait is a recessive allele on the X chromosome. Because males have only one X chromosome, a male with this recessive allele on his X chromosome is color-blind. However, a color-blind female occurs only when both of her X chromosomes have the allele for this trait. ☑

✔ **Reading Check**

3. **Explain** How is cystic fibrosis inherited?

_____

_____

_____

✔ **Reading Check**

4. **Identify** What is one sex-linked disorder?

_____

_____

_____

Pedigrees Trace Traits

You can trace a trait through a family using a pedigree like the one shown below. Males are represented by squares. Females are represented by circles. A completely filled square or circle shows that the person has the trait. A half-colored square or circle shows that the person carries an allele for the trait, but does not have the trait. The pedigree in the figure below shows how the trait for color blindness is carried through a family. In this pedigree, the grandfather was color blind. He married a woman who did not carry the color-blind allele.

Picture This

5. **Infer** In the pedigree, why are there no color-blind women in this family?

_____

_____

_____

_____

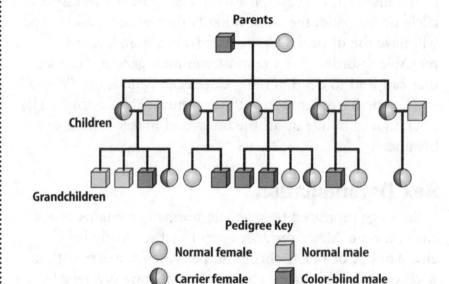

Pedigree Key

○	Normal female	▢	Normal male
◑	Carrier female	■	Color-blind male

Think it Over

6. **Draw Conclusions** Why do you think pedigrees are important for animals bred for show, such as dogs?

_____

_____

_____

How can pedigrees be helpful?

A pedigree can be used by a geneticist to trace a trait in members of a family over several generations. The pedigree allows the geneticist to determine the trait's pattern of inheritance. The geneticist can identify if the trait is recessive, dominant, sex-linked, or follows some other pattern. Geneticists use this information to predict the probability that a baby will be born with a specific trait.

Pedigrees also are used to breed animals and plants for desirable traits. Livestock and plant crops are food sources for humans. Using pedigrees, these organisms can be bred to increase their yield and nutritional content.

● After You Read

Mini Glossary

incomplete dominance: the offspring of two homozygous parents show an intermediate phenotype

polygenic (pah lih JEH nihk) inheritance: a group of gene pairs act together to produce a trait

sex-linked gene: an allele inherited on a sex chromosome

1. Review the terms and their definitions in the Mini Glossary. Choose one term and use it to explain one way that traits can be inherited.

   _____

   _____

   _____

2. Choose one of the question headings in the Read to Learn section. Write the question in the space below. Then write your answer to that question on the lines that follow.

   ┌──┐
   │ **Write your question here.**   │
   │   │
   │   │
   │   │
   └──┘

   _____

   _____

   _____

3. List the words that you circled in the Read to Learn section. Select one of those words and write its definition below.

   _____

   _____

   _____

Science Online Visit **glencoe.com** to access your textbook, interactive games, and projects to help you learn more about genetics since Mendel.

End of Section

chapter 5 Heredity

section ⊜ Biotechnology

LE 3.1c Human activities such as selective breeding and advances in genetic engineering may affect the variations of species.

What You'll Learn
- the importance of advances in genetics
- the steps in making genetically engineered organisms

 Mark the Text

Identify Main Points
Highlight the main idea in each paragraph. Underline the details that support the main idea.

FOLDABLES

C Describe Make a three-tab book, as shown below. Use the Foldable to describe genetic engineering, recombinant DNA, and gene therapy.

| Genetic engineering | Recombinant DNA | Gene Therapy |

● Before You Read

Describe on the lines below what you have heard or read about recent advances in medical research.

_____

_____

_____

● Read to Learn

Why is genetics important?

New developments in genetic research are happening all the time. The principles of heredity are being used to change the world.

Genetic Engineering

Genetic engineering is the use of biological and chemical methods to change the arrangement of DNA that makes up a gene. One use for genetic engineering is to produce large amounts of different medicines. Genes also can be inserted into cells to change how those cells perform their normal functions. Genetic engineering researchers are also looking for new ways to improve crop production and quality.

How is recombinant DNA made?

Making recombinant DNA is one method of genetic engineering. Recombinant DNA is made by inserting a useful section of DNA from one organism into a bacterium. This process is used to make large amounts of insulin, which is used to treat diabetes. Other uses include the production of a growth hormone to treat dwarfism and chemicals used to treat cancer.

How does gene therapy work?

Gene therapy is another kind of genetic engineering. It is used to replace abnormal alleles. In gene therapy, a normal allele is placed in a virus, as shown in the figure below. The virus then delivers the normal allele when it infects the target cell. The normal allele replaces the abnormal one. Scientists are conducting experiments that use gene therapy to test ways of controlling cystic fibrosis and some kinds of cancer. With continued research, gene therapy may be used to cure genetic disorders in the future. ☑

✔ Reading Check

1. **Identify** What is replaced in gene therapy?

_____

_____

_____

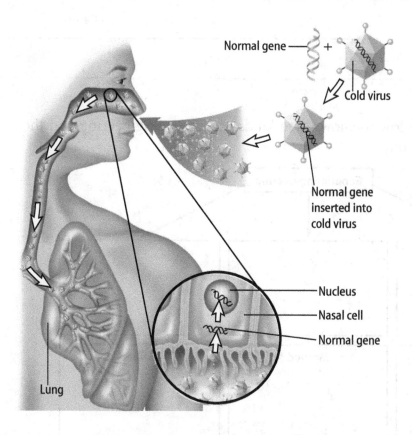

Normal gene — + Cold virus

Normal gene inserted into cold virus

Nucleus
Nasal cell
Normal gene

Lung

Picture This

2. **Explain** Use the figure to explain to a partner how gene therapy works.

How are plants genetically engineered?

Before people knew about genotypes, they selected plants with the most desired traits to breed for the next generation. This process is called selective breeding. Today people also use genetic engineering to improve crop plants. One method is to find the genes that produce desired traits in one plant and then insert those genes into a different plant. Scientists recently made genetically engineered tomatoes with a gene that allows them to be picked green. As these tomatoes are being sent to stores, they continue to ripen. You can then buy ripe, firm tomatoes in the store. The long-term effects of eating genetically engineered plants are not known.

● After You Read

Mini Glossary

genetic engineering: biological and chemical methods to
   change the arrangement of DNA that makes up a gene

1. Review the term and its definition in the Mini Glossary. Write a sentence that explains
   how genetic engineering can improve crop plants.

_____

_____

_____

2. Complete the concept web below to show three kinds of genetic engineering and the
   methods used to carry them out.

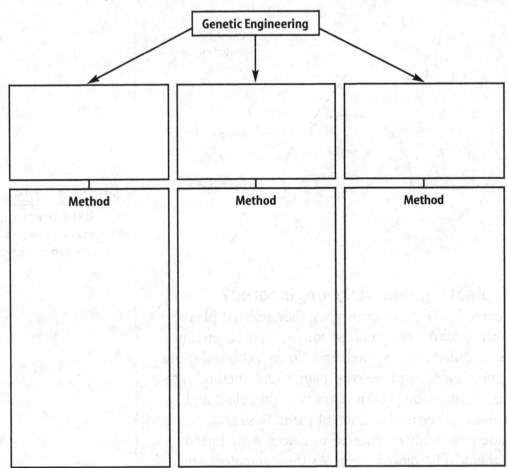

Science **Online** Visit **glencoe.com** to access your textbook, interactive games,
and projects to help you learn more about advances
in genetics.

Regulation and Reproduction

section ❶ The Endocrine System

 LE 1.2h The nervous and endocrine systems interact to control and coordinate the body's responses to changes in the environment, and to regulate growth, development, and reproduction. Hormones are chemicals produced by the endocrine system; hormones regulate many body functions. **Also covered:** LE 1.2a

● Before You Read

Have you ever been suddenly frightened? On the lines below, explain how your body reacted.

_____

_____

What You'll Learn
- how hormones function
- the endocrine glands and the hormones they produce
- how a feedback system works in your body

● Read to Learn

Body Controls

Your endocrine system and your nervous system are your body's control systems. The nervous system sends messages to and from the brain to the rest of your body. The endocrine system sends chemical messages to different parts of your body.

Your body reacts very quickly to messages from the nervous system. Your body reacts more slowly to chemical messages from the endocrine system.

Endocrine Glands

Endocrine glands are tissues that produce hormones. **Hormones** (HOR mohnz) are chemicals that can speed up or slow down certain cell processes. Each endocrine gland releases its hormones directly into the blood. The blood carries the hormone to other parts of the body.

Endocrine glands produce hormones that control the body in many ways. Some endocrine glands help the body handle stressful situations. Other endocrine glands help the body grow and develop. Endocrine glands coordinate the circulation of the blood and help the body digest and absorb food. The endocrine glands and their functions are listed in the table on the next page.

Mark the Text

Identify the Main Point
Underline the main point of each paragraph. Review the main points after you have finished reading the section.

FOLDABLES

Ⓐ **Compare** Make a three-tab book Foldable, as shown below. Use it to compare the functions and the structure of the endocrine system. Include the names of glands and organs that are part of the endocrine system.

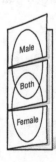

Male

Both

Female

Picture This

1. **Identify** Highlight the names of the endocrine glands located in your brain. Then circle the names of the glands and organs that are involved in reproduction. Which gland is both highlighted and circled?

The Endocrine System		
Endocrine Glands and Organs	**Location in the Body**	**Major Function**
Pineal	in the brain	produces the hormone melatonin that may help regulate your body clock
Pituitary	in the brain	produces hormones that regulate various body activities including growth and reproduction
Thymus	upper chest	produces hormones that help the body fight infections
Thyroid	below the larynx	produces hormones that regulate metabolism (the chemical reactions in the body)
Parathyroid	below the larynx	produces hormones that regulate the body's calcium levels
Adrenals	on top of each kidney	produce several hormones that help your body respond to stress and keep your blood sugar levels stable
Pancreas	between the kidneys	produces hormones that help control blood sugar levels in the bloodstream
Testes (male)	in the scrotum	produce testosterone, a male reproductive hormone
Ovaries (female)	in the pelvic cavity	produce estrogen and progesterone, hormones that regulate the female reproductive cycle

A Negative-Feedback System

The organs and glands of the endocrine system control the amount of hormones in your body by sending chemical messages back and forth to each other. This process is called a negative-feedback system. Follow each step in the figure below to learn more about how a negative feedback system works.

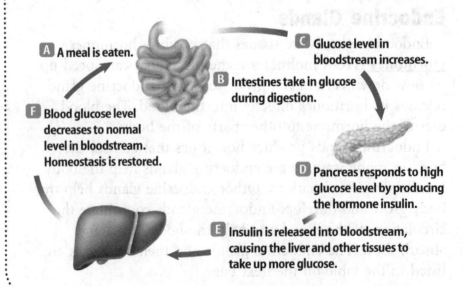

A A meal is eaten.

B Intestines take in glucose during digestion.

C Glucose level in bloodstream increases.

D Pancreas responds to high glucose level by producing the hormone insulin.

E Insulin is released into bloodstream, causing the liver and other tissues to take up more glucose.

F Blood glucose level decreases to normal level in bloodstream. Homeostasis is restored.

Picture This

2. **Identify** Circle the name of the organ that produces insulin.

After You Read

Mini Glossary

hormones (HOR mohnz) chemical messages in the body that speed up or slow down certain cell processes

1. Review the term and its definition in the Mini Glossary. Write a sentence that explains the purpose of hormones in your body.

   _____

   _____

   _____

2. Use the **terms** in the box below to complete the sentences that follow.

adrenals	ovaries	parathyroid	pituitary
testes	thymus	thyroid	

   a. The _____ produces a hormone that helps the body fight infection.

   b. The _____ produces testosterone, while the _____ produce estrogen and progesterone.

   c. The glands that help your body react to stress are known as the _____.

   d. The _____ gland in the brain controls growth.

   e. The _____ and the _____ are located below the larynx.

Science Online Visit **glencoe.com** to access your textbook, interactive games, and projects to help you learn more about the endocrine system.

End of Section

Regulation and Reproduction

section ❷ The Reproductive System

 LE 1.2i The male and female reproductive systems are responsible for producing sex cells necessary for the production of offspring. **4.2a** The male sex cell is the sperm. The female sex cell is the egg. The fertilization of an egg by a sperm results in a fertilized egg. **Also covered:** LE 1.2h

What You'll Learn

- the function of the reproductive system
- the major structures of the male and female reproductive systems
- the stages of the menstrual cycle

Create a Quiz As you study the information in this section, create questions about the information you read. The questions can be used to review the section's content.

Picture This

1. **Explain** Use the diagram to explain to a classmate what the pituitary gland does in females and then have the classmate explain what the pituitary gland does in males.

● Before You Read

On the lines below, describe one way in which a male body differs from a female body.

_____

_____

_____

● Read to Learn

Reproduction and the Endocrine System

Most human body systems are the same in males and females, but the reproductive systems are different. As you can see in the figure below, the pituitary gland makes the sex hormones that control the male and female reproductive systems. Sex hormones are needed to develop sexual characteristics. Sex hormones from the pituitary gland begin the process of making eggs in females and sperm in males. Eggs and sperm pass hereditary information from one generation to the next.

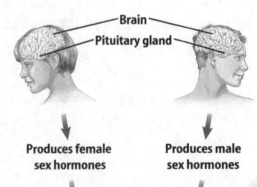

Brain
Pituitary gland

Produces female sex hormones

Produces male sex hormones

Stimulates egg production in ovaries

Stimulates sperm production in testes

The Male Reproductive System

The male reproductive organs are inside and outside the body. As shown in the figure below, the organs outside the body are the penis and the scrotum (SKROH tum). The scrotum contains two organs called testes (TES teez) (singular, *testis*). The **testes** make the male hormone, testosterone (tes TAHS tuh rohn). They also make male reproductive cells, called **sperm**.

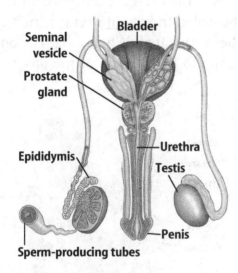

Bladder
Seminal vesicle
Prostate gland
Epididymis
Urethra
Testis
Penis
Sperm-producing tubes

Picture This

2. **Identify** Underline the name of the structure that produces testosterone.

What happens to sperm?

Each sperm cell has a head and tail. The head contains hereditary information. The tail moves back and forth to push the sperm through fluid. Sperm travel out of the testes through sperm ducts that circle the bladder. The seminal vesicle (VEH sih cuhl) provides the sperm with a fluid. The fluid provides energy to the sperm and helps them move. The mixture of sperm and fluid is called **semen** (SEE mun). Semen leaves the body through the urethra. The urethra is the same tube that carries urine from the body.

The Female Reproductive System

Most of the female reproductive organs are inside the body. The female sex organs are called the **ovaries**. The ovaries produce eggs. Eggs are the female reproductive cells.

FOLDABLES

B Explain Make a two-tab book Foldable, as shown below, to record notes about the structures and functions of the male and female reproductive systems.

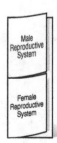

Male Reproductive System

Female Reproductive System

What happens to the eggs?

About once a month, hormones cause one of the ovaries to release an egg. The release of an egg from an ovary is called **ovulation** (ahv yuh LAY shun). After the egg is released, it enters the oviduct. Short, hairlike structures called cilia (SIH lee uh) help move the egg through the oviduct to the uterus (YEW tuh rus). The **uterus** is a muscular organ with thick walls. The fertilized egg develops in the uterus. ✓

As you can see in the figure below, at the lower hollow end of the uterus is the cervix. Connected to the cervix is a muscular tube called the **vagina** (vuh JI nuh). The vagina is also called the birth canal. When a baby is born, it travels through the vagina to the outside of the mother's body.

✔ **Reading Check**

3. Identify the structure the egg enters when it is released from the ovary.

_____

Picture This

4. Explain Trace the path of an egg after ovulation.

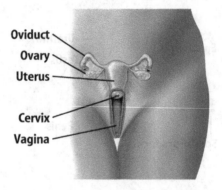

Oviduct
Ovary
Uterus
Cervix
Vagina

The Menstrual Cycle

The **menstrual** (MEN strul) **cycle** is the monthly cycle of changes in the female reproductive system. The menstrual cycle lasts about 28 days. During each cycle, an egg matures, female sex hormones are produced, the uterus prepares to receive a fertilized egg, and menstrual flow occurs. The first menstrual period happens between ages nine and 13 for most females.

What controls the menstrual cycle?

The pituitary gland releases several hormones that control the menstrual cycle. These hormones begin the process that results in the release of the egg from the ovary. They also stimulate the production of two other hormones, estrogen (ES truh jun) and progesterone (proh JES tuh rohn). The interaction of all these hormones causes the menstrual cycle. The menstrual cycle has three parts, or phases.

Phase One of the Menstrual Cycle Phase 1 starts with the menstrual flow, called **menstruation** (men STRAY shun). This flow is made up of blood and tissue cells released from the thickened lining of the uterus. Menstruation lasts up to six days.

Phase Two of the Menstrual Cycle During phase 2 of the menstrual cycle, hormones cause the lining of the uterus to thicken. During phase 2, an egg develops in the ovary. The release of the egg, or ovulation, occurs about 14 days before menstruation begins. The egg must be fertilized within 24 hours or it begins to break down. Sperm can live in a female's body for up to three days, so fertilization can happen soon after ovulation. ☑

Phase Three of the Menstrual Cycle During phase 3, the lining of the uterus continues to thicken. If a fertilized egg arrives, the thickened lining of the uterus begins to support and feed the developing embryo. If the egg is not fertilized, the lining of the uterus breaks down and the menstrual cycle starts over. The changes to the uterus during the phases of the menstrual cycle are shown in the figure below.

✔ **Reading Check**

5. **Explain** For how long after ovulation can an egg be fertilized ?

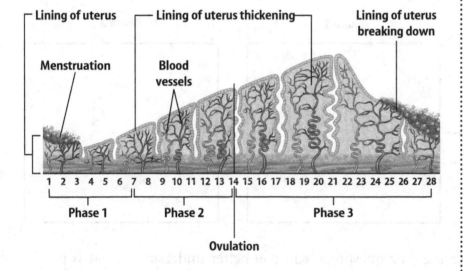

Lining of uterus — Lining of uterus thickening — Lining of uterus breaking down

Menstruation   Blood vessels

1 2 3 4 5 6 7 8 9 10 11 12 13 14 15 16 17 18 19 20 21 22 23 24 25 26 27 28

Phase 1   Phase 2   Phase 3

Ovulation

Picture This

6. **Identify** During which phase is the lining of the uterus the thickest?

What is menopause?

For most females, the menstrual cycle ends between ages 45 and 60. Menopause occurs when the menstrual cycle ends. During menopause, the ovaries produce fewer and fewer sex hormones. The completion of menopause may take several years.

● After You Read

Mini Glossary

menstrual (MEN strul) cycle: the monthly cycle of changes in the female reproductive system

menstruation (men STRAY shun): phase 1 of the menstrual cycle, when blood and tissue cells are released from the thickened lining of the uterus

ovaries: the female sex organs that produce eggs

ovulation (ahv yuh LAY shun): the process that releases an egg from an ovary

semen (SEE mun): a mixture of sperm and fluid

sperm: male reproductive cells

testes (TES teez): male reproductive organs that produce sperm and the male hormone, testosterone

uterus (YEW tuh rus): the female organ in which a fertilized egg develops

vagina (vuh JI nuh): part of the female reproductive system, a muscular tube connected to the cervix

1. Review the terms and their definitions in the Mini Glossary. Use at least two of the terms in a sentence to describe either the male or female reproductive system.

_____

_____

2. Complete the flow chart below by writing a phrase that describes what happens during each phase of the menstrual cycle.

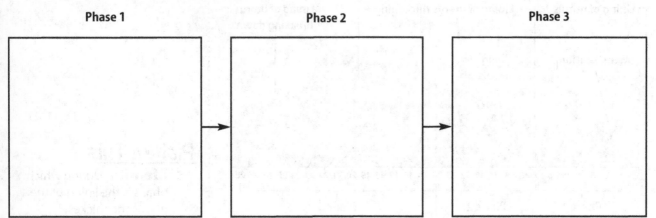

Phase 1 **Phase 2** **Phase 3**

3. How did writing and answering quiz questions help you better understand what you have read?

_____

_____

End of Section

Science Online Visit **glencoe.com** to access your textbook, interactive games, and projects to help you learn more about the reproductive system.

Regulation and Reproduction

section ❸ Human Life Stages

 LE 4.2a The male sex cell is the sperm. The female sex cell is the egg. The fertilization of an egg by a sperm results in a fertilized egg. **4.3a** Multicellular organisms exhibit complex changes in development, which begin after fertilization. The fertilized egg undergoes numerous cellular divisions that will result in a multicellular organism, with each cell having identical genetic information. **Also covered:** LE 4.1c, 4.1d, 4.3b, 4.3c, 4.4c

● Before You Read

Describe the changes that you have seen happen in a young child over a year's time.

_____

_____

What You'll Learn

- how a human egg is fertilized
- how the embryo and fetus develop
- the life stages of infancy, childhood, adolescence, and adulthood

● Read to Learn

Fertilization

A human develops from an egg that has been fertilized by a sperm. As sperm enter the vagina, they come in contact with chemicals given off in the vagina. These chemicals cause changes in the sperm that make it possible for the sperm to fertilize the egg. A sperm that touches the egg releases an enzyme. This enzyme helps the sperm enter the egg. Fertilization takes place when sperm and egg unite.

How does a zygote form?

Once a sperm enters an egg, the nucleus of the sperm joins with the nucleus of the egg. This joining creates a fertilized cell called the zygote (ZI goht).

Multiple Births

Mothers sometimes give birth to two or more babies at once. These are called multiple births. Multiple births can happen when an ovary releases more than one egg at a time or when a zygote divides into two or more zygotes.

Sometimes an ovary releases two eggs at the same time. If both eggs are fertilized, fraternal twins are born. Fraternal twins do not have the same hereditary information because they came from two different eggs. Fraternal twins can be the same or different sexes. ☑

Mark the Text

Locate Information As you read this section, highlight the portions of the text that describe the changes to an embryo and fetus during pregnancy.

☑ Reading Check

1. **Explain** How many eggs must be fertilized for fraternal twins to be born?

_____

Before Birth

Infancy

Childhood

Adolescence

Adulthood

Picture This

2. **Explain** Place the numbers 1, 2, or 3 beside the following words in the figure to show the order in which they happen: Fertilization, Implantation, and Ovulation.

Think it Over

3. **Conclude** Why is the mother's good nutrition important to the embryo?

_____

_____

When are twins identical?

Identical twins develop from one egg that has been fertilized by one sperm. The zygote divides into two separate zygotes. Identical twins have the same hereditary information because they come from the same fertilized egg. Identical twins are always the same sex.

Development Before Birth

As you can see in the figure below, the zygote moves along the oviduct to the uterus. During this time, the zygote goes through many cell divisions. After about seven days, the zygote attaches to the wall of the uterus. This is called implantation. A zygote that attaches to the wall of the uterus will develop into a baby in about nine months. The period of development from fertilized egg to birth is called **pregnancy**.

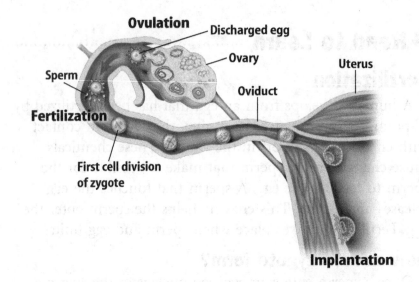

When does a zygote become an embryo?

After the zygote attaches to the wall of the uterus, it is called an **embryo** (EM bree oh).

How does an embryo get food and oxygen?

After an embryo attaches to the uterus, a placenta (pluh SEN tuh) develops from tissues of the uterus and the embryo. An umbilical (um BIH lih kul) cord connects the embryo to the placenta. Blood vessels in the umbilical cord carry nutrients and oxygen from the mother's blood through the placenta to the embryo. Other blood vessels in the umbilical cord carry wastes from the embryo to the mother's blood.

What protects the embryo?

During the third week of pregnancy, a thin membrane called the **amniotic** (am nee AH tihk) **sac** forms around the embryo. The amniotic sac is filled with a clear fluid called amniotic fluid. The amniotic fluid acts as a cushion to protect the embryo. Amniotic fluid also stores nutrients and wastes. ☑

When does the embryo develop body parts?

During the first two months of development, the embryo's major organs form and the heart begins to beat. At five weeks, the embryo has a head with eyes, nose, and mouth. During the sixth and seventh weeks, fingers and toes develop.

How does a fetus develop?

Pregnancy in humans lasts about 38 to 39 weeks. After the first two months of pregnancy, the developing embryo is called a **fetus** (FEE tus). The fetus has all its body organs and is about 8 cm to 9 cm long. By the end of the seventh month of pregnancy, the fetus is 30 cm to 38 cm long. By the ninth month, the fetus is about 50 cm long. It weighs from 2.5 kg to 3.5 kg. During the ninth month, the fetus moves to a head-down position within the uterus. This is the best position for delivery.

The Birthing Process

The process of childbirth begins when the muscles of the uterus start to contract. This is called labor. As the contractions increase, the amniotic sac breaks and the fluid comes out. Over a period of hours, the contractions cause the opening of the uterus to get wider. More powerful and more frequent contractions push the baby out through the vagina into the world. After the baby is born, more contractions push the placenta out of the mother's body. ☑

When are babies delivered through surgery?

Sometimes babies cannot be born through the birth canal. In these cases, a baby is delivered through surgery called a cesarean (suh SEER ee uhn) section. In this surgery, a cut is made in the abdominal wall of the mother, then through the wall of the uterus. The baby is delivered through this opening.

☑ **Reading Check**

4. **Explain** What are the functions of the amniotic fluid?

_____

_____

_____

☑ **Reading Check**

5. **Identify** two things contractions help push from the mother's body.

_____

_____

_____

What happens after birth?

After birth, the baby is still attached to the umbilical cord. Two clamps are placed on the umbilical cord and it is cut between the clamps. The scar where the cord was attached is called the navel.

The experiences that a fetus goes through during childbirth can cause **fetal stress.** After it is born, the fetus must adapt from a dark, watery environment with a constant temperature to an environment with more light, less water, and changes in temperature. The first four weeks after birth are known as the neonatal (nee oh NAY tul) period. Neonatal means "newborn." During this time the baby's body begins to function normally.

Stages After Birth

After birth, four stages of development occur: infancy, childhood, adolescence, and adulthood. Infancy lasts from birth to around 18 months of age. Childhood lasts from the end of infancy to puberty (PYEW bur tee), the time of development when a person becomes physically able to reproduce. Adolescence is the teen years. Adulthood lasts from about the early 20s until death. ☑

How does a baby develop during infancy?

Human babies depend on other humans for their survival. During infancy a baby learns how to coordinate the movements of its body, as shown in the figure below. Its mental abilities increase, and it grows rapidly. Many infants triple their weight in the first year of life.

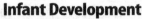

Infant Development

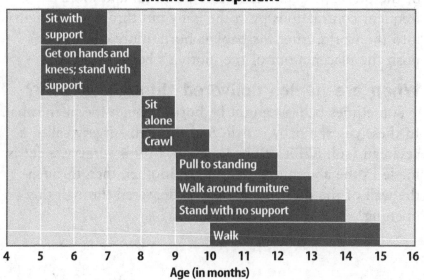

Age (in months)
Sit with support
Get on hands and knees; stand with support
Sit alone
Crawl
Pull to standing
Walk around furniture
Stand with no support
Walk

4 5 6 7 8 9 10 11 12 13 14 15 16
Age (in months)

✔ Reading Check

6. Explain When do humans become physically able to reproduce?

_____

_____

Picture This

7. Identify Study the table to answer the following questions.

a. At what age can most infants sit alone?

_____

b. At what age do infants learn to walk?

_____

What developments take place in childhood?

Childhood lasts from the age of about 18 months to about 12 years. Growth during childhood is rapid. Between two and three years of age, the child learns to control his or her bladder and bowels. Most children also can speak in simple sentences at age two or three. Around age four, the child can get dressed and undressed with some help. By age five, many children can read some words. Throughout childhood, children develop their abilities to speak, read, write, and reason.

What happens during adolescence?

Adolescence begins at about age 12 or 13 and ends at about age 20. Puberty is a part of adolescence. For girls, puberty happens between ages nine and 13. For boys, puberty occurs between ages 13 and 16. During puberty, hormones produced in the pituitary gland cause changes in the body. Females develop breasts, pubic and underarm hair, and fatty tissue around the thighs and buttocks. Males develop deeper voices, increased muscle size, and facial, pubic, and underarm hair. ☑

Adolescence is usually when a final growth spurt occurs. Most girls begin this final growth phase around age 11 and end around age 16. For boys, the final growth spurt begins around age 13 and ends around age 18. However, different people have different growth rates.

What happens during adulthood?

Adulthood begins when adolescence ends, at about age 20, and continues through old age. From about age 45 to age 60, middle-aged adults begin to lose physical strength. Their blood circulation and breathing become less efficient. Bones break more easily, and skin becomes wrinkled. ☑

What changes occur in older adults?

After age 60, adults may have an overall decline in their health. Their body systems do not work as well as they once did. Muscles and joints become less flexible. Bones become thinner and break more easily. Older adults may lose some of their ability to hear and see. Their lungs and heart do not work as well as they used to. Eating well and exercising throughout life can help delay these changes.

☑ **Reading Check**

8. Identify When do most girls experience puberty?

_____

_____

_____

☑ **Reading Check**

9. Explain What physical changes occur during middle age?

_____

_____

_____

● After You Read

Mini Glossary

amniotic (am nee AH tihk) sac: a thin membrane that forms around the embryo, acting as a cushion and a place to store nutrients and wastes

embryo (EHM bree oh): a fertilized egg or zygote after it attaches to the wall of the uterus

fetal stress: the experiences that a fetus goes through during childbirth

fetus (FEE tus): a developing human embryo after two months of pregnancy

pregnancy: the period of development from fertilized egg to birth

1. Review the terms and their definitions in the Mini Glossary. Write one or two sentences that explain the relationship of a zygote, an embryo, and a fetus.

_____

_____

_____

2. Fill in the table below to identify and describe the stages of development after birth.

Stage of Development	Period of Time	Development Changes
	Birth to 18 months	
	18 months to 12 years	
	12 years to 20 years	
	20 years to 60 years	
	After age 60	

End of Section

 Science ◐nline Visit **glencoe.com** to access your textbook, interactive games, and projects to help you learn more about human life stages.

88 Regulation and Reproduction

Adaptations over Time

section ❶ Ideas About Evolution

LE 3.1b Individual organisms with certain traits are more likely to survive and have offspring than individuals without those traits. **3.2d** Although the time needed for change in a species is usually great, some species of insects and bacteria have undergone significant change in just a few years. **Also covered:** LE 7.1a, 7.2b

● Before You Read

In what ways are you like your parents or other relatives?

_____

_____

_____

_____

● Read to Learn

Early Models of Evolution

There are millions of species of plants, animals, and other organisms living on Earth today. A **species** is a group of organisms that share similar characteristics and can reproduce among themselves to produce fertile offspring. The characteristics of a species that are passed from parent to offspring are called inherited characteristics. Change in these inherited characteristics over time is **evolution**.

What was Lamarck's hypothesis?

In 1809, Jean Baptiste de Lamarck proposed a hypothesis to explain how species change over time. He said that characteristics, or traits, that a parent organism develops during its lifetime are inherited by its offspring. Lamarck's hypothesis is called the inheritance of acquired characteristics. According to Lamarck's hypothesis, if a parent develops large muscles through exercise or hard work, the trait of large muscles would be passed on to the offspring. Scientists tested Lamarck's hypothesis by collecting data on traits that are passed from parent to offspring. The data did not support Lamarck's hypothesis.

What You'll Learn

- Lamarck's hypothesis of acquired characteristics
- Darwin's theory of natural selection
- variations in organisms
- the difference between gradualism and punctuated equilibrium

Study Coach

Ask Questions Read each question heading. Then work with a partner to write questions about the information related to the heading. Take turns asking and answering the questions. Use the questions as a study guide about evolution.

🔅 Think it Over

1. **Conclude** Do scientists today support Lamarck's hypothesis? Explain.

_____

_____

_____

_____

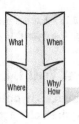

What | When

Where | Why/How

Picture This

2. **Describe** the location of the Galápagos Islands.

_____

_____

_____

☑ **Reading Check**

3. **Identify** How did finches who ate seeds and nuts use their beaks?

_____

_____

_____

Darwin's Model of Evolution

In 1831, Charles Darwin set out on a journey from England that took him to the Galápagos Islands. The Galápagos Islands, shown on the map below, are off the coast of Ecuador. Darwin was amazed by the variety of life he saw on these islands. He hypothesized that plants and animals living on the Galápagos Islands originally came from Central and South America. He noted that the species on the islands were similar in many ways to the species he had seen on the mainland. However, Darwin observed different traits in many species on the islands as well. Darwin studied several species and developed hypotheses to explain the differences in traits he observed.

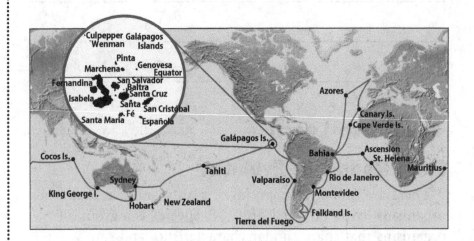

What did Darwin observe?

Darwin observed 13 species of finches on the Galápagos Islands. He noticed that all 13 species were similar except for three characteristics—body size, beak shape, and eating habits. Darwin concluded that the different species of finches must have had to compete with each other for food. Finches that had beak shapes that allowed them to eat available food survived longer and had more offspring than finches without those kinds of beak shapes. After many generations, these groups of finches became separate species.

Darwin observed that the beak shape of each species of Galápagos finch is related to its eating habits. Darwin observed finches that ate nuts and seeds. Their beaks were short and strong for breaking hard shells. He observed finches that fed on insects. They had long, narrow beaks for finding the insects beneath tree bark. ☑

Natural Selection

In the mid-1800s, Darwin developed a theory of evolution that is accepted by most scientists today. He described his ideas in a book called *On the Origin of Species*.

What was Darwin's theory?

Darwin's theory became known as the theory of evolution by natural selection. **Natural selection** means that organisms with traits best suited to their environment are more likely to survive and reproduce. Their traits are passed to more offspring. The principles of natural selection are shown in the table below. ☑

The Principles of Natural Selection
1. Organisms produce more offspring than can survive.
2. Differences, or variations, occur among individuals of a species.
3. Some variations are passed to offspring.
4. Some variations are helpful. Individuals with helpful variations are better able to suvive and reproduce.
5. Over time, the offspring of individuals with helpful variations increase and become a larger percentage of the population. Eventually, they may become a separate species.

Variation and Adaptation

Darwin's theory of evolution by natural selection focuses on the variations of species' members. A **variation** is an inherited trait that makes an individual organism different from other members of its species. Variations happen when there are permanent changes, or mutations, in an organism's genes. Some mutations produce small variations, such as differences in the shape of human hairlines. Other mutations produce large variations, such as fruit without seeds. Over time, more and more members of a species might inherit these variations. If individuals with these variations continue to survive and reproduce over time, a new species can evolve.

Some variations are more helpful than others. An **adaptation** is any variation that makes an organism better suited to its environment. Adaptations can include an organism's color, shape, behavior, or chemical makeup. Camouflage (KA muh flahj) is an adaptation. An organism that is camouflaged can blend into its environment. Camouflage makes it easier for the organism to hide, increasing the chances that it will survive and reproduce. ☑

Copyright © Glencoe/McGraw-Hill, a division of The McGraw-Hill Companies, Inc.

✔ **Reading Check**

4. **Explain** According to the theory of evolution by natural selection, which organisms are most likely to survive and reproduce?

_____

_____

_____

✔ **Reading Check**

5. **Determine** How does camouflage help an organism survive?

_____

_____

_____

How do changes in genes affect species?

Over time, changes in the genes of a species might change the appearance of the species. As the inherited traits of a species of seed-eating Galápagos finch changed, so did the size and shape of its beak. Environmental conditions can help bring about these changes. When individuals of the same species move into an area, they bring genes and variations. When they move out of an area, they remove their genes and variations. Suppose a family from a different country moves to your neighborhood. They might bring different foods, customs, and ways of speaking. In a similar way, when new individuals enter an existing population, they can bring different genes and variations.

Does geographic isolation affect evolution?

Sometimes geologic features such as mountains or lakes can separate a group of individuals from all the other members of the population. Over time, variations that are not found in the larger population might become common in the smaller, separate population. Also, gene mutations could add variations to the smaller population. After many generations, the two populations can become so different that they can no longer breed with each other. They become two different species. For example, Portuguese sailors brought European rabbits to the Canary Islands. European rabbits feed during the day and grow fairly large. In order to survive the warm temperatures of the Canary Islands, the European rabbits, over many generations, developed large eyes and fed at night. The Canary Island rabbits eventually became a separate species. ☑

The Speed of Evolution

Scientists do not agree on how quickly evolution happens. Some hypothesize that it happens slowly, over hundreds of millions of years. Others hypothesize that it can happen quickly. Most scientists agree that there is evidence to support both hypotheses.

What is gradualism?

Darwin hypothesized that evolution happens slowly. His hypothesis is called gradualism. **Gradualism** is a hypothesis that describes evolution as a slow, continuing process in which one species changes to a new species over millions or hundreds of millions of years.

✔ Reading Check

6. Infer What two factors affected the development of new species?

FOLDABLES

B Compare Make a three-tab Foldable, as shown below, to compare gradualism and punctuated equilibrium.

What is punctuated equilibrium?

Gradualism does not explain the evolution of all species. For some species, fossil records show that one species suddenly changes into another. **Punctuated equilibrium** is a hypothesis that describes evolution as a rapid process in which one species changes suddenly to a new species. Rapid evolution happens when the mutation of a few genes results in a new species over a fairly short period of time. The figure below shows how punctuated equilibrium describes the evolution of the brown bear.

Hypothesized Evolution of the Brown Bear

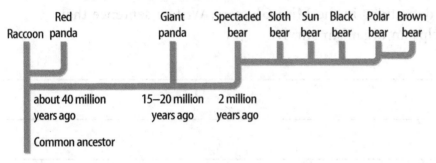

Picture This

7. Identify Circle the name of the common ancestor of the giant panda and the brown bear.

Is punctuated equilibrium happening today?

Evolution by punctuated equilibrium can happen over a few thousand or hundreds of thousands of years. Sometimes, evolution can happen even faster than that. For example, many species of bacteria have changed into new species in only a few decades. Many disease-causing bacteria species were once easily killed by the antibiotic penicillin. Some of these species are no longer harmed by penicillin. These bacteria have become resistant to penicillin.

These penicillin-resistant bacteria evolved quickly. The bacteria changed because some individuals had variations that allowed them to survive even when exposed to penicillin. Other individuals could not survive. The bacteria that had the penicillin-resistant variation survived to reproduce and pass this trait to their offspring. Over a period of time, all of the bacteria in the population had the variation for penicillin resistance.

Think it Over

8. Analyze What allowed some bacteria to survive while other bacteria were killed by penicillin?

_____

_____

_____

● After You Read

Mini Glossary

adaptation: any variation that makes an organism better suited to its environment

evolution: change in inherited characteristics over time

gradualism: hypothesis that describes evolution as a slow, ongoing process by which one species changes to a new species

natural selection: theory that states that organisms with traits best suited to their environment are more likely to survive and reproduce

punctuated equilibrium: hypothesis that says rapid evolution comes about when the mutation of a few genes results in the appearance of a new species over a relatively short period of time

species: group of organisms that share similar characteristics and can reproduce among themselves to produce fertile offspring

variation: inherited trait that makes an individual different from other members of its species

1. Review the terms and their definitions in the Mini Glossary. Write a sentence that describes a variation that helps an organism survive.

_____

_____

_____

2. Complete the chart below to explain the models of evolution listed in the chart.

Theory or Model	Description
Hypothesis of acquired characteristics	
Theory of evolution by natural selection	
Gradualism	
Punctuated equilibrium	

 Visit **glencoe.com** to access your textbook, interactive games, and projects to help you learn more about early models of evolution.

section ② Clues About Evolution

LE 3.2b Extinction of a species occurs when the environment changes and the adaptive characteristics of a species are insufficient to permit its survival.
PS 2.1f Fossils can be used to study past climates and environments. **Also covered:** LE 3.2c

● Before You Read

Have you ever seen a fossil? On the lines below, tell what kind of fossil it was and where you saw it.

_____

_____

_____

What You'll Learn
- why fossils provide evidence of evolution
- how relative and radiometric dating are used to estimate the age of fossils
- five types of evidence for evolution

● Read to Learn

Clues from Fossils

Paleontologists are scientists who study the past by collecting and examining fossils. A fossil is the remains of an ancient organism or an imprint left behind by the organism.

The Green River Formation is one of the richest fossil deposits in the world. It covers parts of Wyoming, Utah, and Colorado. About 50 million years ago, during the Eocene Epoch, this area was covered by lakes. By studying fossils from the Green River Formation, paleontologists have learned that fish, crocodiles, and lizards lived in the lakes. After the animals died, they were covered with silt and mud. Over millions of years, they became fossils.

Types of Fossils

Most of the evidence for evolution comes from fossils. Most fossils are found in sedimentary rock. **Sedimentary rock** is formed when layers of sand, silt, clay, or mud are pressed and cemented together or when minerals are deposited from a solution. Fossils are most often found in a sedimentary rock called limestone. ☑

Mark the Text

Identify Unfamiliar Words Skim the reading and underline any word that you do not know. At the end of each paragraph review the words you have underlined and see if you can define them. If you cannot, look up the word and write its definition in the margin.

✓ Reading Check

1. **Explain** What is the main source of evidence for evolution?

_____

_____

Copyright © Glencoe/McGraw-Hill, a division of The McGraw-Hill Companies, Inc.

ⓒ Describe Make a two-tab concept map Foldable, as shown below, to describe the two methods scientists use to date fossils—relative dating and radiometric dating.

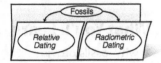

2. Identify Name two things scientists can learn about organisms from fossils.

_____

_____

_____

Determining a Fossil's Age

Paleontologists study the rock layers that fossils are found in. The rocks provide clues about the age of the fossils. Some of these clues include information about the geologic time period in which it was formed. Information may include weather, geology, and other organisms that were alive. Paleontologists have two ways of estimating the age of rocks and fossils—relative dating and radiometric dating.

What is relative dating?

Relative dating is based on the fact that younger rock layers usually lie on top of older rock layers. Relative dating gives only an estimate of a fossil's age. Scientists compare the ages of rock layers found above and below the fossil layer. For example, if a 50-million-year-old rock layer lies below a fossil and a 35-million-year-old rock layer is above the fossil, then the fossil is probably between 35 million and 50 million years old.

What is radiometric dating?

Radiometric dating gives an estimate of the age of a rock layer that is more exact. This method of dating fossils uses radioactive elements. A **radioactive element** gives off a steady amount of radiation as it slowly changes to a nonradioactive element. Each radioactive element gives off radiation at a different rate. Scientists estimate the age of the rock by comparing the amount of radioactive element with the amount of nonradioactive element in the rock.

Fossils and Evolution

Fossils provide a record of organisms that lived in the past. However, the fossil record has gaps, much like missing pages in a book. The gaps exist because most organisms do not become fossils. Even though there are gaps, scientists have still been able to draw conclusions from the fossil records. For instance, they have learned that simple organisms were the first forms of life to appear on Earth. More complex forms of life appeared later.

Fossil discoveries are made all over the world. When scientists find fossils, they make models that show what the organisms might have looked like when they were alive. Scientists can use fossils to find out whether organisms lived in family groups or alone, what they ate, and what kind of environment they lived in. Most fossils are from extinct organisms. ✓

More Clues About Evolution

Besides fossils, there are other clues about evolution. Some kinds of evolution can be observed today. The development of penicillin-resistant bacteria is a direct observation of evolution. Another direct observation of evolution is the development of insect species that are resistant to pesticides.

What is embryology?

The study of embryos and their development is called **embryology** (em bree AH luh jee). An embryo is the earliest growth stage of an organism. The embryos of many different species are similar. The embryos of fish, birds, reptiles, and mammals have tails. As the organisms grow, the fish, birds, and reptiles keep their tails, but many mammals do not. Because the embryos of vertebrates are similar, scientists hypothesize that vertebrates come from a common ancestor.

What are homologous structures?

Body parts that are similar in origin and structure are called **homologous** (hoh MAH luh gus). Some homologous structures have the same function, but others do not. If two or more species have homologous structures, they probably have common ancestors. The figure below shows several homologous structures.

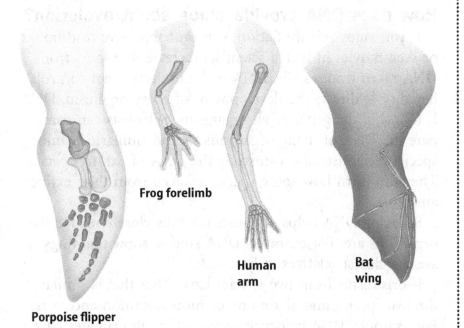

Frog forelimb

Porpoise flipper

Human arm

Bat wing

FOLDABLES

D List Make a half-book Foldable, as shown below, to list examples of evolution and explanations of how the examples show evidence of evolution.

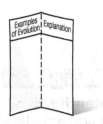

Picture This

3. **Describe** Above each structure, list one way the organism uses that structure.

What are vestigial structures?

The bodies of some organisms have structures known as vestigial (veh STIH jee ul) structures. **Vestigial structures** do not seem to have any use, or function. Vestigial structures provide evidence for evolution. Scientists hypothesize that vestigial structures are body parts that were useful in an ancestor. Humans have three small muscles around each ear that are vestigial. The figure below shows the location of these muscles. In some mammals, such as horses, these muscles are large. They allow a horse to turn its ears toward the source of a sound. ☑

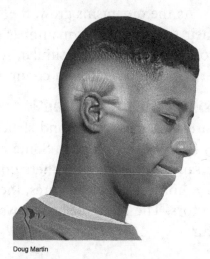

Doug Martin

How does DNA provide clues about evolution?

If you enjoy science fiction, you probably have read books or seen movies in which scientists recreate dinosaurs from DNA taken from fossils. DNA is the molecule that controls heredity. It directs the development of every organism. DNA is found in the genes of all organisms. Scientists can compare the DNA of living organisms to find similarities among species. Scientists also can study the DNA of extinct species. They can learn how some species evolved from their extinct ancestors.

Studying DNA helps scientists see how closely related the organisms are. For example, DNA studies show that dogs are the closest relatives of bears. ☑

If organisms from two species have DNA that is similar, the two species may share one or more common ancestors. For example, DNA evidence suggests that all primates have a common ancestor. Primates include chimpanzees, gorillas, orangutans, and humans.

● After You Read

Mini Glossary

embryology (em bree AH luh jee): the study of embryos and their development

homologous (hoh MAH luh gus): body parts that are similar in origin and structure

radioactive element: an element that gives off a steady amount of radiation as it slowly changes to a nonradioactive element

sedimentary rock: rock in which most fossils are found, formed when layers of sand, silt, clay, or mud are pressed and cemented together, or when minerals are deposited from a solution

vestigial (veh STIH jee ul) structures: structures that do not seem to have a function

1. Review the terms and their definitions in the Mini Glossary. Choose one of the terms and write a sentence that explains how it provides a clue to evolution.

   _____

   _____

   _____

2. In the web diagram below, list the clues that scientists have as evidence of evolution.

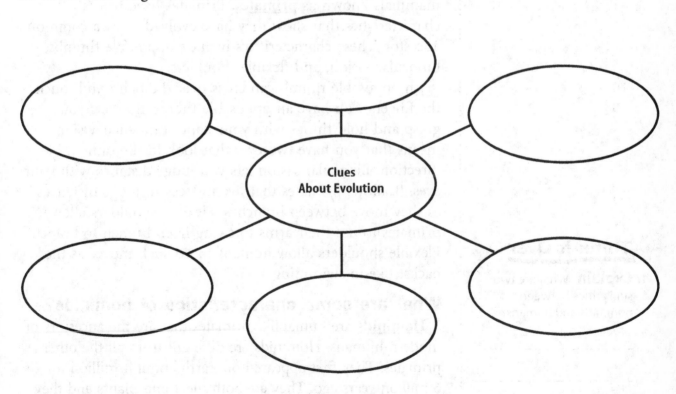

Clues About Evolution

Science Online Visit **glencoe.com** to access your textbook, interactive games, and projects to help you learn more about the clues of evolution.

End of Section

Adaptations over Time

section ❸ The Evolution of Primates

 LE 3.1b Changes in environmental conditions can affect the survival of individual organisms with a particular trait. Individual organisms with certain traits are more likely to survive and have offspring than individuals without those traits. **Also covered:** LE 1.1h, 2.2a, 7.2b

What You'll Learn

- the differences among living primates
- the adaptations of primates
- the evolutionary history of modern primates

● Before You Read

Describe the appearance and behavior of a primate such as monkeys and gorillas.

_____

_____

_____

Mark the Text

Identify Main Points

Underline the main idea of each paragraph. Then circle one supporting detail.

● Read to Learn

Primates

Humans, monkeys, and apes belong to a group of mammals known as **primates**. Primates have several characteristics that show they have evolved from a common ancestor. These characteristics include opposable thumbs, binocular vision, and flexible shoulders.

An opposable thumb can cross over the palm and touch the fingers. You have an opposable thumb that lets you grasp and hold things with your hand. Binocular vision means that you have two eyes that look in the same direction. Binocular vision lets you judge distance with your eyes. It allows primates that live in trees to judge distances as they move between branches. Flexible shoulders allow primates to use their arms to swing from branch to branch. Flexible shoulders allow humans to do such moves as the backstroke in swimming.

What are some characteristics of hominids?

Hominids are humanlike primates that are the ancestors of modern humans. Hominids are different from all the other primates. They first appeared on Earth about 4 million to 6 million years ago. They ate both meat and plants and they walked upright on two legs.

💡 Think it Over

1. **Explain** What are two similarities between hominids and humans?

_____

_____

_____

Where have fossils of hominids been found?

In the 1920s, scientists discovered a fossil skull in South Africa. The skull had a small space for the brain, but it had a humanlike jaw and teeth. The fossil was named *Australopithecus*. It was one of the oldest hominids that had ever been discovered. In 1974, scientists found an almost-complete skeleton of *Australopithecus* in northern Africa. It had a small brain and may have walked upright. This fossil shows that modern hominids might have evolved from a common ancestor. ☑

Who were the ancestors of early humans?

In the 1960s, scientists discovered a hominid fossil named *Homo habilis* that was estimated to be 1.5 million to 2 million years old. Scientists hypothesize that *Homo habilis* changed into another species, called *Homo erectus*, about 1.6 million years ago. These two hominids are thought to be ancestors of humans because they had larger brains and more humanlike features than *Australopithecus*.

Humans

Fossil records show that **_Homo sapiens_** evolved about 400,000 years ago. By 125,000 years ago, two early human groups probably lived in parts of Africa and Europe. These two groups were the Neanderthals (nee AN dur tawlz) and Cro-Magnon humans.

Who were the Neanderthals?

Neanderthals had short, heavy bodies with thick bones, small chins, and heavy browridges. They lived in caves in family groups. They used stone tools to hunt large animals. Neanderthals are probably not direct ancestors of modern humans.

Who were the Cro-Magnon humans?

The fossils of Cro-Magnon humans have been found in Europe, Asia, and Australia. They are between 10,000 and about 40,000 years old. Cro-Magnon humans looked very much like modern humans. They lived in caves, made stone carvings, and buried their dead. Cro-Magnon humans are thought to be direct ancestors of early humans. Early humans are called *Homo sapiens*. Modern humans are called *Homo sapiens sapiens*. Fossil evidence shows that modern humans evolved from *Homo sapiens*.

✔ **Reading Check**

2. Identify two characteristics of *Australopithecus*.

_____

_____

💡 **Think it Over**

3. Compare Name two ways that Neanderthals and Cro-Magnon humans were similar.

_____

_____

_____

● After You Read

Mini Glossary

hominids: humanlike primates that lived about 4 million to 6 million years ago and were different from the other primates

Homo sapiens: direct ancestors of humans

primate: group of mammals to which humans, monkeys, and apes belong

1. Review the terms and their definitions in the Mini Glossary. Choose one term and write a sentence that describes how it is related to modern humans.

_____

_____

_____

2. In the boxes below, show the sequence of the evolution of the ancestors of modern humans. Write down how long ago scientists believe each of the following human ancestors first appeared: hominids, *Homo habilis, Homo erectus, Homo sapiens,* Neanderthals and Cro-Magnon humans. The first box has been completed for you.

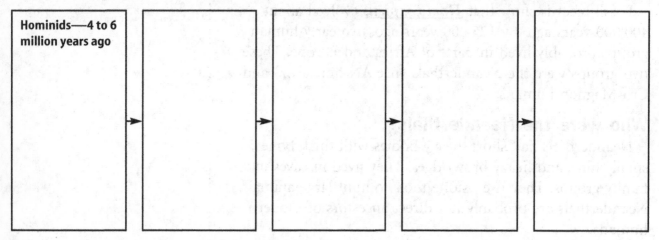

Hominids—4 to 6 million years ago →   →   →   →

3. How did you benefit from underlining main ideas in paragraphs?

_____

_____

_____

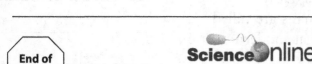

End of Section

Science Online Visit **glencoe.com** to access your textbook, interactive games, and projects to help you learn more about the evolution of primates.

chapter 8 Conserving Resources

section ❶ Resources

 PS 4.1a The Sun is a major source of energy for Earth. Other sources of energy include nuclear and geothermal energy. **4.1b** Fossil fuels contain stored solar energy and are considered nonrenewable resources. Solar energy, wind, moving water, and biomass are some examples of renewable energy resources.

● Before You Read

Identify two objects in the room you are in. What products from the environment were used to make them?

_____

_____

● Read to Learn

Natural Resources

An earthworm eats decaying plant material. A robin catches the worm and flies to a tree. The leaves of the tree use sunlight during photosynthesis. Leaves fall to the ground and decay. What do these living things have in common? They rely on Earth's natural resources. **Natural resources** are the parts of the environment that are useful or necessary for the survival of living organisms. Like other organisms, humans need food, air, and water. Humans also use resources to make everything from clothes to cars.

What are renewable resources?

A **renewable resource** is any natural resource that is recycled or replaced constantly by nature. For example, the Sun provides a constant supply of heat and light. Plants add oxygen to the air when they carry out photosynthesis. Rain fills lakes and streams with water.

Why are some resources in short supply?

Although renewable resources are recycled or replaced, they are sometimes in short supply. Sometimes there may not be enough rain or water provided from melting snow to supply water to people, plants, and animals. In desert regions, water and other resources are often scarce.

What You'll Learn

- the difference between renewable and nonrenewable resources
- how fossil fuels are used
- alternatives to using fossil fuels

▶ **Study Coach**

Identify the Main Idea As you read this section, organize notes into two columns. On the left, list a main idea about the material in each subhead. On the right, list the details that support the main idea.

FOLDABLES

A **Identify** Make a vocabulary book using notebook paper. As you read the section, add each boldface underlined term. Write the definitions under the tabs.

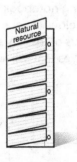

What are nonrenewable resources?

Natural resources that are used up more quickly than they can be replaced by natural processes are **nonrenewable resources**. Earth's supply of nonrenewable resources is limited. For example, plastics and gasoline are made from a nonrenewable resource called petroleum, or oil. **Petroleum** is formed mostly from the remains of microscopic marine organisms buried in Earth's crust. Petroleum is nonrenewable because it takes hundreds of millions of years for it to form. ☑

Fossil Fuels

Coal, oil, and natural gas are nonrenewable resources that supply energy. Most of the energy you use comes from these fossil fuels, as you can see in the figure below. **Fossil fuels** are fuels formed in Earth's crust over hundreds of millions of years. Cars are powered by gasoline, which is made from oil. Many power plants use coal to produce electricity. Natural gas is used for heating and cooking.

Sources of Energy in the United States

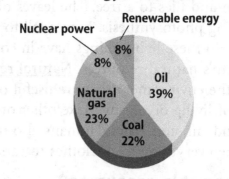

Why should fossil fuels be conserved?

People all over the world use fossil fuels every day. Earth's supply of these fuels is limited. In the future, fossil fuels may become more expensive and harder to get.

The use of fossil fuels can cause environmental problems. Layers of soil and rock are often stripped away when mining for coal. This destroys ecosystems. Another problem with fossil fuels is that they have to be burned to release energy. The burning results in waste gases that cause air pollution. Two forms of air pollution are smog and acid rain. To reduce the problems caused by fossil fuels, many people suggest using fossil fuels less and finding other sources of energy.

☑ **Reading Check**

1. **Explain** why petroleum is a nonrenewable resource.

_____

_____

_____

Picture This

2. **Identify** On the circle graph, outline the sections that represent fossil fuels. On the line below, write the percentage of U.S. energy that comes from sources other than fossil fuels.

_____

FOLDABLES

Ⓑ **Explain** Make a two-tab book using notebook paper, as shown below. Make notes about the effects of fossil fuels and alternatives to fossil fuels.

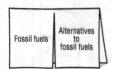

Reducing the Use of Fossil Fuels You can turn off the television when you are not watching it. This will reduce the use of electricity. You can ride in a car pool or use public transportation to reduce the use of gasoline. Walking or riding a bicycle also can reduce the use of fossil fuels.

Alternatives to Fossil Fuels

Another way of reducing the use of fossil fuels is to find other sources of energy. Power plants use fossil fuels to power the turbines that produce electricity. Alternative energy sources such as water, wind, and nuclear energy can be used instead of the fossil fuels to turn the turbines. Another alternative is solar cells that use only sunlight to produce electricity.

How can water generate electricity?

Water is a renewable resource that can be used to produce electricity. **Hydroelectric power** is electricity that is made when the energy of falling water is used to turn the turbines of an electric generator. Hydroelectric power does not burn fuel, so it does not cause air pollution. However, this type of power can cause environmental problems. To build a hydroelectric plant, usually a dam needs to be constructed across a river. The dam raises the water level to produce the energy that is needed to make electricity. Many acres of land behind the dam are flooded, destroying land habitats and turning part of the river into a lake.

How can wind be used to produce energy?

Wind power is another renewable energy source that can be used to make electricity. Wind turns the blades of a turbine, which powers an electric generator. Wind power does not cause air pollution. However, electricity can be produced only when the wind is blowing.

Where does geothermal energy come from?

The hot, molten rock that lies beneath Earth's surface is another energy source. You can see the effects of this energy when a volcano erupts. **Geothermal energy** is the heat energy contained in Earth's crust. Geothermal power plants use this energy to produce steam to produce electricity. Geothermal energy is available only where there are natural geysers or volcanoes. Iceland, an island nation, was formed by volcanoes. Geothermal energy supplies most of Iceland's power. ☑

Think it Over

3. **Identify** one advantage and one disadvantage of hydroelectric power.

_____

_____

_____

Reading Check

4. **Explain** the source of geothermal energy.

_____

_____

_____

What is nuclear power?

Another alternative to fossil fuels is nuclear energy. **Nuclear energy** is released when billions of atomic nuclei from uranium, a radioactive element, are split apart in a nuclear fission reaction as shown below. This energy is used to make the steam that turns the turbines of an electric generator.

Nuclear power does not cause air pollution, but it does cause other problems. Mining uranium can harm ecosystems. Nuclear power plants produce radioactive wastes that can harm living organisms. Disposing of these wastes can be a problem. Accidents also are a danger.

Picture This

5. **Describe** Use the figure to explain to a partner how heat is produced from uranium.

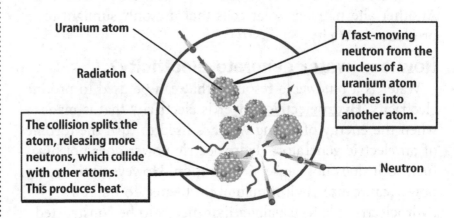

Uranium atom

Radiation

A fast-moving neutron from the nucleus of a uranium atom crashes into another atom.

The collision splits the atom, releasing more neutrons, which collide with other atoms. This produces heat.

Neutron

What is solar energy?

Solar energy is another alternative to fossil fuels. Solar energy comes from the Sun. It is an inexhaustible source of energy—it cannot be used up. One use of solar energy is to heat buildings. During winter in the northern hemisphere, the parts of a building that face south receive the most sunlight. Large windows on the south side of the building let in warm sunshine during the day. The floors and walls of solar-heated buildings are made of materials that absorb heat during the day. At night, the heat is slowly released, keeping the building warm.

What are solar cells?

A solar-powered calculator uses photovoltaic (foh toh vohl TAY ihk) cells to turn sunlight into electric current. Photovoltaic (PV) cells, also known as solar cells, are small and easy to use. But they can produce electricity only in sunlight. Batteries are needed to store electricity for use at night or on cloudy days. PV cells are considered too expensive to use to make large amounts of electricity. ☑

6. **Determine** What do PV cells use to produce electricity?

_____

_____

_____

● After You Read

Mini Glossary

fossil fuel: fuel formed in Earth's crust over hundreds of millions of years

geothermal energy: heat energy within Earth's crust that is available only where geysers and volcanoes are found

hydroelectric power: electricity produced when the energy of falling water turns the blades of a turbine that generates electricity

natural resource: part of the environment that is useful or necessary for the survival of living organisms

nonrenewable resource: natural resource that is used up more quickly than it can be replaced by natural processes

nuclear energy: energy released when billions of uranium nuclei are split apart in a nuclear fission reaction

petroleum: nonrenewable resource formed from the remains of microscopic marine organisms buried in Earth's crust

renewable resource: natural resource that is recycled or replaced constantly by nature

1. Review the terms and their definitions in the Mini Glossary. Write a sentence that explains the difference between renewable and nonrenewable resources.

_____

_____

2. Complete the chart below to compare the advantages and disadvantages of using each of the following forms of energy.

Energy Source	Advantages	Disadvantages
fossil fuels		
hydroelectric power		
wind power		
nuclear power		
geothermal power		
solar power		

Copyright © Glencoe/McGraw-Hill, a division of The McGraw-Hill Companies, Inc.

Science Online Visit **glencoe.com** to access your textbook, interactive games, and projects to help you learn more about resources.

End of Section

Conserving Resources

section ❷ Pollution

LE 7.2d Since the Industrial Revolution, human activities have resulted in major pollution of air, water, and soil. Pollution has cumulative ecological effects such as acid rain, global warming, or ozone depletion. The survival of living things on our planet depends on the conservation and protection of Earth's resources.

What You'll Learn

- the types of air pollution
- the causes of water pollution
- how erosion can be prevented

Study Coach

Make Flash Cards to help you learn more about the section. Write a quiz question for each paragraph on one side of the flash card and the answer on the other side. Keep quizzing yourself until you know all of the answers.

FOLDABLES™

Ⓒ **Describe** Make a trifold book using notebook paper, as shown below. Use the Foldable to describe the three types of pollution.

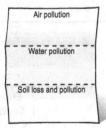

Air pollution

Water pollution

Soil loss and pollution

● Before You Read

What do you think are the major causes of pollution in your community?

_____

_____

_____

● Read to Learn

Keeping the Environment Healthy

More than six billion people live on Earth. This puts a strain on the environment. You can help protect the environment by paying attention to how your use of natural resources affects air, water, and land.

Air Pollution

On a still, sunny day in most large cities, you might see a dark haze in the air. The haze comes from pollutants that form when wood or fuels are burned. A **pollutant** is a substance that contaminates the environment. Air pollution is likely wherever there are cars, airplanes, factories, homes, and power plants. Volcanic eruptions and forest fires also can cause air pollution.

What is smog?

Smog is a form of pollution that is created when sunlight reacts with pollutants produced by burning fuels. Smog can irritate the eyes and make it difficult for people who have lung diseases to breathe. Smog can be reduced if more people take buses or trains instead of driving. Other vehicles, such as electric cars, that produce fewer pollutants also can help reduce smog.

Acid Precipitation

Water vapor condenses on dust particles in the air to form droplets. The droplets create clouds. Eventually, the droplets become large enough to fall as precipitation—mist, rain, snow, sleet, or hail. Air pollutants from the burning of fossil fuels can react with water in the atmosphere to form strong acids. Acidity is measured by a value called pH. **Acid precipitation** has a pH below 5.6, as shown in the figure below. ☑

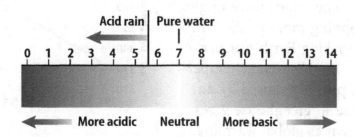

What are the effects of acid rain?

Acid precipitation, or acid rain, washes nutrients from the soil. This can cause trees and plants to die. Acid rain runs off into lakes and ponds, lowering the pH of the water. If the water is too acidic, it can kill the algae and microscopic organisms in the water. This means that fish and other organisms that depend on them for food also die.

How can acid rain be prevented?

When factories burn coal, sulfur is released into the air. Vehicle exhaust contains nitrogen oxide. Sulfur and nitrogen oxide are the main pollutants that cause acid rain. Using low-sulfur fuels, such as low-sulfur coal or natural gas, can reduce acid rain. However, these fuels are more expensive than high-sulfur coal. Smokestacks that remove sulfur dioxide before it enters the air can also help reduce acid rain. Reducing automobile use or using electric cars can help reduce acid rain caused by nitrogen oxide pollution.

Greenhouse Effect

When sunlight reaches Earth's surface, some of it is reflected back into space. The rest is trapped by atmospheric gases. This heat-trapping feature of the atmosphere is the **greenhouse effect**. Without it, temperatures on Earth would probably be too cold to support life.

☑ **Reading Check**

1. **Explain** the causes of acid precipitation.

_____

_____

_____

Picture This

2. **Identify** You measure the pH of rainwater several times. For each reading below, use the scale to determine if it is acid precipitation. Write *Yes* or *No* beside each measurement.

pH of 3.2 _____

pH of 8.5 _____

pH of 6.0 _____

What are greenhouse gases?

The gases in the atmosphere that trap heat are called greenhouse gases. Carbon dioxide (CO_2) is one of the most important greenhouse gases. CO_2 is a normal part of the atmosphere. It is also a by-product of burning fossil fuels. Over the past century, more fossil fuels have been burned than ever before. This is increasing the percentage of CO_2 in the atmosphere, as you can see in the graph above. The atmosphere might be trapping more of the Sun's heat, making Earth warmer. A rise in Earth's average temperature, possibly caused by an increase in greenhouse gases, is known as global warming.

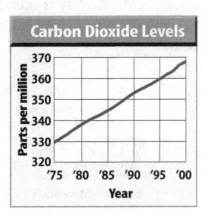

Carbon Dioxide Levels

Is Earth's average temperature changing?

Between 1895 and 1995, Earth's average temperature increased 1°C. No one is certain whether the rise in temperature was caused by human activities or is a natural part of Earth's weather cycle.

Global warming might have several effects. It might cause a change in rainfall patterns, which can affect ecosystems. The rate of plant growth and the plants that can be grown in different parts of the world may change. The number of storms might increase. The polar ice caps might begin to melt, raising sea levels and flooding coastal areas. Many people think that the possibility of global warming is a good reason to reduce the use of fossil fuels. ☑

Ozone Depletion

Ozone (OH zohn) is a form of oxygen in the atmosphere. Ozone molecules are made of three oxygen atoms. They are formed in a chemical reaction between sunlight and oxygen. The oxygen you breathe has two oxygen atoms in each molecule.

The ozone layer is found about 20 km above Earth's surface, as shown in the figure at the top of the next page. The ozone layer in Earth's atmosphere absorbs some of the Sun's harmful ultraviolet (UV) radiation. This radiation can damage living cells.

Picture This

3. **Describe** the trend shown on this graph.

_____

_____

_____

☑ Reading Check

4. **Identify** What are two possible effects of global warming?

_____

_____

_____

CFCs The ozone layer becomes thinner over each polar region during the spring. This thinning of the ozone layer is called **ozone depletion**. It is caused by pollutant gases, especially chlorofluorocarbons (klor oh FLOR oh kar bunz) (CFCs). These gases are sometimes used in the cooling systems of refrigerators and air conditioners. When CFCs leak into the air, they rise in the atmosphere until they reach the ozone layer. CFCs react chemically with ozone, breaking apart the ozone molecules.

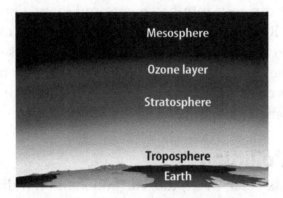

Mesosphere

Ozone layer

Stratosphere

Troposphere

Earth

Picture This
5. **Identify** Add the approximate height at which the ozone layer can be found to the figure.

Why is ozone depletion a problem?

Because of ozone depletion, the amount of UV radiation that reaches Earth could be increasing. This radiation may be causing an increase in the number of skin cancer cases in humans. The ozone layer is important to the survival of life on Earth. For this reason, many countries and industries have agreed to stop making and using CFCs.

The ozone that is high in the atmosphere protects life on Earth. However, ozone that is near Earth's surface can be harmful. Ozone is produced when fossil fuels are burned. This ozone stays lower in the atmosphere and pollutes the air. Ozone damages lungs and other tissues of animals and plants.

Indoor Air Pollution

Air pollution also can occur indoors. Buildings today are better insulated to conserve energy. The insulation reduces the flow of air into and out of a building, so air pollutants can build up indoors. Burning cigarettes release hazardous particles and gases into the air. Even people who do not smoke can be affected by this secondhand cigarette smoke. For this reason, smoking is not allowed in many buildings. Other dangerous gases in buildings are released by paints, carpets, and photocopiers.

6. Explain why carbon monoxide is hard to detect.

_____

_____

_____

7. Identify What are two causes of water pollution?

_____

_____

_____

💡 **Think it Over**

8. Explain how a polluted river will eventually affect an ocean.

_____

_____

_____

Carbon Monoxide Carbon monoxide (CO) is a poisonous gas. It is produced when fuels such as charcoal and natural gas are burned. CO is colorless and odorless, so it is difficult to detect. CO poisoning can cause illness or even death. Today, fuelburning stoves and heaters have to be designed to prevent CO from building up indoors. Many buildings today have alarms that warn of buildups of CO. ☑

Radon Radon is a naturally occurring, radioactive gas that is given off by some types of rock and soil. It has no color or odor. It can seep into basements and lower floors in buildings. Radon exposure is the second leading cause of lung cancer in the United States. Radon detectors sound an alarm if the levels of radon in a building are too high. If radon is present, increasing a building's ventilation can eliminate any damaging effects.

Water Pollution

Pollutants enter water, too. Air pollutants can drift into water or be washed out of the sky by rain. Wastewater from factories and sewage-treatment plants is often released into waterways. Pollution also occurs when people dump litter and waste into rivers, lakes, and oceans. ☑

What happens when surface water is polluted?

Some water pollutants can poison fish and other animals. People who swim in or drink the polluted water can be harmed. Pesticides used on farms can wash into lakes and streams. The chemicals can harm the insects that fish eat. The fish may die from a lack of food.

Another effect of water pollution is algal blooms. Fertilizers and raw sewage contain large amounts of nitrogen. If they are washed into a lake or pond, they can cause algae to grow quickly. When the algae die, bacteria decompose them. The bacteria use up much of the oxygen in the water during this process. Fish and other organisms can die from a lack of oxygen in the water.

How is ocean water polluted?

Rivers and streams flow into oceans, bringing their pollutants along. Ocean water can be polluted by the wastewater from factories and sewage-treatment plants along the coast. Oil spills also cause pollution. About 4 billion kg of oil are spilled into ocean waters every year.

How is groundwater polluted?

Groundwater comes from precipitation and runoff that soaks into the soil. This water moves slowly through layers of rock called aquifers. If the water comes in contact with pollutants as it moves through the soil, the aquifer could become polluted. Polluted groundwater is difficult to clean.

Soil Loss

Most plants need fertile topsoil in order to grow. New topsoil takes hundreds or thousands of years to form. Topsoil can be blown away by wind and washed away by rain. The movement of soil from one place to another is called **erosion** (ih ROH zhun). Eroded soil that washes into a river or stream can block sunlight and slow photosynthesis. It also can harm fish and other organisms. Erosion happens naturally, but human activities increase the rate of erosion. For example, when a farmer plows a field, soil is left bare. Bare soil is more easily carried away by rain and wind. Some methods of farming can help reduce soil erosion. ☑

Soil Pollution

Soil becomes polluted when air pollutants fall to the ground or when water leaves pollutants behind as it flows through the soil. Soil also becomes polluted when people throw litter on the ground or dump trash in landfills.

What happens to solid wastes?

Most of the trash that people throw away every week is dumped in landfills. Most landfills are designed to seal out air and water to keep pollutants from seeping into surrounding soil. However, this also slows normal decay processes. Food scraps and paper, which usually break down quickly, can last for many years in landfills. By reducing the amount of trash that people produce, the need for new landfills can also be reduced.

What happens to hazardous wastes?

Waste materials that are harmful to human health or poisonous to living organisms are **hazardous wastes**. Pesticides and oil are hazardous wastes. Many household items such as leftover paint and batteries also are hazardous wastes. Hazardous wastes should be treated separately from regular trash to prevent them from polluting the environment.

☑ **Reading Check**

9. **Identify** What is erosion?

_____

_____

_____

💡 **Think it Over**

10. **Explain** why hazardous wastes should not be dumped into landfills.

_____

_____

_____

● After You Read

Mini Glossary

acid precipitation: precipitation that has a pH below 5.6
erosion: the movement of soil from one place to another
greenhouse effect: the heat-trapping feature of the atmosphere that keeps Earth warm enough to support life

hazardous waste: waste materials that are harmful to human health or poisonous to living organisms
ozone depletion: the thinning of the ozone layer
pollutant: a substance that contaminates the environment

1. Review the terms and their definitions in the Mini Glossary. Choose one of the terms and write a sentence explaining how it can harm the environment.

_____

_____

_____

2. Choose one of the question headings in the Read to Learn section. Write the question in the space below. Then write your answer to that question on the lines that follow.

Write your question here.

_____

_____

_____

3. How do flash cards help you remember what you have read?

_____

_____

_____

End of Section

 **Science Online** Visit **glencoe.com** to access your textbook, interactive games, and projects to help you learn more about pollution.

Conserving Resources

section ❸ The Three Rs of Conservation

 LE 7.2d Since the Industrial Revolution, human activities have resulted in major pollution of air, water, and soil. Pollution has cumulative ecological effects such as acid rain, global warming, or ozone depletion. The survival of living things on our planet depends on the conservation and protection of Earth's resources. **Also covered:** PS 4.1b

● Before You Read

In what ways do you and your family help to conserve natural resources?

_____

_____

_____

What You'll Learn

- how use of natural resources can be reduced
- how resources can be reused
- that many materials can be recycled

● Read to Learn

Conservation

Conserving resources can help prevent shortages of natural resources. It also can slow the growth of landfills and lower levels of pollution. You can conserve resources in several ways. The three Rs of conservation are reduce, reuse, and recycle.

Reduce

You help conserve natural resources when you reduce your use of them. For example, you use less fossil fuel when you walk instead of ride in a car. You also can reduce your use of natural resources by buying only the things that you need. You can buy products that use less packaging or that use packaging made from recycled materials.

Reuse

Another way to conserve natural resources is to use items more than once. Reusing an item means that it can be used again without changing it or reprocessing it. Bring reusable canvas bags to the grocery store to carry home your purchases. Donate outgrown clothes to charity so that others can reuse them.

Mark the Text

Identify Main Ideas
Highlight the main idea of each paragraph. Then underline the details that support the main idea.

FOLDABLES

Ⓓ Describe Make a layered-look Foldable using notebook paper, as shown below. Make notes describing the three Rs of conservation.

The Three Rs of Conservation
Reduce
Reuse
Recycle

Recycle

If you cannot avoid using an item, and if you cannot reuse it, then you may be able to recycle it. **Recycling** is a form of reuse that requires changing or reprocessing an item or natural resource. Many communities have a curbside recycling program. Items that can be recycled include glass, paper, and plastics. The figure below shows the rates at which some household items are recycled in the United States.

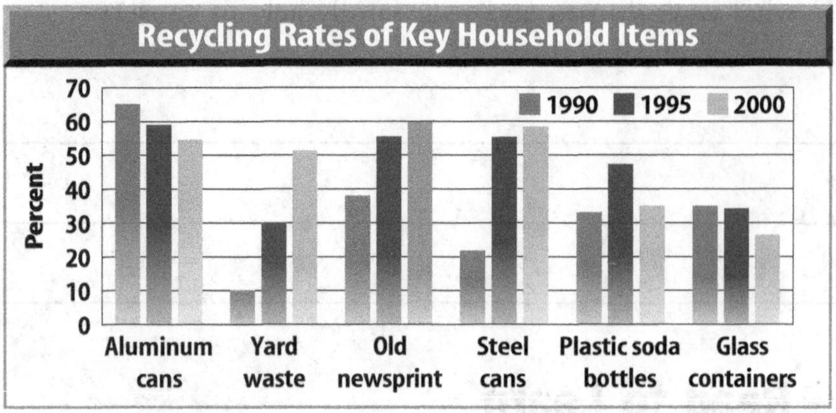

Recycling Rates of Key Household Items

	1990	1995	2000

Percent

Aluminum cans · Yard waste · Old newsprint · Steel cans · Plastic soda bottles · Glass containers

Source: U.S. EPA, 2003

What makes plastic difficult to recycle?

Plastic is more difficult to recycle than other items because there are several types of plastic. Every plastic container is marked with a code that tells the type of plastic it is made of. Plastic soft-drink bottles are the type of plastic easiest to recycle. Some types of plastics cannot be recycled at all because they are made of a mixture of different plastics. Before plastic can be recycled, it has to be separated carefully. One piece of a different type of plastic can ruin an entire batch.

How are metals recycled?

About one quarter of steel used in cans, appliances, and automobiles is recycled steel. Using recycled steel saves iron ore and coal, the resources needed to make steel. Metals such as iron, copper, and aluminum also can be recycled.

You can conserve metals by recycling food cans, which are mostly steel, and aluminum cans. It takes less energy to make a can from recycled aluminum than from raw materials. Also, a can that is recycled is not taking up space in landfills.

How is glass recycled?

Glass bottles and jars can be sterilized and then reused. They also can be melted and made into new bottles. Glass can be recycled again and again. Most glass bottles today already contain at least 25 percent recycled glass. Recycling glass saves the mineral resources needed to make glass. Recycling glass requires less energy than making new glass.

What are some uses of recycled paper?

Used paper can be recycled to make paper towels, newsprint, and cardboard. Ranchers and farmers sometimes use shredded paper instead of straw for bedding in barns and stables. Used paper can be made into compost. Recycling one metric ton of paper saves 17 trees. It also saves water, oil, and electric energy. You can help by recycling newspapers, notebook paper, and junk mail. ☑

Why is composting useful?

When grass clippings, leaves, and fruit and vegetable scraps are dumped in landfills, they stay there for many years without breaking down. Instead, these items can be turned into compost, which can help to enrich the soil. Many communities distribute compost bins to encourage residents to recycle fruit and vegetable scraps and yard waste.

How are recycled materials used?

Many people have learned to recycle. As a result, many recyclable materials are piling up just waiting to be put to use. When you shop, check labels and buy products that contain recycled materials. Buying products made of recycled material will reduce the backlog of recyclable material.

☑ **Reading Check**

2. Explain In addition to trees, what resources are saved when paper is recycled?

_____

_____

_____

● After You Read

Mini Glossary

recycling: a form of reuse that requires changing or reprocessing an item or natural resource

1. Review the term and its definition in the Mini Glossary. Write a sentence explaining how you can participate in recycling.

_____

_____

_____

2. Use the web diagram below to explain the three Rs of conservation. In the ovals, identify the three Rs and include an example of each.

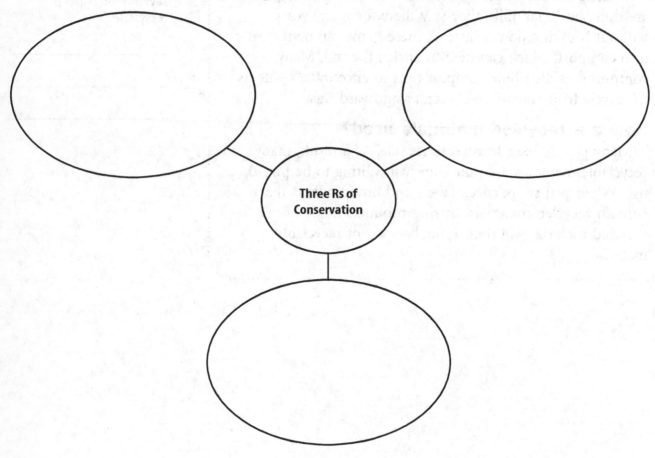

Three Rs of Conservation

End of Section

Science nline Visit **glencoe.com** to access your textbook, interactive games, and projects to help you learn more about the three Rs of conservation.

 **Conserving Life**

section ❶ Biodiversity

 LE 5.1a Animals and plants have a great variety of body plans and internal structures that contribute to their ability to maintain a balanced condition.
7.2d Since the Industrial Revolution, human activities have resulted in major pollution of air, water, and soil. **Also covered:** LE 3.1b, 3.2b, 5.1b, 7.1a, 7.1b, 7.2c

● Before You Read

On the lines below, explain what happened to the dinosaurs. Tell why you think it happened.

_____

_____

_____

What You'll Learn
- about biodiversity
- why biodiversity is important in an ecosystem
- factors that limit biodiversity in an ecosystem

● Read to Learn

The Variety of Life

When you walk through a forest, you see different kinds of trees, shrubs, and animals. Hundreds of species live in the forest. When you walk through a wheat field, you see wheat plants, insects, and weeds. Only a few species live in the wheat field. The forest has a higher biodiversity than the wheat field. <u>Biodiversity</u> refers to the variety of life in an ecosystem.

How is biodiversity measured?

The common measure of biodiversity is the number of species that live in an area. For example, a coral reef can be home to thousands of species including corals, fish, algae, sponges, crabs, and worms. The biodiversity of a coral reef is greater than that of the shallow waters around it.

Scientists once thought that the biodiversity of dark, deep-sea waters was low. Deep-sea exploration has helped scientists discover that species biodiversity is great.

What explains differences in biodiversity?

Biodiversity tends to increase the closer you move toward the equator, where temperatures tend to be warmer. Ecosystems that have the highest biodiversity are usually located in warm, moist climates. The tropical regions of the world are home to two-thirds of Earth's land species. ☑

Mark the Text

Identify Main Ideas
Underline the main idea in each paragraph. Then circle the details that support the main idea.

☑ **Reading Check**

1. **Explain** What are the characteristics of climates that have the highest biodiversity?

_____

_____

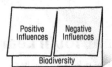
Why is biodiversity important?

Biodiversity is important for many reasons. It provides people with food, medicines, building products, and fiber for clothing. Every species on Earth plays a certain role in the cycling of matter. As a result of biodiversity, soils are richer, pollutants break down, and climates are stable.

Why do humans need biodiversity?

Eating a variety of foods is a good way for people to stay healthy. Hundreds of species help feed the human population all around the world.

Biodiversity can help improve food crops. Crossbreeding food crops with wild species helps develop plant strains that are resistant to many diseases. In the 1970s, American farmers began using a new strain of crossbred corn that resists fungal disease.

Most medicines used today originally came from wild plants. Scientists are still discovering new species. The next plant species discovered could be the cure for cancer.

Biodiversity strengthens an ecosystem. For example, if a disease infects a grapevine in a vineyard, it can easily move from one plant to the next because vines grow close together. Soon, the whole vineyard can become infected with the disease. Farmers may plant one row of grapevines and the next row of another crop. By alternating rows, farmers may help prevent a disease from spreading.

Why is stability important to biodiversity?

If one type of plant in a forest disappears, the forest still exists. Imagine that a forest had only one plant species, one herbivore species that ate the plant, and one carnivore species that ate the herbivore. What would happen if the plant species died out? Biodiversity helps keep the stability of an ecosystem.

What changes biodiversity?

About 100 years ago, passenger pigeons flew across North America. Today, however, the passenger pigeon is extinct. An **extinct species** is a species that was once present on Earth but has died out. ☑

Extinction is a normal part of nature. Fossil records show that many species have become extinct since life appeared on Earth. Species can become extinct because of competition from other species. They can become extinct because of changes in the environment.

☑ **Reading Check**

2. **Define** What is an extinct species?

_____

_____

_____

Mass Extinction A mass extinction happens when a disaster causes many species to die out. One occurred on Earth about 65 million years ago. That extinction, shown on the graph below, occurred in the Mesozoic Era. It wiped out almost two-thirds of all species living on Earth at that time, including dinosaurs.

This extinction might have happened because a huge meteorite crashed into Earth's surface. The impact may have caused dust to block sunlight from reaching Earth's surface leading to climate changes that many species could not survive. After a mass extinction, new species eventually appear. After the dinosaurs disappeared, many new species of mammals appeared on Earth.

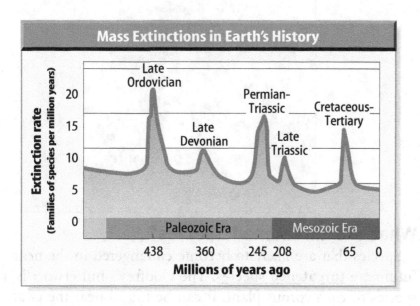

Mass Extinctions in Earth's History

Picture This

3. Identify Circle the names of the mass extinctions that occurred during the Mesozoic Era.

What causes species to die out?

Humans did not have anything to do with the dinosaurs becoming extinct. Today, however, human activities probably contribute to the extinction of many species. The rate of extinctions appears to be rising. About 40 species of plants and animals in the United States became extinct between 1980 and 2000. Hundreds of tropical species became extinct during that same period of time. As the human population increases, more species could be lost.

What are endangered species?

To prevent species from becoming extinct, it is important to know which species could soon disappear. A species in danger of becoming extinct is an **endangered species**.

Think it Over

4. Infer How might a growing human population lead to more species becoming extinct?

_____

_____

_____

Human Impact The Florida panther is the most endangered species in the world. This species originally lived in all parts of Florida, as far west as Louisiana, and as far north as Tennessee. Now they are only found in a small part of southwest Florida, as shown on the map below. Human actions have led to the decline in the Florida panther population. Much of their habitat has been lost as cities have expanded to fill the land. Pollutants have entered their food chain and diseases have greatly reduced their numbers. Now, only a small breeding population exists in national and state parks.

Present Range of the Florida Panther

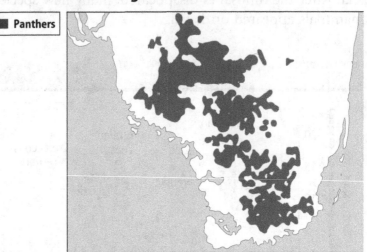

■ Panthers

What are threatened species?

Species that are likely to become endangered in the near future are **threatened species**. The Godfrey's butterwort is a species of carnivorous plant. It can be found near the Gulf coast between Tallahassee and Panama City. The plant already had a limited range. Now, the pine grown for logging has blocked the sunlight from these plants. This has reduced their population even more.

What causes habitat loss?

When people change an ecosystem, such as replacing a forest with a parking lot, the habitats of many species that lived in the forest may become smaller or disappear. Biodiversity can be reduced if many species lose their habitats. ☑

The loss of habitat is a major reason why many species become endangered, threatened, or extinct. For example, the Key Largo cotton mouse lived on all the northern Florida Keys. The keys have become popular tourist destinations. The increase in buildings and people has led to a decrease in habitat available for the Key Largo cotton mouse.

Picture This

5. Synthesize Using a road map of Florida, add the major cities of south Florida to the map.

Reading Check

6. Explain how changing an ecosystem might affect biodiversity.

_____

_____

_____

Protecting Habitats The Key Largo cotton mouse has become a threatened species because of habitat loss. At first, scientists tried to introduce the Key Largo cotton mouse to a new habitat in the Keys. This effort did not succeed. A new strategy limits building in North Key Largo's forests.

How can a divided habitat reduce biodiversity?

Biodiversity can be reduced when a habitat is divided by roads, cities, or farms. Small areas of habitat usually have less biodiversity than large areas of habitat. Divided habitats are a problem for large animals that need large hunting territories. If their habitats are divided, the animals are forced to move somewhere else. ☑

Small habitat areas make it difficult for species to recover from a disaster. If a fire destroys a small part of a forest, the salamanders living in that part are destroyed. After new trees have grown in that part of the forest, salamanders from the part of the forest that was not damaged move in to replace those that had died. However, if a fire destroys a grove of trees surrounded by paved parking lots, salamanders might never return. No salamanders live nearby to move into the area.

How can introduced species affect ecosystems?

An **introduced species** is a species that moves into an ecosystem as a result of human actions. These species usually have no predators or competitors in the new area, so the population of this species grows quickly. Introduced species can crowd out native species. **Native species** are the original organisms in an ecosystem. ☑

In the early 1900s, much of southern Florida was swampland. People wanted to drain the swamps and build on the land. They brought the melaleuca tree from Australia to "dry up" the swamps. The trees quickly took over. Native species died, and animals that ate those native species lost their food source. The trees have reduced biodiversity in southern Florida.

Pollution

Pollution of land, water, or air also affects biodiversity. Soil that is contaminated with chemicals or other pollutants can harm plants or limit their growth. Plants provide habitats for many species. Any change in plant growth can limit biodiversity.

Copyright © Glencoe/McGraw-Hill, a division of The McGraw-Hill Companies, Inc.

✔ **Reading Check**

7. Determine What problem does a divided habitat cause for large animals?

_____

_____

_____

✔ **Reading Check**

8. Describe Why does the population of an introduced species often grow rapidly?

_____

_____

_____

9. Apply How does water pollution affect aquatic organisms?

_____

_____

_____

B Describe Make a two-tab Foldable, as shown below. Use the Foldable to describe global warming and ozone depletion.

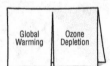

Global Warming | Ozone Depletion

What causes water pollution?

Pollutants that contaminate the water harm organisms that live in the water. These pollutants come from factories, ships, or runoff from lawns and farms. The pollutants can kill aquatic plants, fish, insects, and the organisms they depend on for food. ☑

What causes air pollution?

A form of water pollution known as acid rain is caused by air pollution. **Acid rain** forms when sulfur dioxide and nitrogen oxide released by industries and automobiles combine with water vapor in the air. Acid rain damages trees. It washes away calcium and other nutrients from the soil, making the soil less fertile. Acid rain also harms fish and other organisms that live in lakes and streams. Acid rain makes the water too acidic for many species of fish.

Air pollution from factories, power plants, and automobiles can harm tissues of many organisms. Air pollution can damage the leaves or needles of some trees. This can weaken the trees and make them less able to survive diseases or environmental disasters such as drought or flooding.

What is global warming?

Carbon dioxide (CO_2) is released into the air when wood, coal, gas, or any other fuel is burned. Humans burn large amounts of fuel. This contributes to an increase in the percentage of CO_2 in the atmosphere. An increase in CO_2 may raise Earth's average temperature. This rise in temperature, called global warming, can lead to changes in climate that could affect biodiversity.

What is ozone depletion?

The ozone layer is the part of the atmosphere that is made up of ozone gas. It is about 15 km to 30 km above Earth's surface. The ozone layer protects life on Earth by preventing damaging amounts of the Sun's ultraviolet (UV) radiation from reaching Earth's surface.

The ozone layer is becoming thinner. This thinning is called **ozone depletion**. The thinning ozone layer allows more of the UV radiation that can harm organisms to reach Earth's surface. Increased amounts of UV radiation can lead to more cases of skin cancer in humans.

● After You Read

Mini Glossary

acid rain: results when sulfur dioxide and nitrogen oxide released by industries and automobiles combine with water vapor in the air

biodiversity: the variety of life in an ecosystem

endangered species: species that is in danger of becoming extinct

extinct species: species that was once present on Earth but has died out

introduced species: species that moves into an ecosystem as a result of human actions

native species: the original organisms in an ecosystem

ozone depletion: the thinning of the ozone layer

threatened species: species that is likely to become endangered in the near future

1. Review the terms and their definitions in the Mini Glossary. Write a sentence that explains the difference between introduced species and native species.

_____

_____

_____

2. Complete this diagram by listing three things that reduce biodiversity.

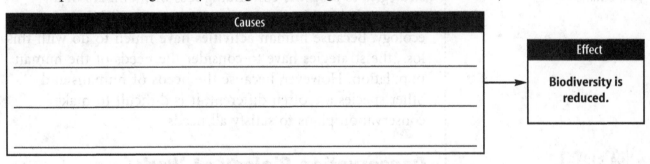

Causes

→

Effect
Biodiversity is reduced.

3. How did highlighting the main idea and circling supporting details help you remember what you read about biodiversity?

_____

_____

_____

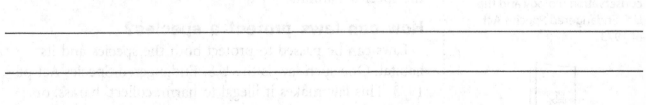

Science Online Visit **glencoe.com** to access your textbook, interactive games, and projects to help you learn more about biodiversity.

End of Section

Conserving Life

section ❷ Conservation Biology

LE 7.2d Since the Industrial Revolution, human activities have resulted in major pollution of air, water, and soil. Pollution has cumulative ecological effects such as acid rain, global warming, or ozone depletion. The survival of living things on our planet depends on the conservation and protection of Earth's resources.
Also covered: LE 3.2b, 7.1b, 7.1e, 7.2c

What You'll Learn

- the goals of conservation biology
- ways to prevent the extinction of species
- how an endangered species can be reintroduced into its original habitat

Study Coach

Make an Outline Make an outline of the information you learn about in this section. Use the headings in the reading as a starting point for organizing your outline.

FOLDABLES

C Describe Make a two-tab Foldable, as shown below. Use the Foldable to describe conservation biology and the U.S. Endangered Species Act of 1973.

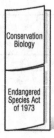

Conservation Biology

Endangered Species Act of 1973

● Before You Read

On the lines below, tell why you think zoos exist.

_____

_____

_____

● Read to Learn

Protecting Biodiversity

The study of methods for protecting biodiversity is called **conservation biology.** Conservation biologists develop strategies to stop the continuing loss of members of a species. Their strategies are based on the principles of ecology. Because human activities have much to do with this loss, the strategies have to consider the needs of the human population. However, because the needs of humans and other species are often different, it is difficult to make conservation plans to satisfy all needs.

Conservation Biology at Work

Most conservation plans have two goals. One goal is to protect the species from harm. The other goal is to protect the species' habitats.

How can laws protect a species?

Laws can be passed to protect both the species and its habitat. One such law is the U.S. Endangered Species Act of 1973. This law makes it illegal to harm, collect, harass, or disturb the habitat of any species on the endangered or threatened species lists. The law also prevents the U.S. government from spending money on projects that might harm these species or their habitats.

Enforcement The U.S. Endangered Species Act is enforced by the United States Fish and Wildlife Service. The Florida Department of Environmental Protection enforces the law in Florida. The Act has helped several species come back from near extinction.

What is CITES?

The United States works with other countries to protect endangered or threatened species. In 1975, The Convention on International Trade in Endangered Species of Wild Fauna and Flora (CITES) was set up. One of its goals is to protect certain species by controlling international trade in these species or any part of the species, such as elephant ivory tusks. Under this agreement about 5,000 animal species and 25,000 plant species are protected.

How are habitats being protected?

A species that is protected by law cannot survive unless its habitat also is protected. Conservation biology works to protect habitats. One way is to set up nature preserves. Nature preserves include national parks and protected wildlife areas.

Protecting the Flordia Everglades For many years, a group of conservationists worked hard to find ways to protect the Florida Everglades. In 1947, President Harry S Truman dedicated the Everglades National Park. It was the first national park set aside for biological reasons. Without national parks and wildlife areas, some animals would be closer to extinction. Visitors to the Everglades National Park can view a mix of tropical and temperate species. Its rare mix of freshwater and saltwater habitats are now protected by law.

What is the purpose of wildlife corridors?

Some large-animal species, such as the Florida panther, need large amounts of land to survive. However, it is not always possible to create large nature preserves. One way to solve this land problem is to link smaller parks together with wildlife corridors. ☑

Wildlife corridors are part of a strategy for saving the endangered Florida panther. A male panther needs a territory of at least 712 km^2. This area is larger than many of the protected panther habitats. Wildlife corridors allow panthers to move from one preserve to another without crossing roads or entering areas where humans live.

FOLDABLES

D Identify Make a three-tab Foldable, as shown below. Use the Foldable to identify the importance of habitat preservation, habitat restoration, and wildlife corridors.

Habitat Preservation

Habitat Restoration

Wildlife Corridors

✓ Reading Check

1. **Explain** What is the purpose of a wildlife corridor?

_____

_____

How are habitats being restored?

Habitats that have been harmed by human activities can be restored. **Habitat restoration** is the process of taking action to bring a damaged habitat back to a healthy condition.

Project Greenshores, shown below, began in 2001 as a habitat restoration effort. Its goal is to return an oyster reef and salt marsh to the Pensacola Bay ecosystem. Workers placed 20,000 tons of recycled concrete and limestone rock in the salt marsh off the coast. The materials formed a man-made reef, which protects aquatic plants from the waves and gives oysters a habitat. The reef also provides a place for bird and marine wildlife.

Project Greenshores is managed by the Florida Department of Environmental Protection. Students and volunteers have been important to the success of the project.

©ZUMA Press, Inc/Alamy Stock Photo

What is the purpose of wildlife management?

Wildlife parks and preserves do not automatically protect species living there from harm. People are needed to manage the areas. For example, in South Africa, guards patrol wildlife parks to prevent poachers from killing elephants for their ivory tusks. Some wildlife preserves do not allow visitors other than biologists who are studying the area.

Wildlife managers and hunters often work together to protect certain animal species. People usually are not allowed to hunt or fish in a park unless they buy a license. The sale of licenses provides money for taking care of the wildlife area. It also helps prevent overhunting. Licenses usually limit the number of animals a hunter is allowed. Hunting rules also can help prevent a population from becoming too large for an area. ☑

Reading Check

3. **Explain** What is one purpose of hunting and fishing licenses?

_____

_____

_____

How can keeping animals in captivity preserve biodiversity?

Sometimes endangered or threatened animals are placed in zoos. Often these animals are no longer found in the wild. A **captive population** is a population of organisms that is cared for by humans. Often, with human care, the numbers of the species increase.

Keeping endangered or threatened animals in captivity can help preserve biodiversity. However, it is not an ideal solution. Providing food, space, and care can be expensive. Sometimes captive animals lose their wild behaviors. If that happens, these animals might not survive if they are returned to their habitats.

What is the purpose of reintroduction programs?

Sometimes members of captive populations can be put back into the wild to help restore biodiversity. **Reintroduction programs** return captive organisms to an area where the species once lived. Once reintroduced, researchers may observe the animals from a distance. These programs can be successful only if the reasons that caused the species to become endangered are removed. Plants also can be reintroduced into their original habitats. Often this is done by replanting seedlings in the original habitats.

How are seed banks used?

Seed banks store the seeds of many endangered plants species. There are seed banks throughout the world. If a species becomes extinct in the wild, the stored seeds can be planted to reintroduce the plants to their original habitats.

Why are some species relocated?

Reintroduction programs do not always involve captive populations. The most successful reintroduction programs happen when wild organisms are moved to a suitable new habitat. The brown pelican relocation is an example of this.

The pelican was once common along the Gulf of Mexico. In the mid-1900s, a pesticide known as DDT ended up in the food that pelicans ate. Because of DDT, the pelican's eggshells became so thin that they broke before the chicks could hatch. Soon, pelicans disappeared from Louisiana and most of Texas. In 1971, pelicans were reintroduced to the area. By the year 2000, more than 7,000 brown pelicans lived in Louisiana and Texas. The United States banned the use of DDT in 1972.

Copyright © Glencoe/McGraw-Hill, a division of The McGraw-Hill Companies, Inc.

Think it Over

4. **List** one advantage and one disadvantage of captive population?

_____

_____

_____

_____

Think it Over

5. **Analyze** Why might reintroduction programs be more successful with wild species than with captive species?

_____

_____

_____

● After You Read

Mini Glossary

captive population: a population of organisms that is cared for by humans

conservation biology: the study of methods for protecting biodiversity

habitat restoration: the process of taking action to bring a damaged habitat back to a healthy condition

reintroduction program: a program that returns captive organisms to an area where the species once lived

1. Review the terms and their definitions in the Mini Glossary. Using two of the terms, write a sentence explaining what is being done to protect biodiversity.

_____

_____

_____

2. Use the web diagram below to identify different strategies used to protect biodiversity.

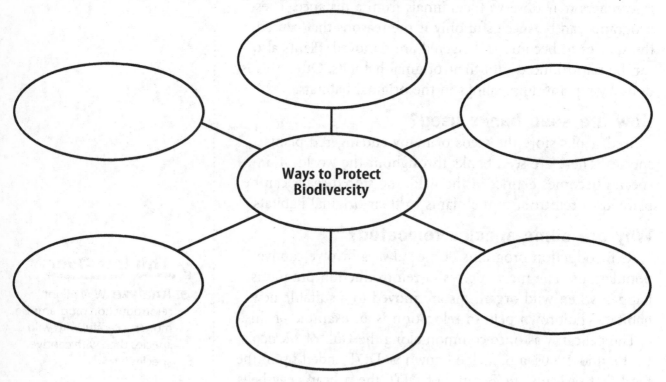

End of Section

Science Online Visit **glencoe.com** to access your textbook, interactive games, and projects to help you learn more about conservation biology.

Immunity and Disease

section ❶ The Immune System

 LE 1.2a Each system is composed of organs and tissues which perform specific functions and interact with each other. **LE 1.2j** Disease breaks down the structures or functions of an organism. Specialized cells protect the body from infectious disease. The chemicals they produce identify and destroy microbes that enter the body.

● Before You Read

Think about the last time that you had a cold. On the lines below, describe three ways your body reacted to the cold.

_____

_____

_____

● Read to Learn

Lines of Defense

Your body has many ways to defend itself from illness. Your first-line defenses are general. First-line defenses work against harmful substances and all types of disease-causing organisms, called **pathogens** (PA thuh junz). Your second-line defenses are specific. They work against specific pathogens. The combination of first-line and second-line defenses is called your **immune system**.

What are your body's first-line defenses?

Your skin and your respiratory, digestive, and circulatory systems are your first-line defenses against pathogens. Your skin stops many pathogens from entering the body. Sweat and oils produced by your skin cells can slow the growth of some pathogens.

Respiratory System Defenses The respiratory system traps pathogens with hairlike structures, called cilia (SIH lee uh), and mucus. Mucus has enzymes (EN zimez) that weaken the cell walls of some pathogens. Coughs and sneezes help get rid of pathogens from your lungs and nasal passages. ☑

What You'll Learn
- the body's natural defenses
- the difference between an antigen and an antibody
- the differences between active and passive immunity

Mark the Text

Locate Information Read all the headings for this section and circle any word you cannot define. Then review the circled words and underline the part of the text that helps you define the words.

✔ Reading Check

1. **Explain** What do cilia do?

_____

_____

Copyright © Glencoe/McGraw-Hill, a division of The McGraw-Hill Companies, Inc.

Reading Essentials **131**

Digestive System Defenses Your digestive system has four defenses against pathogens—saliva, enzymes, hydrochloric acid, and mucus. Saliva contains substances that kill bacteria. Enzymes in your stomach, pancreas, and liver help destroy pathogens. Hydrochloric acid in your stomach kills some bacteria and stops some viruses that enter your body on the food you eat. The mucus in your digestive tract has a chemical that prevents bacteria from attaching to the inner lining of your digestive organs.

Circulatory System Defenses Your circulatory system contains white blood cells that surround and destroy foreign organisms and chemicals. White blood cells constantly patrol your body, destroying harmful bacteria. If the white blood cells cannot destroy the bacteria fast enough, you may develop a fever. A fever is a slight increase in body temperature that slows the growth of pathogens. A fever speeds up your body's defenses. ☑

How do you know when tissue is damaged?

When tissue is damaged by injury or infected by pathogens, it becomes inflamed. Signs that tissue is inflamed include redness, an increase in temperature, swelling, and pain. Damaged cells release chemicals that cause nearby blood vessels to widen, allowing more blood to flow into the inflamed area. Other chemicals released by damaged cells attract white blood cells that surround and destroy the pathogens. If pathogens get past these first-line defenses, your body uses its second-line defenses. Second-line defenses work against specific pathogens.

What are antigens?

Molecules that are foreign to your body are called __antigens__ (AN tih junz). Antigens can be separate molecules, or they can be attached to the surface of pathogens. When your immune system recognizes antigens in your body, it releases special kinds of white blood cells that fight infection. White blood cells that fight infections are called lymphocytes.

The first lymphocytes to respond to an antigen are the T cells. There are two kinds of T cells, killer T cells and helper T cells. Killer T cells release enzymes that help destroy foreign matter. Helper T cells cause the body to produce another kind of lymphocyte, called a B cell.

2. Determine What does a fever do?

_____

_____

_____

FOLDABLES

Ⓐ Explain Use quarter-sheets of notebook paper to make Foldables to define and explain antigens and antibodies.

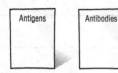

| Antigens | Antibodies |

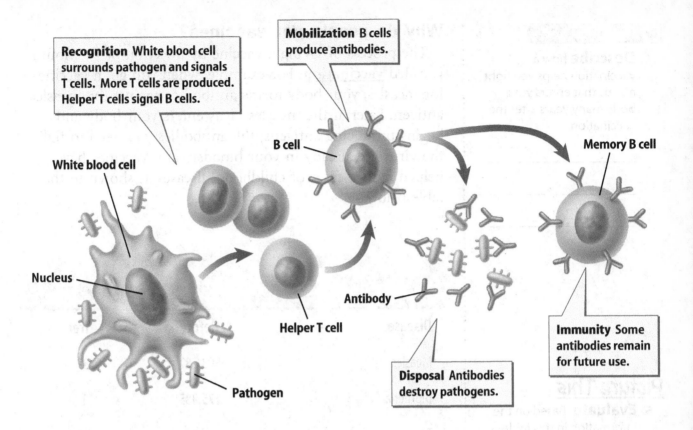

Recognition White blood cell surrounds pathogen and signals T cells. More T cells are produced. Helper T cells signal B cells.

Mobilization B cells produce antibodies.

White blood cell

Nucleus

Pathogen

Helper T cell

B cell

Antibody

Disposal Antibodies destroy pathogens.

Memory B cell

Immunity Some antibodies remain for future use.

What are antibodies?

B cells form antibodies to specific antigens. An **antibody** is a protein your body makes to fight a specific antigen. The antibody can attach to the antigen and make the antigen harmless. The antibody can also make it easier for a killer T cell to destroy the antigen.

Other lymphocytes, called memory B cells, also have antibodies against specific pathogens. Memory B cells stay in the blood ready to destroy that same pathogen if it invades your body again. The response of your immune system to a pathogen is summarized in the figure above.

What are active and passive immunity?

Antibodies help your body build defenses in two ways—actively and passively. In **active immunity**, your body makes its own antibodies in response to an antigen. In **passive immunity**, the antibodies have been produced in another animal and put into your body. Vaccines are antigens produced in another organism and then placed in your body to build immunity against a disease. Passive immunity does not last as long as active immunity does.

Picture This

3. Identify Circle the name of the step in which antibodies are produced. Highlight the name of the step in which pathogens are destroyed.

FOLDABLES

B Describe Make a three-tab Foldable, as shown below, to compare and contrast active immunity and passive immunity.

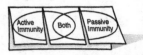

4. Describe how a vaccination helps you fight a virus that enters your body many years after the vaccination.

_____

_____

_____

Picture This

5. Evaluate Based on the information in this table, have vaccines been effective? Explain.

_____

_____

_____

Why do people get vaccines?

The process of giving a vaccine by injection or by mouth is called **vaccination**. For example, when you get a vaccine for measles, your body forms antibodies against the measles antigen. Later, if the measles virus enters your body and begins producing antigens, the antibodies you need to fight the virus are already in your bloodstream. Vaccines have helped reduce cases of childhood diseases as shown in the table below. ✔

Annual Cases of Disease Before and After Vaccine Availability in the U.S.		
Disease	**Before**	**After**
Measles	503,282	89
Diptheria	175,885	1
Tetanus	1,314	34
Mumps	152,209	606
Rubella	47,745	345
Pertussis (whooping cough)	147,271	6,279

Antibodies that protect you from one virus may not help you fight another virus. Each year a different set of flu viruses causes the flu. As a result, people get a new flu shot each year.

What is tetanus?

Tetanus is a disease caused by bacteria in the soil. Bacteria can enter the body through an open wound. The bacteria that causes tetanus produces a chemical that makes muscles unable to move. In early childhood, you received several tetanus vaccines to help you develop immunity to this disease. You need to continue to get tetanus vaccines every 10 years to stay protected.

● After You Read

Mini Glossary

active immunity: long-lasting immunity that results when the body makes its own antibodies in response to an antigen

antibody: a protein made in response to a specific antigen

antigen (AN tih jun): any molecule that is foreign to your body

immune system: the complex group of defenses against harmful substances and disease-causing organisms

passive immunity: immunity that results when antibodies produced in another animal are introduced into your body

pathogen (PA thuh jun): a disease-causing organism

vaccination: the process of giving a vaccine by injection or mouth to provide active immunity

1. Review the terms and their definitions in the Mini Glossary. Write a sentence or two that explains the difference between an antigen and an antibody.

_____

_____

_____

2. Complete the concept web below to identify four first-line defenses your body has against disease.

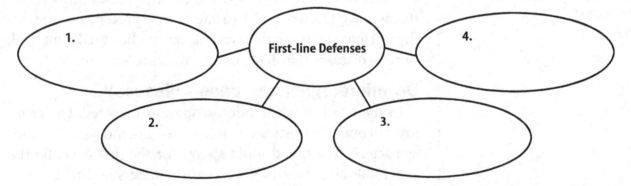

3. How did finding definitions of unfamiliar words help you understand the immune system?

_____

_____

Science Online Visit **glencoe.com** to access your textbook, interactive games, and projects to help you learn more about the immune system.

End of Section

Immunity and Disease

section ❷ Infectious Diseases

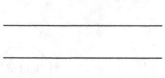 **LE 1.2j** Disease breaks down the structures or functions of an organism. Other diseases are the result of damage by infection from other organisms (germ theory). Specialized cells protect the body from infectious disease. **Also covered:** LE 1.2a, 5.2f

What You'll Learn

- the work done by scientists to discover and prevent disease
- diseases caused by viruses and bacteria
- the causes of sexually transmitted diseases

Read-and-Say Work with a partner. Read the information under a heading to yourselves. Then discuss together what you learned. Continue until you both understand the main ideas of this section.

💡 Think it Over

1. **Infer** What liquids do you drink that you think have undergone pasteurization?

_____

_____

_____

● Before You Read

How do you think washing hands helps prevent disease?

_____

_____

_____

● Read to Learn

Disease in History

In the past, there were no treatments for diseases such as the plague, smallpox, and influenza. These diseases killed millions of people worldwide. Today the causes of these diseases are known, and treatments can prevent or cure them. However, some diseases still cannot be cured. Outbreaks of new diseases that have no known cure also occur.

Do microorganisms cause disease?

In the late 1700s, the microscope was invented. Under a microscope, scientists were able to see microorganisms such as bacteria, yeast, and mold spores for the first time. By the late 1800s and early 1900s, scientists understood that microorganisms could cause diseases and carry them from one person to another.

What did Louis Pasteur discover?

The French chemist Louis Pasteur discovered that micro-organisms could spoil wine and milk. He then realized that microorganisms could attack the human body in the same way, causing diseases. Pasteur invented **pasteurization** (pas chuh ruh ZAY shun), which is the process of heating liquid to a specific temperature that kills most bacteria.

Which microorganisms cause diseases?

Many diseases are caused by bacteria, viruses, protists (PROH tihsts), or fungi. Bacteria can slow the normal growth and activities of body cells and tissues. Some bacteria produce toxins, or poisons, that kill body cells on contact. The table below lists some of the diseases caused by different groups of pathogens.

Human Diseases and the Pathogens that Cause Them	
Pathogens	**Diseases Caused**
Bacteria	Tetanus, tuberculosis, typhoid fever, strep throat, bacterial pneumonia, plague
Protists	Malaria, sleeping sickness
Fungi	Athlete's foot, ringworm
Viruses	Colds, influenza, AIDS, measles, mumps, polio, smallpox

Viruses A <u>virus</u> is a tiny piece of genetic material surrounded by a protein coating that infects host cells and multiplies inside them. The host cells die when the viruses break out of them. These new viruses infect other cells. Viruses destroy tissues or interrupt important body activities.

Other Pathogens Protists can destroy tissues and blood cells. They also can interfere with normal body functions. Fungus infections work in a similar way and can cause athlete's foot, nonhealing wounds, and chronic lung disease.

What did Robert Koch develop?

In the 1880s, Robert Koch developed a way to isolate and grow one type of bacterium at a time. Koch developed rules for identifying which organism causes a particular disease. Koch's rules are still used by doctors today.

What did Joseph Lister discover?

Today we know that washing hands kills bacteria and other organisms that spread disease. But until the late 1800s, people, including doctors, did not know this. Joseph Lister, an English surgeon, saw that infection and cleanliness were related. Lister learned that carbolic (kar BAH lik) acid kills pathogens. He greatly reduced the number of deaths among his patients by washing their skin, his hands, and his surgical instruments with carbolic acid. ☑

Picture This

2. Identify What type of pathogen causes strep throat?

_____

FOLDABLES

C Organize Make a folded table with three columns and three rows, as shown below. Use the Foldable to record facts about types of diseases.

	Diseases Caused By	How Caused
Bacteria		
Viruses		

What operating procedures are followed today?

Today special soaps are used to kill pathogens on skin. Every person who helps perform surgery must wash his or her hands thoroughly and wear sterile gloves and a covering gown. The patient's skin is cleaned around the area of the body to be operated on and then covered with sterile cloths. Surgery instruments and all operating equipment are sterilized. The air in the operating room is filtered to keep out pathogens. ☑

✔ **Reading Check**

3. **List** two operating procedures followed today.

_____

_____

_____

How Diseases Are Spread

An **infectious disease** is a disease that is spread from an infected organism or the environment to another organism. An infectious disease can be caused by a virus, bacterium, protist, or fungus. Infectious diseases are spread in many ways. They can be spread by direct contact with the infected organism, through water and air, on food, or by contact with contaminated objects. They can also be spread by disease-carrying organisms called **biological vectors**. Rats, birds, and flies are examples of biological vectors.

People also can be carriers of diseases. When you have the flu and sneeze, you send thousands of virus particles into the air. These particles can spread the virus to others. Colds and many other diseases also can be spread by contact. Everything you touch may have disease-causing bacteria or viruses on it. Washing your hands regularly is an important way to avoid disease.

Sexually Transmitted Diseases

Infectious diseases that are passed from person to person during sexual contact are called **sexually transmitted diseases (STDs)**. STDs are caused by bacteria or viruses.

What are bacterial STDs?

STDs caused by bacteria are gonorrhea (gah nuh REE uh), chlamydia (kluh MIH dee uh), and syphilis (SIH fuh lus). The symptoms for gonorrhea and chlamydia may not appear right away, so a person may not know that he or she is infected. The symptoms for these STDs are pain when urinating, genital discharge, and genital sores. Bacterial STDs can be treated with antibiotics. If left untreated, gonorrhea and chlamydia can damage the reproductive system, leaving the person unable to have children.

FOLDABLES

Ⓓ **Explain** Use a quarter-sheet of notebook paper to define, list the types of, and explain STDs.

STDs

What are the symptoms for syphilis?

Syphilis has three stages. In stage 1, a sore that lasts 10 to 14 days appears on the mouth or sex organ. Stage 2 may involve a rash, fever, and swollen lymph glands. In stage 3, syphilis may infect the cardiovascular and nervous systems. Syphilis can be treated with antibiotics in all stages. However damage to body organs in stage 3 cannot be reversed and may lead to death.

What is genital herpes?

Genital herpes is a lifelong STD caused by a virus. The symptoms include painful blisters on the sex organs. Genital herpes can be passed from one person to another during sexual contact or from an infected mother to her child during birth. The herpes virus hides in the body for long periods of time without causing symptoms and then reappears suddenly. The symptoms for genital herpes can be treated with medicine, but there is no cure or vaccine for the disease.

HIV and Your Immune System

Human immunodeficiency virus (HIV) can exist in blood and body fluids. This virus can hide in body cells, sometimes for years. HIV can be passed on by an infected person through sexual contact. A person can also be infected by reusing an HIV-contaminated needle for an injection. A sterile needle, however, cannot pass on HIV. The risk of getting HIV through blood transfusion is small because all donated blood is tested for HIV. An HIV-infected pregnant woman can infect her unborn child. A baby can get HIV after birth when nursing from an HIV-infected mother. ☑

What is AIDS?

An HIV infection can lead to Acquired Immune Deficiency Syndrome (AIDS). AIDS is a disease that attacks the body's immune system.

HIV is different from other viruses. It attacks the helper T cells in the immune system. HIV enters the T cell and multiples. When the infected T cell bursts open, it releases more HIV that infects more T cells. Soon, so many T cells are destroyed that not enough B cells are formed to produce antibodies. Once HIV has reached this stage, the infected person has AIDS. The immune system can no longer fight HIV or any other pathogen. There is no cure for AIDS, but several kinds of medicines help treat AIDS in some patients.

Think it Over

4. **Determine** At which stage does syphilis cause permanent damage?

_____

_____

_____

✔ Reading Check

5. **Identify** What are two ways that a teenager or adult can get HIV?

_____

_____

_____

Fighting Disease

The first step to preventing infections is to wash small wounds with soap and water. Cleaning the wound with an antiseptic and covering it with a bandage also help fight infection.

Washing your hands and body helps prevent body odor. Washing also removes and destroys microorganisms on your skin. Health-care workers, such as the one shown below, wash their hands between patients. This reduces the spread of pathogens from one person to another.

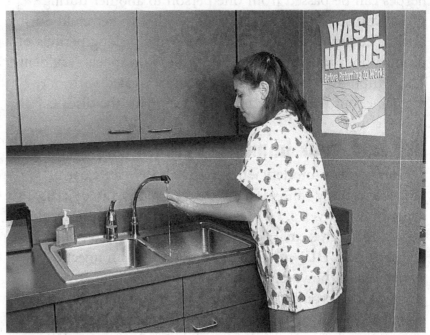

Mark Burnett

Microorganisms in your mouth cause mouth odor and tooth decay. Brushing and flossing your teeth every day keep these microorganisms under control.

Exercising, eating healthy foods, and getting plenty of rest help keep you healthy. You are less likely to get a cold or the flu if you have good health habits. Having checkups every year and getting the recommended vaccinations also help you stay healthy.

Picture This

6. **Identify** other types of jobs where workers should wash their hands often.

_____

_____

Think it Over

7. **Apply** List two things you do every day to keep healthy.

_____

_____

● After You Read

Mini Glossary

biological vector: a disease-carrying organism

infectious disease: a disease that is caused by a virus, bacterium, protist, or fungus and is spread by an organism or the environment to another organism

pasteurization (pas chuh ruh ZAY shun): the process of heating a liquid to a specific temperature that kills most bacteria

sexually transmitted disease (STD): an infectious disease that is passed from person to person during sexual contact

virus: a small piece of genetic material surrounded by a protein coating that infects and multiplies in host cells

1. Review the terms and their definitions in the Mini Glossary. Choose one term that identifies a way a person gets a disease. Write a sentence about how the term you selected causes infection.

_____

_____

_____

2. Complete the table below to identify the causes, symptoms, and treatments of STDs.

Kinds of STDs	Causes (Bacteria or Virus)	Symptoms	Treatment
Gonorrhea			
Chlamydia			
Syphilis			
Genital herpes			

Science Online Visit **glencoe.com** to access your textbook, interactive games, and projects to help you learn more about infectious diseases.

End of Section

chapter 10 — Immunity and Disease

section ❸ Noninfectious Diseases

LE 1.2j Disease breaks down the structures or functions of an organism. Some diseases are the result of failures of the system. Other diseases are the result of damage by infection from other organisms (germ theory). Specialized cells protect the body from infectious disease. The chemicals they produce identify and destroy microbes that enter the body. **4.4d** Cancers are a result of abnormal cell division. **Also covered:** LE 1.2a, 5.2f

What You'll Learn

- the causes of noninfectious diseases
- what happens during an allergic reaction
- the characteristics of cancer
- how chemicals in the environment can harm humans

Mark the Text

Identify the Main Point

Underline the main point of each paragraph. Review these ideas as you study the section.

✓ Reading Check

1. **Explain** How are allergens and asthma related?

_____

_____

_____

● Before You Read

Explain on the lines below why it is important to read labels and follow directions when using household products.

_____

_____

_____

● Read to Learn

Chronic Disease

Diseases and disorders that are not caused by pathogens are called **noninfectious diseases**. Allergies, diabetes, asthma, cancer, and heart disease are noninfectious diseases. Many are chronic (KRAH nihk) diseases, or can become chronic diseases if not treated. A chronic disease is an illness that can last a long time. Some chronic diseases can be cured, but others cannot be cured.

Allergies

An **allergy** is an overly strong reaction of the immune system to a foreign substance. Allergic reactions include itchy rashes, sneezes, and hives. Most allergic reactions do not cause major problems. However, some allergic reactions can cause shock and even death if not treated right away.

What causes allergies?

A substance that causes an allergic reaction is called an **allergen**. Examples of allergens include dust, chemicals, certain foods, pollen, and some antibiotics. Asthma (AZ muh) is a lung disorder that is caused by allergens. The symptoms of asthma include shortness of breath, wheezing, and coughing. ✓

Copyright © Glencoe/McGraw-Hill, a division of The McGraw-Hill Companies, Inc.

How does the body react to allergens?

When you come in contact with an allergen, your immune system usually forms antibodies. Your body also reacts to allergens by releasing chemicals called histamines (HIHS tuh meenz) that cause red, swollen tissues. Antihistamines are medications that can be used to treat allergic reactions and asthma.

Diabetes

Diabetes is a chronic disease that has to do with the levels of insulin made by the pancreas. Insulin is a hormone that helps glucose, a form of sugar, pass from the bloodstream into your cells. There are two types of diabetes. Type I diabetes is the result of too little or no insulin production. Type II diabetes happens when your body does not properly use the insulin it produces. Symptoms of diabetes include tiredness, great thirst, the need to urinate often, and tingling feelings in the hands and feet. ☑

People with Type I diabetes often need daily injections of insulin to control their glucose levels. People with Type II diabetes usually can control the disease by watching their diet and their weight.

If diabetes is not treated, health problems can develop. These problems include blurred vision, kidney failure, heart attack, stroke, loss of feeling in the feet, and the loss of consciousness, or a diabetic coma.

Chemicals and Disease

Chemicals are everywhere—in your body, the foods you eat, cosmetics, and cleaning products. Most chemicals used by consumers are safe, but a few are harmful. A chemical that is harmful to living things is called a toxin. Toxins can cause a variety of diseases, as well as birth defects, tissue damage, and death. Some toxins and the damage they cause are shown in the table below.

Toxin	Effect
asbestos	lung disease
lead-based paints	damage to central nervous system
alcohol (consumed during pregnancy)	birth defects

2. List four symptoms of diabetes.

_____

_____

_____

_____

FOLDABLES™

E **Explain** Make a four-tab Foldable to explain the causes of noninfectious diseases.

Allergies

Diabetes

Chemicals

Cancer

3. Explain How can cancer cells spread through the body?

_____

_____

Cancer

Cancer is a group of closely related diseases that are caused by uncontrolled cell growth. The table below shows characteristics of cancer cells.

Characteristics of Cancer Cells
Cell growth is out of control.
Cells do not function as part of the body.
Cells take up space and cause problems with normal body functions.
Cells travel throughout the body by way of blood and lymph vessels.
Cells produce tumors and unusual growths anywhere in the body.

What are some types of cancers?

Leukemia (lew KEE mee uh) is a cancer of white blood cells. The cancerous white blood cells cannot fight diseases. These cancer cells multiply and crowd out normal blood cells. Cancer of the lungs makes breathing difficult. Cancer of the large intestine is a leading cause of death in men and women. Breast cancer causes tumors to grow in the breast. Cancer of the prostate gland, an organ that surrounds the urethra, is the second most common cancer in men.

What are some causes of cancer?

Carcinogens (kar SIH nuh junz) are substances that can cause cancer. Some of these substances are shown in the photograph below. Coming in contact with carcinogens increases your chance of getting cancer. Carcinogens include asbestos, some cleaning products, heavy metals, tobacco, alcohol, and some home and garden products. Smoking has been linked to lung cancer. Exposure to X rays and radiation increase your chances of getting cancer. Some foods, such as smoked or barbecued meats, can give rise to cancers. ✓

Reading Check

4. Identify three carcinogens.

_____

_____

_____

KS Studios

Genetics and Cancer The genetic makeup of some people increases their risk of developing cancer. That does not mean they will definitely get cancer, but it increases their chances of developing cancer.

How is cancer treated?

Finding cancer in its early stages is important for successful treatment. The early warning signs of cancer are listed in the table below.

Early Warning Signs of Cancer
Changes in bowel movements or urination
A sore that does not heal
Unusual bleeding or discharge
Thickening or lump in the breast or elsewhere
Difficulty in digesting or swallowing food
Changes in a wart or mole
Cough or hoarseness that will not go away

Surgery to remove cancerous tissue is one treatment for cancer. Radiation with X rays may be used to kill cancer cells. In **chemotherapy** (kee moh THER uh pee), chemicals are used to kill cancer cells.

What can you do to help prevent cancer?

Knowing the causes of cancer can help you prevent it. One way to help prevent cancer is to follow a healthy lifestyle. Avoiding tobacco and alcohol products can help prevent mouth and lung cancers. Eating a healthy diet that is low in fats, salt, and sugar can help prevent cancer. Using sunscreen and limiting the amount of time you spend in the sunlight are ways to prevent skin cancer. Avoid harmful home and garden chemicals. If you choose to use them, read all the labels and carefully follow the directions for their use.

Picture This

5. **Conclude** What should a person do if they notice one of these early warning signs?

_____

_____

Think it Over

6. **Identify** one thing that you need to avoid or that you need to start doing to help prevent cancer.

_____

_____

_____

● After You Read

Mini Glossary

allergen: a substance that causes an allergic response

allergy: an overly strong reaction of the immune system to a foreign substance

chemotherapy (kee moh THER uh pee): the use of chemicals to destroy cancer cells

noninfectious disease: a disease not caused by pathogens

1. Review the terms and their definitions in the Mini Glossary. Write a sentence that describes an allergy that you have or that someone you know has.

   _____

   _____

   _____

2. Fill in the table below to identify the causes of some noninfectious diseases.

Noninfectious Diseases	Causes
Asthma	
Diabetes Type I	
Diabetes Type II	
Lung cancer	
Skin cancer	

3. How did reviewing the main ideas help you study this section?

   _____

   _____

   _____

End of Section

 **Science Online** Visit **glencoe.com** to access your textbook, interactive games, and projects to help you learn more about noninfectious diseases.

The Sun-Earth-Moon System

section ❶ Earth

 PS 1.1h The apparent motions of the Sun, Moon, planets, and stars across the sky can be explained by Earth's rotation and revolution. **1.1j** The shape of Earth, the other planets, and stars is nearly spherical. **Also covered:** PS 1.1c, 1.1e, 1.1i

● Before You Read

What do you already know about Earth's shape, its size, and how it moves? Write what you know on the lines below.

_____

_____

_____

What You'll Learn

- Earth's shape, size, and movements
- the difference between rotation and revolution
- what causes the seasons

● Read to Learn

Properties of Earth

In the morning, the Sun rises in the east. It moves across the sky during the day. Finally, the Sun sets in the west. Is the Sun moving—or are you?

People once thought that Earth was a flat object at the center of the universe. They believed that the Sun went around Earth in a big circle each day. Now, most people know that Earth is not flat, and the Sun only looks like it is moving around Earth. Scientists have discovered that Earth spins and that Earth moves around the Sun. It is the spinning motion of Earth that makes it look like the Sun is moving across the sky.

What is Earth's shape?

Basketballs, tennis balls, and Earth have something in common. They are all round, three-dimensional objects called **spheres** (SFIHRZ). The distance from the center of a sphere to any point on the surface is the same.

Aristotle, a Greek astronomer and philosopher who lived around 350 B.C., observed that Earth made a curved shadow on the Moon during an eclipse. His observations led him to think that Earth was a sphere.

Study Coach

Make a Sketch As you read, draw your own sketches to help you understand and remember new information.

FOLDABLES

Ⓐ Find Main Ideas Make the following six-tab Foldable to identify and record the main ideas about Earth.

How do we know Earth is a sphere?

Today, we have observations from astronauts and pictures from artificial satellites and space probes to show us Earth's shape. Now we also know Earth is not a perfect sphere. It bulges at the equator and is somewhat flat at the poles. The table below shows the differences in Earth's diameter at the equator and from pole to pole.

Copyright © Glencoe/McGraw-Hill, a division of The McGraw-Hill Companies, Inc.

Physical Properties of Earth	
Diameter (pole to pole)	12,714 km
Diameter (equator)	12,756 km
Circumference (poles)	40,008 km
Circumference (equator)	40,075 km
Mass	5.98×10^{24} kg
Average density	5.52 g/cm^3
Average distance to the Sun	149,600,000 km
Period of rotation (1 day)	23 h, 56 min
Period of revolution (1 year)	365 days, 6 h, 9 min

Applying Math

1. **Solve a One-Step Equation** On the table, find the numbers for Diameter (equator) and for Diameter (pole to pole). Subtract the number for Diameter (pole to pole) from the number for Diameter (equator). What does this tell you about Earth's shape?

_____

_____

Does Earth spin?

Earth spins like a top. The imaginary center line around which Earth spins is called Earth's **axis.** The poles are at the north and the south ends of Earth's axis. The spinning of Earth on its axis is called **rotation**.

Earth's rotation causes day and night. As Earth rotates, your area of Earth faces toward the Sun in the morning and away from the Sun at night. Earth rotates once each day. A rotation takes about 24 hours.

Magnetic Field

Scientists hypothesize that the movement of material inside Earth's core, along with Earth's rotation, generates a magnetic field. Like a bar magnet, Earth has opposite north and south magnetic poles. Earth's magnetic field protects you from harmful radiation. It does this by trapping many charged particles that reach Earth from the Sun. ☑

Reading Check

2. **Explain** How is Earth like a bar magnet?

_____

_____

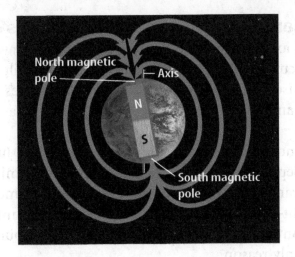

Picture This

3. Draw lines through Earth's magnetic axis and Earth's rotational axis to show they do not line up.

What is Earth's magnetic axis?

When a compass needle points north, you are seeing proof of Earth's magnetic field. The line that joins Earth's north and south magnetic poles is called its magnetic axis. As shown in the figure above, the magnetic axis does not line up with Earth's rotational axis. In fact, the location of the magnetic axis changes slowly over time. A compass whose needle points north will lead you to Earth's magnetic north pole, not the rotational north pole.

What causes changing seasons?

Flowers bloom as the days get warmer. The Sun appears higher in the sky, and daylight lasts longer. Spring seems like a fresh, new beginning. What causes these changes?

Does Earth's orbit cause seasons?

Recall that Earth's rotation causes day and night. Another movement of Earth is called revolution. **Revolution** is Earth's orbit, or the path of Earth, as it goes around the Sun. It takes a year for Earth to orbit the Sun. ☑

The shape of Earth's path around the Sun is an **ellipse** (ee LIHPS)—a long, curved shape, similar to a stretched-out circle. The Sun is not located in the center of the ellipse but is a little toward one end. Earth is closest to the Sun around January 3, and farthest from the Sun around July 4.

Although Earth's orbit takes it nearer and farther from the Sun, the change in distance is small and does not cause seasons. If Earth's distance from the Sun caused the seasons, January—when the Earth is nearest to the Sun—would have the warmest days. This is not the case, however, in the northern hemisphere.

Copyright © Glencoe/McGraw-Hill, a division of The McGraw-Hill Companies, Inc.

✔ Reading Check

4. Define What is Earth's revolution?

_____

_____

Does Earth's tilted axis cause seasons?

Earth's axis is tilted 23.5 degrees from a line drawn perpendicular to the plane of its orbit. It is this tilt that causes seasons. The tilt explains why Earth receives such a different amount of solar energy from place to place during the year.

In the northern hemisphere, summer begins in June and ends in September. This is when the northern hemisphere is tilted toward the Sun. During summer, there are more hours of sunlight—or solar energy. Longer periods of sunlight are one reason that summer is warmer than winter, but this is not the only reason.

How does Earth's tilt affect solar radiation?

Earth's tilt causes the Sun's radiation to strike the hemispheres at different angles. Sunlight strikes the hemisphere tilted toward the Sun at an angle closer to 90 degrees than the hemisphere tilted away. Thus the hemisphere tilted toward the Sun receives more solar radiation than the hemisphere tilted away from the Sun.

Summer occurs in the hemisphere tilted toward the Sun, when its radiation strikes Earth at a high angle and for longer periods of time. The hemisphere receiving less radiation experiences winter.

Solstices

The __solstice__ is the day when the Sun reaches its greatest distance north or south of the equator. In the northern hemisphere, the summer solstice occurs on June 21 or 22, and the winter solstice occurs on December 21 or 22. The position of Earth in relation to the Sun at different times of the year is shown in the figure on the next page. In the southern hemisphere, the winter solstice is in June and the summer solstice is in December.

Summer solstice is the longest period of daylight of the year. From the summer solstice to the winter solstice, the number of daylight hours keeps decreasing. The winter solstice is the shortest period of daylight of the year. Then the number of daylight hours begins increasing again.

Think it Over

5. Infer In the winter, are daylight hours longer or shorter than in summer?

_____

_____

Think it Over

6. Infer If it is winter in the northern hemisphere, which hemisphere is getting more of the Sun's radiation?

_____

_____

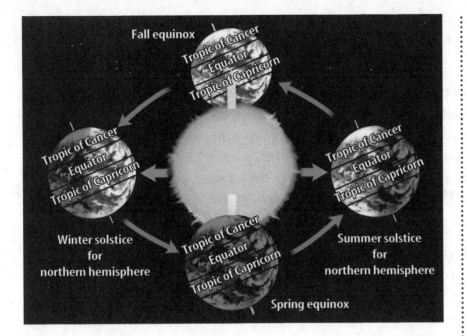

Fall equinox

Tropic of Cancer
Equator
Tropic of Capricorn

Tropic of Cancer
Equator
Tropic of Capricorn

Tropic of Cancer
Equator
Tropic of Capricorn

Winter solstice
for
northern hemisphere

Summer solstice
for
northern hemisphere

Tropic of Cancer
Equator
Tropic of Capricorn

Spring equinox

Picture This

7. Explain Use the figure to explain over which part of Earth the Sun is located during the winter solstice in the northern hemisphere.

_____

_____

Equinoxes

An **equinox** (EE kwuh nahks) occurs when the Sun is directly above Earth's equator. The tilt of Earth's axis means that the Sun's position relative to the equator is constantly changing. Most of the time, the Sun is either north or south of the equator. But two times a year the Sun is directly over the equator. This results in the spring and fall equinoxes. At an equinox, the Sun strikes the equator at the highest possible angle, 90 degrees. This can be seen in the figure above. ☑

During an equinox, neither the northern hemisphere nor the southern hemisphere is tilted toward the Sun. The number of daylight hours and nighttime hours is nearly equal all over the world.

In the northern hemisphere, the spring equinox occurs on March 20 or 21, and the fall equinox occurs on September 22 or 23. In the southern hemisphere, the spring equinox occurs in September, while the fall equinox occurs in March.

☑ Reading Check

8. Define When does an equinox occur?

_____

_____

● After You Read

Mini Glossary

axis: imaginary center line around which Earth spins

ellipse (ee LIHPS): elongated, closed curve that described Earth's yearlong orbit around the sun

equinox (EE kwuh nahks): twice-yearly time—each spring and fall—when the Sun is directly over the equator and the number of daylight and nighttime hours are equal worldwide

revolution: Earth's yearlong elliptical orbit around the Sun

rotation: spinning of Earth on its axis

solstice: twice-yearly point at which the Sun reaches its greatest distance north or south of the equator

sphere (SFIHR): a round, three-dimensional object whose surface is the same distance from its center at all points

1. Review the terms and their definitions in the Mini Glossary. Write a sentence or two about the effects of Earth's rotation and its tilted axis.

_____

_____

_____

2. Complete the table by labeling the statements true or false.

Earth's Properties and Seasons	True or False?
Earth's shape is a slightly flattened sphere.	_____
Earth's seasons are caused by its tilt.	_____
The shape of Earth's orbit is a circle.	_____
The shape of Earth's orbit is an ellipse.	_____
After the summer solstice, daylight hours increase.	_____
During a solstice, the Sun is at its farthest point north or south of the equator.	_____

End of Section

 Visit **glencoe.com** to access your textbook, interactive games, and projects to help you learn more about Earth.

The Sun-Earth-Moon System

section ❷ The Moon—Earth's Satellite

 PS 1.1g Moons are seen by reflected light. Our Moon orbits Earth, while Earth orbits the Sun. The Moon's phases as observed from Earth are the result of seeing different portions of the lighted area of the Moon's surface. The phases repeat in a cyclic pattern in about one month. **Also covered:** PS 1.1c, 1.1e

● Before You Read

What do you already know about the moon? List physical characteristics or phases of the moon on the lines below. Check your information as you read the section.

_____

_____

_____

What You'll Learn

- the phases of the Moon
- why solar and lunar eclipses occur
- the Moon's physical characteristics

● Read to Learn

Motions of the Moon

The Moon's movements are similar to Earth's movements. Just as Earth rotates on its axis, the Moon rotates on its axis. Earth revolves around the Sun, while the Moon revolves around Earth. The Moon's revolution around Earth is responsible for the changes in the Moon's appearance.

If the Moon rotates on its axis, why can't you see it spin around in space? The Moon's rotation takes 27.3 days—the same amount of time it takes to revolve once around Earth. Because these two motions take the same amount of time, the same side of the Moon always faces Earth. So, even though the Moon rotates on its axis, the same side is always visible from Earth.

What lights the Moon?

The surface of the Moon reflects the light of the Sun. Just as half of Earth experiences day as the other half experiences night, half of the Moon is lighted while the other half is dark. As the Moon revolves around Earth, different portions of its lighted side can be seen. This is why the Moon appears to change form or shape.

Study Coach

Create a Quiz As you read the text, create a quiz question for each subject. When you have finished reading, see if you can answer your own questions correctly.

FOLDABLES

B Classify Make the following six-tab Foldable to identify the main ideas about Earth's Moon.

Phases of the Moon

Moon phases are the different ways the Moon appears from Earth. The phase of the Moon depends on the relative positions of the Moon, Earth, and the Sun, as shown in the figure below.

A **new moon** occurs when the Moon is between Earth and the Sun. During a new moon, the lighted half of the Moon is facing the Sun and the dark side of the Moon faces Earth. Even though the Moon is in the sky, it cannot be seen. A new moon rises and sets in the sky at the same time as the Sun.

Picture This

1. **Identify** Highlight the lighted side of each figure of the Moon.

Moon Phases

Waxing gibbous · 1st qtr. · Waxing crescent · Sunlight · Full · New · Earth · Waning gibbous · 3rd qtr. · Waning crescent

Reading Check

2. **Apply** What is happening when the moon is in its waxing phases?

_____

_____

Waxing Phases After the new moon, the phases begin waxing. **Waxing** means that more of the lighted half of the Moon can be seen each night. About 24 h after a new moon, a thin slice of the Moon can be seen. This phase is called the waxing crescent. About a week after a new moon, you can see half of the lighted side of the Moon, or about one quarter of the Moon's surface. This is the first quarter phase. ☑

The phases continue to wax. When more than one quarter of the Moon's surface is visible, it is called waxing gibbous. *Gibbous* is the Latin word for "humpbacked." A **full moon** occurs when all of the Moon's surface that faces Earth reflects light.

Waning Phases After the full moon, the phases are said to be waning. <u>Waning</u> means that you can see less and less of the lighted half of the Moon each night. About 24 h after a full moon, you begin to see the waning gibbous moon. About a week after a full moon, you can again see half of the lighted side of the Moon, or one quarter of the Moon's surface. This is the third-quarter phase. As the waning phases continue, you see less and less of the Moon. The last of the waning phases is the waning crescent, when just a small slice of the Moon is visible. This takes place just before another new moon.

It takes about 29.5 days for the Moon to complete its cycle of phases. Recall that it takes about 27.3 days for the Moon to revolve around Earth. The difference in the numbers is due to Earth's revolution. It takes about two extra days for the Sun, Earth, and the Moon to return to their same relative positions.

Eclipses

Imagine living 10,000 years ago. You are gathering nuts and berries when, without warning, the Sun disappears. The darkness lasts only a short time, and the Sun soon returns to full brightness. You know something strange has happened, but you don't know why or how. It will be almost 8,000 years before anyone can explain what you just experienced.

The event just described was a total solar eclipse (ih KLIPS). Today, most people know what causes eclipses. What causes the day to become night and then change back into day?

What causes an eclipse?

The revolution of the Moon around Earth causes eclipses. Eclipses take place when Earth blocks light from reaching the Moon, or when the Moon blocks light from reaching a part of Earth. Sometimes, during a new moon, the Moon's shadow falls on Earth. This causes a solar eclipse. During a full moon, Earth may cast a shadow on the Moon. This causes a lunar eclipse.

An eclipse can take place only when the Sun, the Moon, and Earth are lined up perfectly. Because the Moon's orbit is not in the same plane as Earth's orbit around the Sun, lunar eclipses take place only a few times each year.

Applying Math

3. **Calculate** About how many times does the moon complete its cycle of phases around Earth in one year?

_____

_____

Think it Over

4. **Infer** What is between the Sun and the Moon during a lunar eclipse?

_____

_____

What is an eclipse of the Sun?

A <u>solar eclipse</u> occurs when the Moon moves directly between the Sun and Earth and casts its shadow over part of Earth. A solar eclipse is shown in the figure below. Depending on where you are on Earth, you may be in a total eclipse or a partial eclipse. Only a small area of Earth is part of the total solar eclipse during the eclipse event.

The darkest portion of the Moon's shadow on Earth is called the umbra (UM bruh). A person standing within the umbra experiences a total solar eclipse. During a total solar eclipse, the only part of the Sun that is visible is a white glow around the edge of the eclipsing Moon.

Surrounding the umbra is a lighter shadow on Earth's surface. This lighter shadow is called the penumbra (puh NUM bruh). Those who are standing in the penumbra experience a partial solar eclipse. **WARNING:** *Regardless of which eclipse you view, never look directly at the Sun. The light can permanently damage your eyes.*

Picture This

5. Label On the diagram, label the umbra and the penumbra.

Solar Eclipse

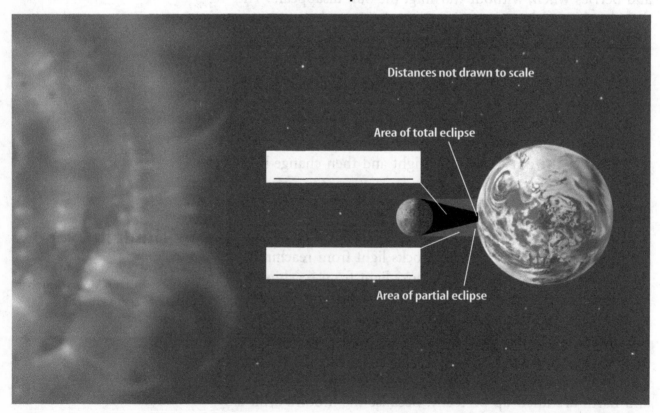

Distances not drawn to scale

Area of total eclipse

Area of partial eclipse

What is an eclipse of the Moon?

When Earth moves directly between the Sun and the Moon and its shadow falls on the Moon, a **lunar eclipse** occurs. A lunar eclipse begins when the Moon moves into Earth's penumbra. As the Moon continues to move, it enters Earth's umbra, and you can see a curved shadow on the Moon's surface. As the Moon moves completely into Earth's umbra, it goes dark. This is a total lunar eclipse. A total lunar eclipse is shown in the figure above. Sometimes sunlight bent through Earth's atmosphere will cause the eclipsed Moon to have a reddish appearance.

A partial lunar eclipse occurs when only a portion of the Moon moves into Earth's shadow. Then, the rest of the Moon is in Earth's penumbra and still gets some direct sunlight. When the Moon is totally within Earth's penumbra, it is called a penumbral lunar eclipse. It is difficult to tell when a penumbral lunar eclipse happens because some sunlight continues to fall on the side of the Moon facing Earth.

Picture This

6. Label On the diagram, label the umbra and penumbra.

During which lunar phase do eclipses occur?

Lunar eclipses do not happen every month. Lunar eclipses happen only during the full moon phase. ✔

A total lunar eclipse can be seen by anyone on the nighttime side of Earth as long as the Moon is not hidden by clouds. Only a few people get to witness a total solar eclipse, however. Only those in the small area where the Moon's umbra strikes Earth can witness it.

The Moon's Surface

When you look at the Moon, you can see many depressions called craters. Meteorites, asteroids, and comets striking the Moon's surface created most of these craters. When the objects struck the Moon, cracks may have formed in the Moon's crust, allowing lava to reach the surface and fill up the large craters. Dark, flat regions formed as the lava spread. These regions are called **maria** (MAHR ee uh). ✔

The igneous rocks of the maria are 3 billion to 4 billion years old. So far, they are the youngest rocks to be found on the Moon. This shows that craters formed after the Moon's surface had cooled. The maria formed early while molten rock still remained in the Moon's interior. The Moon must once have been as geologically active as Earth is today. As the Moon cooled, the interior separated into distinct layers.

The Moon's Origin

Before the Apollo space missions in the 1960s and 1970s, there were three leading theories about the origin of the Moon. One theory was that the Moon was captured by Earth's gravity. Another stated that the Moon and Earth condensed from the same cloud of dust and gas. An alternative theory proposed that Earth ejected molten material that became the Moon.

💡 **Think it Over**

9. **Recognize Cause and Effect** What was a result of the data gathered in the Apollo missions?

_____

_____

What is the impact theory?

The data gathered by the Apollo missions led many scientists to support a new theory. This theory, called the impact theory, states that the Moon formed billions of years ago from condensing gas and debris thrown off when Earth collided with a Mars-sized object. The blast that resulted ejected material from both objects into space. A ring of gas and debris formed around Earth. Finally, particles in that ring joined together to form the Moon.

Inside the Moon

Just as scientists study earthquakes to gather information about Earth's interior, scientists study moonquakes to understand the structure of the Moon. The information scientists gather from moonquakes has helped them make several possible models of the Moon' interior. One model is shown in the figure below. In it, the Moon's crust is about 60 km thick on the side facing Earth. On the side facing away from Earth, the Moon's crust is thought to be about 150 km thick. Under the crust, another solid layer, the mantle, may be 1,000 km deep. A zone of the mantle where the rock is partly melted may extend even farther down. Below this mantle, there may be a solid, iron-rich core.

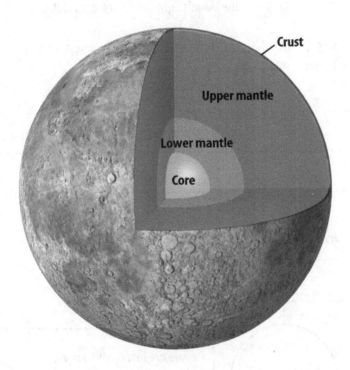

Crust

Upper mantle

Lower mantle

Core

What has been learned about the Moon in history?

Much has been learned about the Moon and Earth by studying the Moon's phases and eclipses. Earth and the Moon are in motion around the Sun. From studying the curved shadow that Earth casts on the Moon, early scientists learned that Earth is a sphere. When Galileo first used his telescope to look at the Moon, he saw that it was not smooth but had craters and maria. Today, scientists study rocks collected from the Moon. By doing so, they hope to learn more about Earth.

Applying Math

10. **Calculate** About what is the difference in thickness between the Moon's crust on the side facing Earth and the crust facing away from Earth?

_____

Picture This

11. **Interpret Scientific Illustrations** List the layers of the Moon in order from the interior to the surface.

_____

_____

_____

_____

● After You Read

Mini Glossary

full moon: phase that occurs when all of the Moon's surface facing Earth reflects light

lunar eclipse: occurs when Earth passes directly between the Sun and the Moon and Earth's shadow falls on the Moon

maria (MAHR ee uh): dark-colored, relatively flat regions of the Moon formed when ancient lava reached the surface and filled craters on the Moon's surface

moon phase: change in appearance of the Moon as viewed from the Earth, due to the relative positions of the Moon, Earth, and the Sun

new moon: moon phase that occurs when the Moon is between Earth and the Sun, at which point the Moon cannot be seen because its lighted half is facing the Sun and its dark side faces Earth

solar eclipse: occurs when the Moon passes directly between the Sun and Earth and casts a shadow over part of Earth

waning: describes phases that occur after a full moon, as the visible lighted side of the Moon grows smaller

waxing: describes phases following a new moon, as more of the Moon's lighted side becomes visible

1. Review the terms and their definitions in the Mini Glossary. Write two sentences explaining different phases of the Moon.

_____

_____

_____

2. Fill in the concept map with what you know about eclipses.

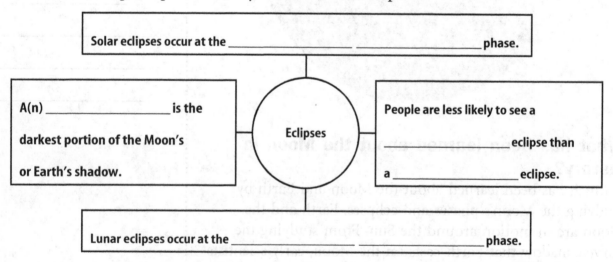

Solar eclipses occur at the _____ _____ phase.

A(n) _____ is the darkest portion of the Moon's or Earth's shadow.

Eclipses

People are less likely to see a _____ eclipse than a _____ eclipse.

Lunar eclipses occur at the _____ _____ phase.

End of Section

Copyright © Glencoe/McGraw-Hill, a division of The McGraw-Hill Companies, Inc.

Science Online Visit **glencoe.com** to access your textbook, interactive games, and projects to help you learn more about Earth's satellite, the Moon.

The Sun-Earth-Moon System

section ❸ Exploring Earth's Moon

 PS1.1c The Sun and the planets that revolve around it are the major bodies in the solar system. Other members include comets, moons, and asteroids. Earth's orbit is nearly circular. **Also covered:** PS 1.1e, 1.1g

● Before You Read

People have always been curious about the Moon. What would you like to know about the Moon? In the space below, write some questions you have about the Moon.

_____

_____

_____

What You'll Learn

■ recent discoveries about the Moon
■ facts that might affect future space travel to the Moon

● Read to Learn

Missions to the Moon

For centuries, scientists have tried to discover what the Moon is made of and how it formed. In 1959, the former Soviet Union launched the first *Luna* spacecraft. This spacecraft made it possible to study the Moon up close.

Two years later, the United States began a similar space program. The United States launched the first *Ranger* spacecraft and a series of *Lunar Orbiters*. The spacecraft in these early missions took detailed photographs of the Moon.

The *Surveyor* spacecraft were the next step. The *Surveyor* spacecraft were designed to take more detailed photographs and to actually land on the Moon. Five of these spacecraft landed on the Moon's surface and analyzed lunar soil. The goal of the *Surveyor* program was to gather information about the Moon that would allow astronauts to land there one day.

In 1969, the astronauts of *Apollo 11* landed on the Moon. Between 1969 and 1972, when the *Apollo* missions ended, 12 U.S. astronauts had walked on the Moon.

Mark the Text

Identify the Main Point
Highlight the main point in each paragraph. Using a different color, highlight an example that helps explain the main point.

FOLDABLES

● Organize Information
Make the following 2-tab Foldable to organize information about Moon missions and Moon mapping.

Copyright © Glencoe/McGraw-Hill, a division of The McGraw-Hill Companies, Inc.

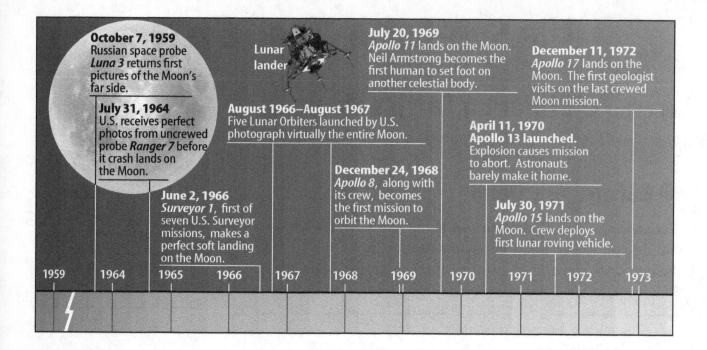

October 7, 1959
Russian space probe *Luna 3* returns first pictures of the Moon's far side.

July 31, 1964
U.S. receives perfect photos from uncrewed probe *Ranger 7* before it crash lands on the Moon.

Lunar lander

July 20, 1969
Apollo 11 lands on the Moon. Neil Armstrong becomes the first human to set foot on another celestial body.

December 11, 1972
Apollo 17 lands on the Moon. The first geologist visits on the last crewed Moon mission.

August 1966–August 1967
Five Lunar Orbiters launched by U.S. photograph virtually the entire Moon.

April 11, 1970
Apollo 13 launched. Explosion causes mission to abort. Astronauts barely make it home.

June 2, 1966
Surveyor 1, first of seven U.S. Surveyor missions, makes a perfect soft landing on the Moon.

December 24, 1968
Apollo 8, along with its crew, becomes the first mission to orbit the Moon.

July 30, 1971
Apollo 15 lands on the Moon. Crew deploys first lunar roving vehicle.

1959 1964 1965 1966 1967 1968 1969 1970 1971 1972 1973

Picture This

1. Use Tables Which Apollo mission deployed the first lunar roving vehicle?

_____

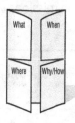
Is the Moon being studied today?

The time line above shows important events in the exploration of the Moon. But, there is still much to learn about the Moon. The United States has started to study the Moon again. In 1994, the spacecraft *Clementine* was placed into lunar orbit. *Clementine's* purpose was to conduct a survey of the Moon's surface. An important part of the study was to collect data on the mineral content of Moon rocks. While in orbit around the Moon, *Clementine* also mapped features on the Moon's surface, including huge impact basins.

What is an impact basin?

An **impact basin,** or impact crater, is a depression left behind when a meteorite or other object strikes the Moon. The South Pole-Aitken Basin is the oldest impact basin that has been identified so far.

Impact basins like the South Pole-Aitken Basin are very interesting to scientists. Because this deep crater is located at one of the poles, the Sun's rays never reach the bottom of the crater. Therefore, the bottom of the crater is always in shadow. The temperatures there are extremely cold. Scientists hypothesize that if a comet collided with the Moon, ice could have been deposited there. Some of that ice might still be found in the shadows at the bottom of the crater. In fact, *Clementine* sent information that showed the presence of water, just as scientists had hypothesized.

Mapping the Moon

Photographs taken by *Clementine* were used to create detailed maps of the Moon's surface. Data from *Clementine* showed that the Moon's crust did not have the same thickness all over the Moon. The crust on the side of the Moon that faces Earth is much thinner than the crust on the far side. Additional information showed that the Moon's crust is thinnest under impact basins.

What is the *Lunar Prospector*?

In 1998, NASA sent the small *Lunar Prospector* spacecraft into orbit around the Moon. For one year the spacecraft circled the Moon from one pole to the other. It flew around the Moon once every two hours.

The *Lunar Prospector* collected data that confirmed that the Moon has a small, iron-rich core at its center. This finding supports the impact theory of how the Moon was formed. The small core is a result of a small amount of iron that could have blasted away from Earth. ☑

Where is there ice on the Moon?

In addition to photographing the surface, *Lunar Prospector* carried instruments that gathered information for mapping the Moon. The maps were of the Moon's gravity, its magnetic field, and how much and where certain elements were found in the Moon's crust. Scientists finally had data from the entire surface of the Moon, rather than just the areas around the Moon's equator.

The *Lunar Prospector* confirmed that ice was present in deep craters at both poles of the Moon. Using data from *Lunar Prospector*, scientists made maps that show the location of ice at each pole. At first scientists thought that ice crystals were mixed with lunar soil. More recent information suggests that the ice deposit may be in the form of more compact deposits. ☑

✔ **Reading Check**

2. **Describe** What is in Moon's core that supports the impact theory?

_____

_____

✔ **Reading Check**

3. **Identify** Where is there ice on the Moon's surface?

_____

_____

● After You Read

Mini Glossary

impact basin: a depression left on the surface of the Moon
caused by an object striking its surface

1. Review the term and its definition in the Mini Glossary. Write a sentence explaining what causes impact basins to form.

_____

_____

2. Complete the chart to review missions that gathered information about the Moon.

Spacecraft	Mission
Ranger and Lunar Orbiters	To photograph the Moon
Surveyor	
Clementine	
Lunar Prospector	

3. How did highlighting help you read this section? Reread the sentences you highlighted in the text. Now that you have read the entire section, do you think you highlighted the right sentences? Make any corrections you think would help you.

_____

_____

_____

End of Section

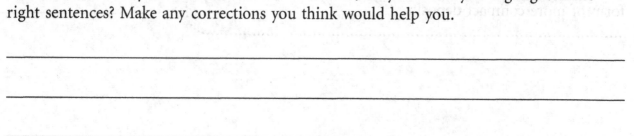

Science Online Visit **glencoe.com** to access your textbook, interactive games, and projects to help you learn more about exploring Earth's moon.

Ocean Motion

section ❶ Ocean Water

 PS 4.1b Fossils fuels contain stored solar energy and are considered nonrenewable resources. They are a major source of energy in the United States. Solar energy, wind, moving water, and biomass are some examples of renewable energy resources. **Also covered:** PS 3.1a, 2.1e, 2.2a

● Before You Read

What comes to mind when you think about the ocean? What resources do you know about that come from the ocean?

_____

_____

_____

What You'll Learn
- the origin of the water in Earth's oceans
- how substances such as dissolved salts get into seawater
- the composition of seawater

● Read to Learn

Importance of Oceans

It is easy to enjoy the ocean on a sunny day. You can lie on the beach and listen as the waves roll onto the shore. But the ocean is also useful. It provides us with many of the resources we need.

What resources come from oceans?

Oceans are important sources of food, energy, and minerals. Humans get foods such as shrimp, fish, crabs, and clams from oceans. Kelp, a seaweed found in the ocean, is used in making ice cream, salad dressing, and medicines. Sources of energy can also come from the ocean. Oil and natural gas are often found beneath the ocean floor. Mineral resources can be found in the oceans too. Gold and copper are often mined in shallow waters. Almost one-third of all the table salt in the world comes from oceans. It is removed from the seawater through evaporation. ☑

Transportation Oceans also allow for the efficient transportation of goods. Millions of tons of oil, coal, and grains are shipped over the oceans each year.

▶ **Mark the Text**

Identify the Main Point
Highlight the main point in each paragraph. Then use a different color to highlight a detail or example that helps explain each main point.

☑ **Reading Check**

1. **Identify** Name some foods that humans get from oceans.

_____

_____

Origin of Oceans

Earth had many volcanoes during its first billion years. When the volcanoes erupted, they sent out lava, ash, and large amounts of water vapor, carbon dioxide, and other gases. This is shown in the figure on the left below. Scientists hypothesize that about 4 billion years ago, this water vapor began to be stored in Earth's early atmosphere.

Over millions of years, the water vapor cooled enough to condense into storm clouds. Rain fell from these clouds and filled low areas on Earth called **basins**. You can see this in the figure on the right below. Earth's oceans formed in the basins. Today, oceans cover over 70 percent of Earth's surface.

How Water Vapor Formed Earth's Oceans

Composition of Oceans

Ocean water contains dissolved gases such as oxygen, carbon dioxide, and nitrogen. These gases enter the ocean from the atmosphere, the air that surrounds Earth. Oxygen also enters the ocean from organisms that photosynthesize. Organisms that use oxygen to breathe produce carbon dioxide which is released when they exhale. This is another way carbon dioxide enters the ocean.

Salts If you've ever tasted ocean water, you know that it is salty. Ocean water contains many dissolved salts. Chloride, sodium, sulfate, magnesium, calcium, and potassium are some of the ions in seawater. An ion is a charged atom or group of atoms. Some of these ions come from rocks that are dissolved slowly by rivers and groundwater. These include calcium, magnesium, and sodium. Rivers carry these chemicals to the oceans. Erupting volcanoes add other ions, such as bromide and chloride.

<u>Picture This</u>

2. Describe How did land forms affect where oceans were formed?

_____

_____

_____

FOLDABLES

A **Classify** Make the following Foldable to help you organize information about the composition of seawater.

water +

dissolved gases +

dissolved salts

Is seawater always salty?

Seawater is about 96.5 percent pure water. Many ions are found dissolved in seawater. When seawater evaporates, these ions combine to form minerals called salts. The chart below shows that chloride and sodium are the most common ions in seawater. During evaporation, these two ions combine. They form a salt called halite. Halite is the salt used every day to flavor foods. The dissolved halite and other salts give ocean water its salty taste.

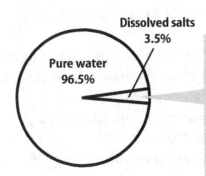

Dissolved salts 3.5%

Pure water 96.5%

Ions Found in Seawater

Ion	Percentage
Chloride	55.0
Sodium	30.6
Sulfate	7.7
Magnesium	3.7
Calcium	1.2
Potassium	1.1
Other	0.7

Applying Math

3. **Calculate** What percentage of all the ocean's ions are either chloride or sodium? Use the information shown on the chart to help you.

What is salinity?

<u>Salinity</u> (say LIH nuh tee) is a measure of the amount of salts dissolved in seawater. Salinity is usually measured in grams of dissolved salt in one kilogram of seawater. One kilogram of ocean water contains about 35 g of dissolved salts, or 3.5 percent. The amount of salts in seawater has stayed nearly constant for hundreds of millions of years. This tells you that the oceans are not getting saltier.

How does the ocean stay in balance?

New elements and ions are constantly being added to water. Rivers, volcanoes, and the atmosphere all add material to the oceans. But, the ocean is said to be in balance. Elements are being removed from the ocean at the same rate that they are being added. Dissolved salts are removed when they become solid salts. Then they become part of the ocean sediment.

Some marine organisms, such as oysters, use dissolved calcium to make shells. Because many organisms use calcium, it is removed more quickly from seawater. Chloride and sodium are removed from seawater more slowly.

Think it Over

4. **Summarize** How many grams of salts will be left if you evaporate 1 kg of ocean water?
   a. 1,000 g
   b. 35 g
   c. 85.6 g
   d. 3.5 g

How can salt be removed from ocean water?

If you have ever swum in the ocean, you may have noticed a white, flaky substance on your skin when it dried. That substance is salt. When seawater evaporates, salt is left. As the demand for fresh drinking water increases around the world, scientists are working on creating an efficient way to remove salt from seawater. Desalination (dee sa luh NAY shun) is the process of removing salt from seawater. Some desalination plants use evaporation to remove the salt.

How is ocean water desalinated?

Scientists are working on several methods for turning saltwater into freshwater.

In some plants, seawater is passed through a membrane. The membrane filters out salt ions. Freshwater also can be obtained by melting frozen seawater. Frozen seawater contains less salt than liquid seawater. The ice can be washed and melted to produce freshwater.

Another method of desalination uses solar energy. A building is filled with seawater. The building has a glass roof. Solar energy heats the water until it evaporates. Then, the freshwater is collected from the glass roof. Look at the figure below. It shows a solar desalination plant.

Picture This

5. Interpret Scientific Illustrations Use a marker to trace the path taken by seawater in a desalination plant. Then, use another color to trace the path taken by freshwater.

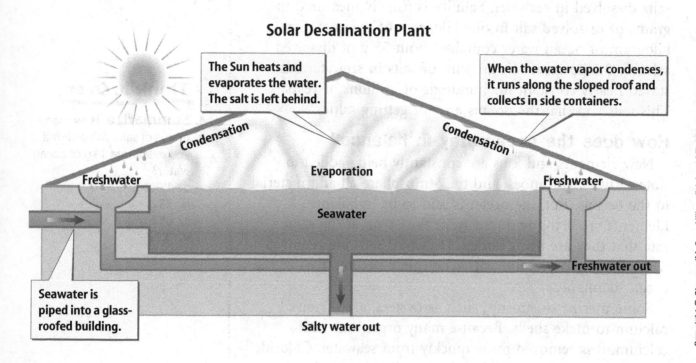

Solar Desalination Plant

The Sun heats and evaporates the water. The salt is left behind.

When the water vapor condenses, it runs along the sloped roof and collects in side containers.

Condensation

Condensation

Freshwater

Evaporation

Freshwater

Seawater

Freshwater out

Seawater is piped into a glass-roofed building.

Salty water out

● After You Read

Mini Glossary

basin: low area on Earth in which an ocean formed

salinity: a measure of the amount of salts dissolved in seawater

1. Review the terms and their definitions in the Mini Glossary. Choose one word and write a sentence to explain the meaning in your own words.

_____

_____

_____

2. Use the chart to describe how a solar desalination plant works.

Solar Desalination

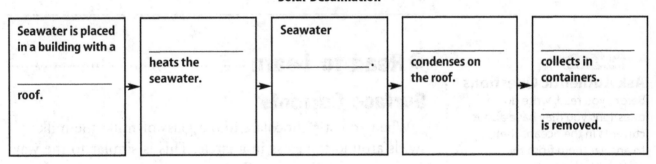

| Seawater is placed in a building with a _____ roof. | → | _____ heats the seawater. | → | Seawater _____. | → | _____ condenses on the roof. | → | _____ collects in containers. _____ is removed. |

3. Choose one of the question headings in the Read to Learn section. Write the question in the box. Then answer it in your own words.

Write your question here.

_____

_____

_____

Science Online Visit **glencoe.com** to access your textbook, interactive games, and projects to help you learn more about ocean water.

End of Section

Ocean Motion

section ❷ Ocean Currents

🗽 **PS 3.1h** Density can be described as the amount of matter that is in a given amount of space. If two objects have equal volume, but one has more mass, the one with more mass is denser. **Also covered:** PS 4.2a, 4.2b, 4.2e

What You'll Learn

- the Coriolis effect
- what influences surface currents
- the temperature of coastal waters
- about density currents

Study Coach

Ask Authentic Questions

Before you read, write down questions you may have about currents in the ocean. Then, try to answer them from the material in this section.

FOLDABLES

❽ Organize Information

Make the following Foldable from a half sheet of notebook paper to summarize information about currents in the northern and southern hemispheres.

N
Clockwise currents

Equator

Counter-clockwise currents

S

● Before You Read

Imagine that you are stirring chocolate into a glass of milk with a spoon. How does the milk move? What happens when you stir faster?

● Read to Learn

Surface Currents

When you stir chocolate into a glass of milk, the milk swirls around the glass in a circle. This is similar to the way an ocean current moves. Ocean currents are a mass movement, or flow, of ocean water. Think of an ocean current as a river moving within the ocean.

A **surface current** is a current that moves water horizontally, or parallel to Earth's surface. Surface currents are powered by wind blowing over the water. The wind forces the water in the ocean to move in huge, circular patterns. In fact, the currents on the ocean's surface are related to the circulation of the winds on Earth. However, these currents don't affect the deep sections of the ocean. They move only the upper few hundred meters of seawater.

Some seeds and plants are carried between continents by surface currents. Sailors have relied on surface currents and winds to make sailing easier. You can see some surface currents in the figure on the next page. The arrows show the circular direction that the currents follow. Some of the currents are caused by warm winds and some are caused by cool winds.

Major Surface Currents of Earth's Oceans

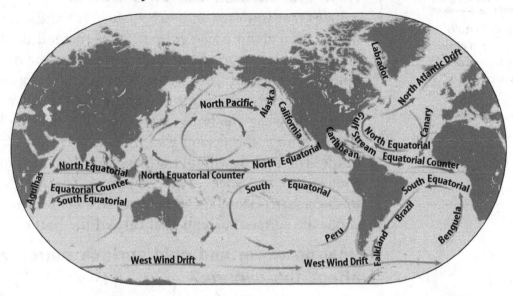

How do surface currents form?

Surface ocean currents and surface winds are affected by the Coriolis (kor ee OH lus) effect. The **Coriolis effect** is the shifting of winds and surface currents from their expected paths because of Earth's rotation.

Earth rotates toward the east. Because of this, winds in the northern hemisphere turn to their right and winds in the southern hemisphere turn to their left. These surface winds can cause water to pile up in certain parts of the ocean. When gravity pulls water off the pile, the Coriolis effect turns the water. This causes surface water in oceans to spiral, or circle, around the piles of water.

Look again at the map of major surface currents. The circular patterns that you see are caused by the Coriolis effect. The currents north of the equator circle to their right. Currents south of the equator circle to their left.

What is the Gulf Stream?

Much of what is known about surface currents comes from records that were kept by sailors in the nineteenth century. Sailors always have used surface currents to make traveling easier. Sailors heading west use surface currents that flow west. Sailors heading east use currents such as the Gulf Stream. The Gulf Stream is a 100-km-wide surface current in the Atlantic Ocean. When America was still a colony of England, sailors noticed that trips to England were faster than trips from England. Going eastward with the Gulf Stream made the journey quicker. ☑

Picture This

1. Identify Name one current that affects the oceans around North America's coasts.

_____

_____

✔ Reading Check

2. Summarize How can surface currents be helpful to ships?

_____

_____

Think it Over

3. Infer What could scientists learn about currents from a drift bottle's trip?

_____

_____

How are surface currents tracked?

Items that wash up on beaches, such as bottles, can provide information about ocean currents. One method used to track surface currents is to release drift bottles into the ocean. Drift bottles are released from a variety of coastal locations.

Inside each bottle, a message and a numbered card state where and when the bottle was released. When the bottle washes ashore, the person who finds it may notice the card inside. The person will fill out the card with the information about when and where it washed ashore. The card is returned to the research team and provides valuable information about the surface currents that carried the bottle.

How do warm and cold surface currents affect the climate?

Look at the map of surface currents again. Notice that some currents start near the north and south poles, and other currents start near the equator. Currents on the west coasts of continents begin near the poles where the water is colder. The California Current is an example of such a current. It starts near the north pole and is a cold surface current.

Currents on the east coast of continents start near the equator where the water is warmer. The Gulf Stream starts in waters near the equator and is a warm surface current.

As a warm surface current flows away from the equator, heat is released to the atmosphere. The atmosphere is warmed. The transfer of heat helps determine climate.

Upwelling

Recall that surface currents carry water horizontally—parallel to Earth's surface. Water also travels vertically, from the bottom to the top of the ocean. **Upwelling** is a vertical circulation in the ocean that brings deep, cold water to the ocean surface. ☑

Along some coasts of continents, wind blowing parallel to the coast carries water away from the land because of the Coriolis effect. Cold water from deep in the ocean rises up to replace it. The cold water is full of nutrients from organisms that died, sank to the bottom, and decayed. Fish are attracted to these nutrient-rich areas. Areas of upwelling are important fishing grounds. The figure on the next page illustrates upwelling off the coast of Peru.

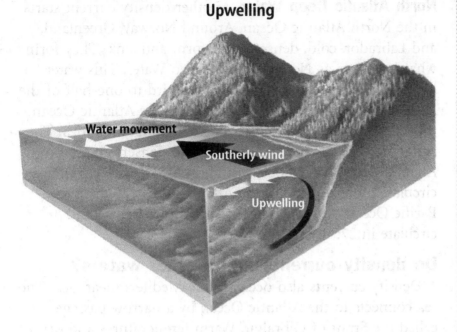

Upwelling

Water movement

Southerly wind

Upwelling

5. Infer Why does upwelling around Peru make Peru a rich fishing ground?

_____

_____

_____

Density Currents

Deep in the ocean, there is no wind to move the water. Instead, differences in density cause water to circulate or move. Cold water is more dense than warm water. Salty water is more dense than less salty water.

A **density current** forms when a mass of seawater becomes more dense than the surrounding water. Gravity causes this dense water to sink beneath less dense seawater. The deep, dense water spreads to the rest of the ocean. Changes in temperature and salinity work together to create density currents. A density current moves water very slowly.

Where are density currents found?

One important density current begins in Antarctica. In winter, the seawater there is more dense than at any other time. When seawater freezes, the salt is left behind in the unfrozen water. This extra salt increases the seawater's density and causes it to sink. Slowly, the water begins to spread along the ocean bottom toward the equator forming a density current. In the Pacific Ocean, it could take up to 1,000 years for the water in this density current to reach the equator.

Think it Over

6. Sequence of Events
Number the events to show the order in which a density current forms in Antarctica.

_____ seawater freezes

_____ unfrozen seawater sinks

_____ dense seawater spreads along ocean floor

North Atlantic Deep Water Another density current starts in the North Atlantic Ocean. Around Norway, Greenland, and Labrador, cold, dense waters form and sink. They form what is known as North Atlantic Deep Water. This water covers the floor of the northern one-third to one-half of the Atlantic Ocean. In the southern part of the Atlantic Ocean, this current meets the density current from Antarctica. The Antarctic density current is colder and denser. The North Atlantic Deep Water floats just above it. Density currents circulate more quickly in the Atlantic Ocean than in the Pacific Ocean. In the Atlantic, a density current could circulate in 275 years. ☑

Do density currents affect other waters?

Density currents also occur in the Mediterranean Sea. The sea connects to the Atlantic Ocean by a narrow passage called the Strait of Gibraltar. Warm temperatures and dry air in the Mediterranean region cause the seawater to evaporate. The salts remain behind. This increases the salinity and density of the sea. The dense, salty water travels through the Straits of Gibraltar into the Atlantic Ocean. Because it is much denser than water at the surface of the ocean, it sinks. However, it is not as dense as the very cold, salty water of the North Atlantic Deep Water. So, the water from the Mediterranean floats above it. It forms a middle layer known as the Mediterranean Intermediate Water. You can see the different water layers in the figure below.

Copyright © Glencoe/McGraw-Hill, a division of The McGraw-Hill Companies, Inc.

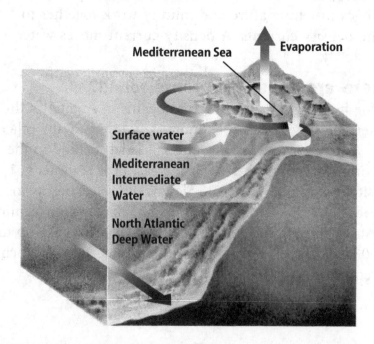

Mediterranean Sea   Evaporation

Surface water

Mediterranean Intermediate Water

North Atlantic Deep Water

✔ Reading Check

7. Think Critically Which is more dense, the Antarctic current or the North Atlantic Deep Water?

_____

_____

Picture This

8. Interpret Scientific Illustrations Which layer of water shown in the figure is most dense?

_____

_____

● After You Read

Mini Glossary

Coriolis effect: the shifting of winds and surface currents from their expected paths that is caused by Earth's rotation

density current: a current that forms in the ocean because a mass of seawater becomes more dense than the surrounding water and sinks

surface current: a current in the ocean that moves water horizontally, or parallel to Earth's surface

upwelling: a vertical circulation in the ocean that brings deep, cold water to the ocean surface

1. Review the terms and their definitions in the Mini Glossary. Write a sentence that explains where density currents and surface currents are found.

_____

_____

_____

2. Complete the spider map about the Coriolis effect. List some of the results on ocean currents of the Coriolis effect.

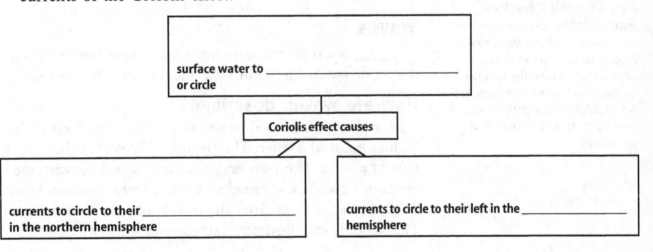

surface water to _____
or circle

Coriolis effect causes

currents to circle to their _____ in the northern hemisphere

currents to circle to their left in the _____ hemisphere

3. Before you read this section, you wrote down questions you had about ocean currents. Were you able to answer any of those questions? What information would you still like to learn about ocean currents?

_____

_____

Science Online Visit **glencoe.com** to access your textbook, interactive games, and projects to help you learn more about ocean currents.

End of Section

Ocean Motion

section ❸ Ocean Waves and Tides

PS 1.1e Most objects in the solar system have a regular and predictable motion. These motions explain such phenomena as a day, a year, phases of the Moon, eclipses, tides, meteor showers, and comets. **Also covered:** PS 1.1d, 4.4a, 4.4c, 5.1b, 5.2d

What You'll Learn

- wave formation
- how water particles move within waves
- the movement of a wave
- how ocean tides form

Study Coach

Read-Recall-Check-Summarize *Read* the section on waves. *Recall* the main ideas by brainstorming them on paper. Then reread the section to *check* that your brainstorming was right. Finally, use your own notes to *summarize* what you read.

Before You Read

Where have you seen a water wave? How would you describe the wave?

_____

_____

_____

Read to Learn

Waves

A **wave** is a rhythmic movement that carries energy through matter or space. An ocean wave moves through seawater.

How are waves described?

Several terms are used to describe waves. The **crest** is the highest point of a wave. The **trough** (TRAWF) is the lowest part of a wave. The wavelength is the distance between the crests or between the troughs of two adjoining waves. Wave height is the distance from the trough of a wave to the crest. The figure below illustrates each part of a wave.

Picture This

1. Identify Highlight the crests in the figure. Then use another color to highlight the troughs.

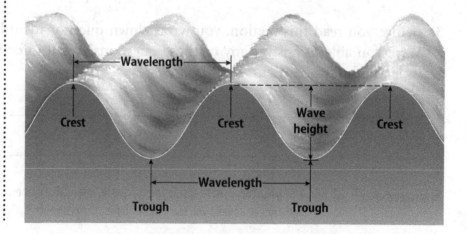

How is a wave's energy measured?

Waves carry energy. This energy can be measured. Half of a wave's height is called the amplitude (AM pluh tewd). To measure the energy carried by a wave, the amplitude is squared. A wave with twice the amplitude of another wave carries four times ($2 \times 2 = 4$) the energy. Small waves have small amplitudes. Amplitude increases as waves grow larger. Large waves can damage ships and coastal property.

How do waves move?

A bobber on a fishing line moves up and down in the water as a wave passes. It does not move outward with the wave. It returns to near its original position after the wave has passed.

Like the bobber, each molecule of water in a wave returns to its original position after a wave passes. The molecule may be pushed forward by the next wave, but it will return again to its original position. The water in waves does not move forward unless the wave is crashing onto shore. The water molecules in a wave move around in circles, coming back to about the same place. Only the energy moves forward. ☑

Below a depth equal to about half the wavelength, water movement stops. Below that depth, water is not affected by waves.

Breakers As a wave reaches the shore, it changes shape. In shallow water, friction with the ocean bottom slows water at the bottom of the wave. The top of the wave keeps moving because it has not been slowed by friction. Eventually, the top of the wave outruns the bottom and it collapses. Water tumbles over on itself, and the wave breaks onto the shore. A **breaker** is a collapsing wave. After a wave breaks onto shore, gravity pulls the water back to sea.

How do water waves form?

On windy days, waves form on lakes and oceans. When wind blows across a body of water, wind energy is transferred to the water. When wind speed is great enough, water piles up forming a wave. As the wind continues to blow, the wave grows in height.

Wave height depends on the speed of the wind, the distance over which the wind blows, and the length of time the wind blows. When the wind stops blowing, waves stop forming. But waves that have already formed will continue to move for long distances. Waves reaching one shore could have formed halfway around the world.

FOLDABLES

C Classify Cut a sheet of paper into eight note cards. Use the cards to record important information about waves and tides.

✔ Reading Check

2. **Summarize** What moves forward in a wave?
   a. molecules
   b. energy
   c. water
   d. bobbers

💡 Think it Over

3. **Recognize Cause and Effect** Would a wave be higher or lower on a very windy day? Why?

_____

_____

_____

Tides

Throughout the day, the level of the sea rises and falls. This rise and fall in sea level is called a **tide**. A tide is caused by a giant wave produced by the gravitational pull of the Sun and the Moon. Although this wave is only 1 m or 2 m high, its wavelength is thousands of kilometers long. As the crest of this wave approaches the shore, sea level seems to rise. This rise in sea level is called high tide. When the trough of this huge wave nears the shore, sea level appears to drop. This drop in sea level is referred to as low tide.

What is the tidal range?

As Earth rotates, Earth's surface passes through the crests and troughs of this giant wave. Many coastal areas, such as the Atlantic and Pacific coasts of the United States, have two high tides and two low tides each day. But because ocean basins vary in size and shape, some coastal locations, such as many along the Gulf of Mexico, have only one high and one low tide each day. A **tidal range** is the difference between the level of the ocean at high tide and the level of the ocean at low tide.

Why do tidal ranges vary in different locations?

Most shorelines have tidal ranges between 1 m and 2 m. However, tidal ranges can be as small as 30 cm or as large as 13.5 m.

The shape of the seacoast and the shape of the ocean floor both affect the ranges of tides. A wide seacoast allows water to spread out farther. At high tide, the water level might only rise a few centimeters. In a narrow gulf or bay, the water cannot spread out. The water will rise many meters at high tide. A narrow gulf or bay will have a greater tidal range than a smooth, wide area of shoreline.

What are tidal bores?

Sometimes, a rising tide enters a river from the sea. If the river is narrow and shallow and the sea is wide, a wave called a tidal bore forms. A tidal bore can have a breaking crest or it can be a smooth wave.

Tidal bores usually are found in places with large tidal ranges. When a tidal bore enters a river, its force causes water in the river to reverse its flow. Waves in a tidal bore might reach 5 m in height and speeds of 65 km/h.

Copyright © Glencoe/McGraw-Hill, a division of The McGraw-Hill Companies, Inc.

Applying Math

4. **Calculate** A sea has a high tide that measures 15 m high. At low tide, it measures 12.5 m high. What is its tidal range?

_____

💡 **Think it Over**

5. **Describe** When a tidal bore enters a river, why does it cause the flow of water in the river to reverse?

_____

_____

_____

How does the Moon affect tides?

The Moon and the Sun exert a gravitational pull on Earth. The Sun is much bigger than Earth, but the Moon is much closer. The Moon has a stronger pull on Earth than the Sun. Earth and the water in Earth's oceans respond to this pull. The water bulges outward as the Moon's gravity pulls it. This results in a high tide. The process is shown in the figure below.

The Moon's gravity pulls at Earth. This creates two bulges of water. One bulge is on the side of Earth closest to the Moon. The other bulge is on the opposite side. The high tide on the side of Earth near the Moon happens because the water is being pulled away from Earth towards the Moon. The high tide on the side of Earth opposite the Moon happens because the gravitational pull on that part of Earth is greater than the pull on the water on that side of Earth. The areas of Earth's oceans that are not toward or away from the Moon are the low tides. As Earth rotates, the bulges follow the Moon. This results in high and low tides happening around the world at different times.

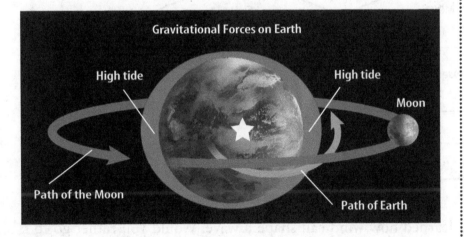

Gravitational Forces on Earth

High tide

High tide

Moon

Path of the Moon

Path of Earth

Picture This

6. **Interpret Scientific Illustrations** Describe the sea level of the ocean in the area of the star in the figure.

_____

_____

_____

What effect does the Sun have on tides?

The Sun's pull can add to or subtract from the gravitational pull of the Moon. Occasionally during Earth's revolution, Earth, the Sun, and the Moon are lined up together. Then, the Moon and the Sun both pull at Earth. The combined gravitational pull results in spring tides on Earth. During spring tides, high tides are higher and low tides are lower than usual. When the Sun, Earth, and the Moon form a right angle, high tides on Earth are lower than usual. Low tides are higher than usual. These are called neap tides.

● After You Read

Mini Glossary

breaker: a collapsing wave
crest: the highest point of a wave
tidal range: the difference between the level of the ocean at high tide and the level of the ocean at low tide

tide: rise and fall in sea level
trough: the lowest part of a wave
wave: a rhythmic movement that carries energy through matter or space

1. Review the terms and their definitions in the Mini Glossary. Write a sentence or two describing a wave's crest and its trough.

   _____

   _____

   _____

2. Complete the Venn diagram to compare and contrast the effects that the Moon and the Sun have on Earth. Use the words *high, low, Moon, strong,* and *weak.*

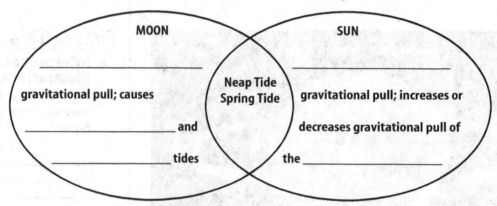

MOON

_____

gravitational pull; causes

_____ and

_____ tides

Neap Tide
Spring Tide

SUN

gravitational pull; increases or

decreases gravitational pull of

the _____

3. Earlier in this section, you learned how wind can shape a wave. Would you rather go to the beach on a windy day, a calm day, or during a storm? Predict what the waves will be like each day.

   _____

   _____

   _____

End of Section

Science Online Visit **glencoe.com** to access your textbook, interactive games, and projects to help you learn more about waves.

chapter 13 # The Solar System

section ❶ The Solar System

PS 1.1c The Sun and the planets that revolve around it are the major bodies in the solar system. Other members include comets, moons, and asteroids. Earth's orbit is nearly circular. **1.1d** Gravity is the force that keeps planets in orbit around the Sun and the Moon in orbit around the Earth.

● Before You Read

Name the planets in the solar system that you already know.

_____

_____

● Read to Learn

Ideas About the Solar System

Based on their observations, early humans believed the Sun and planets moved around Earth. Today, people understand that Earth and the other planets and objects in the solar system orbit, or move around, the Sun.

Earth-Centered Model Early Greek scientists thought the planets, the Sun, the Moon, and the stars rotated around Earth. This is called the Earth-centered model of the solar system. It included Earth, the Moon, the Sun, five planets—Mercury, Venus, Mars, Jupiter, and Saturn—and the stars.

Sun-Centered Model In 1543, Nicholas Copernicus published his model of the solar system. He stated that Earth and the other planets revolved around the Sun and that the Moon revolved around Earth. He explained that the Sun and the planets only looked like they were moving around Earth because Earth rotates. This is the Sun-centered model of the solar system.

Galileo Galilei used his telescope to observe that Venus went through a full cycle of phases like the Moon's. Also, Venus looked smaller when its phase was near full. This could only be explained if Venus were orbiting the Sun, not Earth. Galileo concluded that the Sun is the center of the solar system.

What You'll Learn

- past and present ideas about the solar system
- how the solar system formed
- how the Sun's gravity holds planets in orbit

◀ **Study Coach**

Ask Questions As you read, write down your questions. Use the questions to find out more about topics that are not clear, or topics that are particularly interesting.

FOLDABLES

🅐 **Find Main Ideas** Make the following two-tab Foldable to help you identify the main ideas about past and present views on the solar system.

Past Views

Present Views

What is the modern view of the solar system?

Today, we know that the <u>solar system</u> is made up of eight planets, including Earth, and many smaller objects that orbit the Sun. The Sun and the position of the eight planets relative to the Sun are shown in the figure on this page and the next page. The solar system also includes a huge amount of space that stretches out in all directions from the Sun.

The Sun contains 99.86 percent of the mass in the solar system. Therefore, the Sun has a lot of gravity. The Sun's gravity is strong enough to hold the planets and other objects in their orbits. ☑

How the Solar System Formed

Scientists hypothesize that the solar system formed more than 4.6 billion years ago. They have found clues that it may have formed from a cloud of gas, ice, and dust. Over time, this cloud pulled together to form a large, tightly packed, spinning disk. The center of the disk heated up to about 10 million degrees Celsius, and the reaction known as nuclear fusion began. That is how the star, the Sun, formed at the center of the solar system.

How did the planets form?

Not all of the gas, ice, and dust was pulled into the center of the spinning disk to form the Sun. Some matter collided and stuck together to form planets and asteroids. The eight planets of the solar system are divided into two groups, the inner planets and the outer planets.

Reading Check

1. **Explain** What force holds the planets in their orbits?

_____

_____

Picture This

2. **Interpret Scientific Illustrations** Which planet is closest to the Sun? Which planet is farthest from the Sun? Which is the third planet from the Sun?

_____

_____

_____

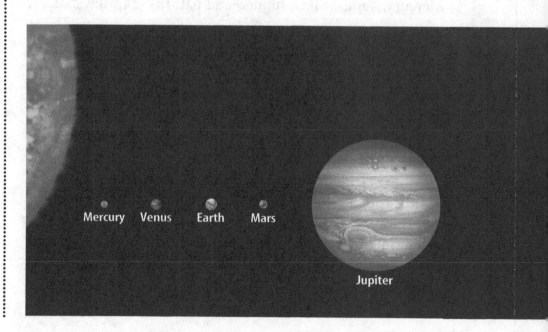

Mercury   Venus   Earth   Mars

Jupiter

What are the eight planets?

The inner planets of the solar system—Mercury, Venus, Earth, and Mars—are small, rocky planets with iron cores. The outer planets are Jupiter, Saturn, Uranus, and Neptune. The outer planets are much larger than the inner planets. They are made up mostly of lighter substances, including hydrogen, helium, methane, and ammonia. ☑

These light substances are not found in great quantities in the inner planets. The high temperatures closer to the Sun turned these substances to gas. They could not cool enough to form solids.

Motions of the Planets

When Nicholas Copernicus developed his Sun-centered model of the solar system, he thought the orbits of the planets were circles. In the early 1600s, Johannes Kepler discovered that the orbits of the planets are oval shaped, or elliptical. He also found that the Sun's position in the orbits is slightly off-center.

Kepler discovered that the planets orbit the Sun at different speeds. Planets closer to the Sun travel faster than planets farther away from the Sun. The outer planets also have longer distances to travel and take much longer to orbit the Sun than the inner planets.

☑ **Reading Check**

3. Identify Name the inner planets.

_____

_____

_____

_____

💡 **Think it Over**

4. Infer Which planet takes longer to orbit the Sun—Mars or Neptune?

_____

Saturn   Uranus   Neptune

● After You Read

Mini Glossary

solar system: system of eight planets, including Earth, and
many smaller objects that orbit the Sun

1. Review the term and its definition in the Mini Glossary. On the lines below, write something you have learned about the solar system.

_____

_____

_____

2. Complete the chart that shows how the solar system may have formed.

1. The solar system formed from a cloud of _____, _____, and _____.
2. The cloud condensed to form a(n) _____.
3. _____ formed first. It was at the center of the new solar system.
4. The other material in the solar system collided and formed _____ planets.
5. The inner planets are _____, _____, _____, and _____.   The outer planets are _____, _____, _____, and _____.

3. Review the questions you wrote as you read this section. What resources could you use to find answers to your questions? Did the questions you write help you understand the information?

_____

_____

End of Section

Science Online Visit **glencoe.com** to access your textbook, interactive games, and projects to help you learn more about the solar system.

The Solar System

section **2** The Inner Planets

 PS 1.1c The Sun and the planets that revolve around it are the major bodies in the solar system. Other members include comets, moons, and asteroids. Earth's orbit is nearly circular. **Also covered:** PS 1.1d, 1.1e, 2.1a

● Before You Read

What do you know about Mercury and Venus? What would you like to know about these inner planets?

_____

_____

_____

● Read to Learn

Inner Planets

Today, people know a great deal about the solar system. Scientists use telescopes to study the planets both from Earth and from space. They also use space probes to study the solar system. Much of the information you will read in this section was gathered by space probes.

Mercury

<u>Mercury</u> is the planet closest to the Sun. The spacecraft *Mariner 10* sent pictures of Mercury to Earth in 1974 and 1975. Scientists learned that Mercury, like Earth's Moon, has many craters. But unlike the Moon, Mercury has cliffs as high as 3 km on its surface. These cliffs might have formed when the crust of the planet broke as the core of the planet was cooling and shrinking.

Scientists learned that Mercury has a weak magnetic field. This shows that Mercury an iron core, the same as Earth. Some scientists think that Mercury's crust solidified while the iron core was still hot and liquid. As the core became more solid, it became smaller. The cliffs resulted from breaks in Mercury's crust caused by the shrinking of the core.

What You'll Learn

■ facts about the inner planets
■ what each inner planet is like
■ compare and contrast Venus and Earth

Study Coach

Make Flash Cards Make four flash cards to help you study this section. On one side of the card, write the name of an inner planet. On the other side, write facts about that planet.

FOLDABLES

B Compare and Contrast Make the following Foldable to understand how the inner planets are similar and different.

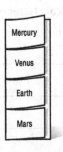

Does Mercury have an atmosphere?

Mercury has no true atmosphere. This is because Mercury has a low gravitational pull and high temperatures during the day. Most gases that could form an atmosphere escape into space. Earth-based observations have found traces of sodium and potassium around the planet. However, these atoms probably come from rocks in Mercury's crust. Therefore, Mercury has no true atmosphere. This lack of atmosphere and its nearness to the Sun cause Mercury to have great extremes in temperature. Mercury's temperature can reach as high as 425°C during the day, and it can fall to as low as −170°C at night. A picture of Mercury and some facts about the planet are shown below. ☑

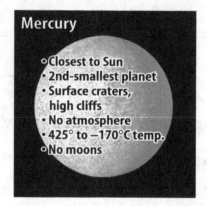

Mercury
- Closest to Sun
- 2nd-smallest planet
- Surface craters, high cliffs
- No atmosphere
- 425° to −170°C temp.
- No moons

Venus

Venus is the second planet from the Sun. Venus is sometimes called Earth's twin because its size and mass are similar to Earth's. When *Mariner 2* flew past Venus in 1962, the satellite sent back information about Venus's atmosphere and rotation. From 1990 to 1994, the U.S. *Magellan* probe used radar to make detailed maps of Venus's surface. A picture of Venus and some facts about the planet are shown below.

Venus
- Like Earth in size and mass
- Carbon dioxide atmosphere
- Air has yellowish color due to sulfuric acid droplets
- Surface craters, cracks, volcanos
- Greenhouse effect: temp. up to 475°C

How hot is it on Venus?

The thick clouds on Venus block most of the Sun's light from reaching the planet's surface. The clouds and carbon dioxide gas in the atmosphere trap heat from the Sun. Temperatures on the surface of Venus range from 450°C to 475°C.

Earth

__Earth__ is the third planet from the Sun. It is about 150 million km from the Sun, or one astronomical unit (AU). Earth is the only planet in the solar system that has large amounts of liquid water. More than 70 percent of Earth's surface is covered by liquid water. Earth is also the only planet that supports life. Earth's atmosphere protects life forms from the Sun's harmful radiation. The atmosphere also causes most meteors to burn up before they reach the surface of the planet. A picture of Earth and some facts about the planet are shown below. ☑

Earth
- Atmosphere protects life
- Water exists as solid, liquid, and gas
- Only planet with known life
- One large moon

✔ **Reading Check**

3. **Apply** How does Earth's atmosphere help support life?

_____

_____

_____

Mars

__Mars__ is the fourth planet from the Sun. It is called the red planet. Its red color is caused by iron oxide in the soil. Polar ice caps on Mars can be seen through telescopes from Earth. The ice caps are made of frozen water covered by a layer of frozen carbon dioxide. A picture of Mars and some facts about the planet are shown below.

Mars
- Red surface due to iron in soil
- Ice caps: water and frozen carbon dioxide
- Channels suggest water once flowed
- Largest volcano in solar system
- Thin atmosphere
- Temp. 35°C to 125°C
- Huge dust storms
- Two small moons

4. Infer Is the volcano Mt. Saint Helens on Earth larger than Olympus Mons on Mars?

_____

_____

5. Explain What were the Viking 1 and 2 probes looking for on Mars?

_____

_____

Picture This

6. List the features that the gullies on Mars and on Mount St. Helens have in common.

_____

_____

_____

What have scientists learned from missions to Mars?

Several spacecraft have made missions to Mars. From these missions, scientists have learned that there are long channels on the planet that might have been carved by flowing water. The largest known volcano in the solar system is on Mars. It is called Olympus Mons. It is probably not an active volcano. There are also large valleys in the Martian crust. ☑

What did the *Viking* probes do?

The *Viking 1* and *2* probes arrived at Mars in 1976. Each probe had two parts—an orbiter and a lander. The orbiters remained in space. They took photographs of the entire surface of Mars. The landers touched down on the surface of Mars. They carried equipment to search for signs of life on the planet. No conclusive evidence of life was found on Mars. ☑

How were *Pathfinder, Global Surveyor,* and *Odyssey* used?

The *Mars Pathfinder* analyzed Martian rock and soil. These data indicated that iron might have reached the surface of Mars from underground. *Global Surveyor* took pictures that showed features like gullies that could have been formed by flowing water. *Mars Odyssey* had instruments that detected frozen water. The water forms a layer of frost under a thin layer of soil. It is possible that volcanic activity might melt frost beneath the Martian surface. The features look similar to those formed by flash floods on Earth, such as on Mount St. Helens. You can see how they compare in the figure below.

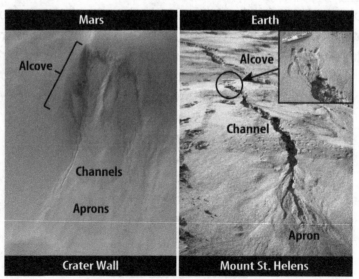

NASA/JPL/Malin Space Science Systems

What makes up Mars's atmosphere?

Mars's atmosphere is much thinner than Earth's atmosphere. It is made up mostly of carbon dioxide with some nitrogen and argon. Temperatures on the surface of Mars can be as high as 35°C and as low as −125°C. The change in temperature between day and night causes strong winds, which in turn cause global dust storms. This information is important if humans ever explore Mars. ☑

Are there seasons on Mars?

Mars's axis is tilted 25°, which is close to Earth's tilt of 23.5°. So, Mars has seasons as it orbits the Sun. The polar ice caps on Mars change with the season. During winter, carbon dioxide freezes at the poles. The polar ice caps get larger. During summer, the carbon dioxide ice changes to gas. The ice caps get smaller. It is winter at one pole when it is summer at the other pole. The color of the ice caps and other areas on Mars also changes with the seasons. This is due to the movement of dust and sand during dust storms.

Does Mars have moons?

Mars has two small moons—Phobos and Deimos. Phobos orbits Mars once every 7 hours. It has a large crater and chains of smaller craters. Deimos orbits Mars once every 31 hours. It is farther away from Mars's surface. Its surface looks smoother than that of Phobos. Its craters have partially filled with soil and rock.

☑ **Reading Check**

7. Recognize Cause and Effect What is the result of extreme change in day and night temperatures on Mars?

_____

_____

💡 **Think it Over**

8. Compare Why does Mars have seasons?

_____

_____

_____

● After You Read

Mini Glossary

Earth: third planet from the Sun; has plenty of liquid water and an atmosphere that protects life

Mars: fourth planet from the Sun; has polar ice caps and a reddish appearance caused by iron oxide in the soil

Mercury: planet closest to the Sun; does not have a true atmosphere; has a surface with many craters and high cliffs

Venus: second planet from the Sun; similar to Earth in mass and size; has thick clouds

1. Review the terms and their definitions in the Mini Glossary. Write something interesting you learned about Mars, Venus, or Mercury.

_____

_____

2. Complete the table to organize the information from this section.

THE INNER PLANETS			
	ORDER FROM SUN	**ATMOSPHERE**	**TEMPERATURES**
MERCURY	Closest	_____	Highs: 425°C Lows: −170°C
VENUS	_____	Heavy clouds Carbon dioxide gas	Highs: _____ Lows: _____
EARTH	3rd	_____ _____	Not given
MARS	_____	Mostly carbon dioxide Some nitrogen and argon	_____

3. Review the flash cards you made. How did this help you learn the content of the section? How could you use the flash cards to prepare for a test on the inner planets?

_____

_____

End of Section

Science●**nline** Visit **glencoe.com** to access your textbook, interactive games, and projects to help you learn more about the inner planets.

The Solar System

section ❸ The Outer Planets

 PS 1.1c The Sun and the planets that revolve around it are the major bodies in the solar system. Other members include comets, moons, and asteroids. Earth's orbit is nearly circular.

● Before You Read

What do you know about the outer planets Jupiter, Uranus, Saturn, or Neptune? What would you like to learn?

_____

_____

_____

What You'll Learn

■ facts about the outer planets: Jupiter, Uranus, Saturn, and Neptune
■ which are the dwarf planets

● Read to Learn

Outer Planets

Voyager, *Galileo*, and *Cassini* were not the first space probes to explore the outer planets. However, much new information about the outer planets has come from these probes.

Jupiter

Jupiter is the fifth planet from the Sun. It is the largest planet in the solar system. Data from space probes show that Jupiter has faint rings around it made of dust. Io, one of Jupiter's moons, has active volcanoes.

What is Jupiter's atmosphere made of?

Jupiter is made up mostly of hydrogen and helium with some ammonia, methane, and water vapor. Scientists hypothesize that the atmosphere of hydrogen and helium gas changes to liquid hydrogen and helium toward the middle of the planet. Below this liquid layer may be a rocky core that is probably different from any rock on Earth.

Jupiter's atmosphere has bands of white, red, brown, and tan clouds. Storms of swirling gas have been observed on the planet. The **Great Red Spot** is the most spectacular of these storms.

Study Coach

Make Flash Cards Make five flash cards to help you study this section. On one side of each card, write the name of one of the outer planets. On the other side, write facts about that planet.

FOLDABLES™

❻ Compare and Contrast Make the following Foldable to help you understand how the outer planets are similar and different.

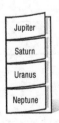

Copyright © Glencoe/McGraw-Hill, a division of The McGraw-Hill Companies, Inc.

How many moons orbit Jupiter?

At least 61 moons orbit Jupiter. In 1610, the astronomer Galileo Galilei was the first person to see the four largest moons. Io (I oh) is the large moon closest to Jupiter.

Jupiter's gravity and the gravity of the next large moon, Europa, pull on Io. This force heats up Io. The result is that Io has the most active volcanoes in the entire solar system.

Europa is made up mostly of rock. It has a thick crust of ice. Under the ice there might be a deep ocean. If this ocean does exist, it would be one of the few places in the solar system with large quantities of liquid water. The next moon is Ganymede. Ganymede is the largest moon in the solar system—larger than the planet Mercury. Callisto, the last of Jupiter's large moons, is made up mostly of ice and rock. Callisto is another place in the solar system where there may be a large quantity of water. Pictures of Jupiter and Callisto, as well as some facts about Jupiter, are shown below. ☑

Saturn

Saturn is the sixth planet from the Sun. It is the second-largest planet in the solar system. Saturn is the least dense planet in the solar system.

What is Saturn's atmosphere like?

Saturn is similar to Jupiter. Both planets are large and made up mostly of gas. Saturn has a thick outer atmosphere made up mostly of hydrogen and helium. Deeper within the atmosphere the gases change to liquid. Below its atmosphere and liquid layers, Saturn might have a small, rocky core.

☑ Reading Check

1. Define What are Io and Callisto?

_____

_____

Picture This

2. Describe List four facts that describe Jupiter.

_____

_____

_____

_____

Jupiter

- Largest planet
- Faint rings
- Atmosphere of hydrogen and helium
- Continual storms, largest is Great Red Spot
- 4 large moons, at least 57 smaller moons

Jupiter's moon Callisto

JPL

What are Saturn's rings and moons like?

Each of Saturn's large rings is made up of thousands of thin rings. These are made of ice and rock particles. Some particles are as tiny as a speck of dust, and some are tens of meters across. Saturn has the most complex ring system in the solar system.

At least 31 moons orbit Saturn. The planet's gravity holds them in their orbits. Titan is the largest of Saturn's moons. It is larger than the planet Mercury. A picture of Saturn and some facts about the planet are shown below.

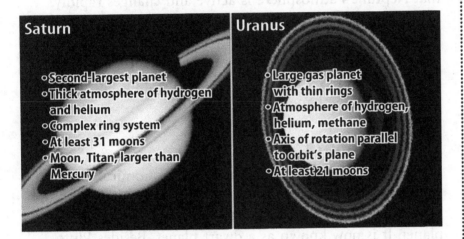

Saturn
- Second-largest planet
- Thick atmosphere of hydrogen and helium
- Complex ring system
- At least 31 moons
- Moon, Titan, larger than Mercury

Uranus
- Large gas planet with thin rings
- Atmosphere of hydrogen, helium, methane
- Axis of rotation parallel to orbit's plane
- At least 21 moons

Uranus

<u>Uranus</u> (YOOR uh nus) is the seventh planet from the Sun. It is a large planet and also is made up mostly of gas. Thin, dark rings surround the equator. Scientists know that Uranus has at least 21 moons. Its largest moon, Titania, has many craters and deep valleys.

What are the characteristics of Uranus?

The atmosphere of Uranus is made up of hydrogen, helium, and some methane. Methane gives the planet a bluish-green color. A few clouds and storms can be seen on Uranus. There may be liquid water under its atmosphere.

Uranus has an unusual rotation. It is tilted on its side. The axes of rotation of the other planets are nearly perpendicular to the planes of their orbits. Uranus's axis of rotation is nearly parallel to the plane of its orbit. Some scientists believe that a collision may have caused Uranus to tip over in this way. A picture of Uranus and some facts about the planet are shown above. ☑

💡 **Think it Over**

3. **Compare and Contrast** Describe two ways that Saturn and Uranus are different.

_____

_____

_____

☑ **Reading Check**

4. **Recognize Cause and Effect** What do scientists believe may have caused Uranus to tilt on its axis?

_____

_____

Neptune

Neptune is the eighth planet from the Sun. However, part of Pluto's orbit crosses inside Neptune's orbit. From 1979 until 1999, Pluto was closer to the Sun than Neptune was.

What characteristics does Neptune have?

Neptune's atmosphere is similar to Uranus's atmosphere. Methane gives the atmosphere of Neptune its bluish-green color, just as it does for Uranus. Neptune has dark-colored storms similar to the Great Red Spot on Jupiter. These storms and bright clouds form and disappear. This shows that Neptune's atmosphere is active and changes rapidly.

There may be a layer of liquid water under Neptune's atmosphere. The planet probably has a rocky core. Neptune has at least 11 moons and several rings. Neptune's largest moon, Triton, has a thin atmosphere made up mostly of nitrogen and methane.

Dwarf Planets

In August, 2006, the International Astronomical Union (IAU) defined the term *planet*. With that definition, Pluto, which became the ninth planet in 1930, was no longer a planet. It is now known as a dwarf planet. Besides Pluto there are two other dwarf planets, Ceres and Eris.

What do we know about dwarf planets?

Ceres was discovered in 1801. It is located in the asteroid belt and is the largest asteroid. Ceres orbits the Sun about once every 4.6 years.

Pluto has a thin atmosphere and a solid, icy-rock surface. Pluto has three moons, Nix, Hydra, and Charon. Pluto orbits the Sun once every 248 years.

Eris, which is slightly larger than Pluto, was discovered in 2005 and originally named UB313. It has a moon named Dysnomia. Eris orbits the Sun once every 557 years.

💡 **Think it Over**

5. **Recognize Cause and Effect** What gas causes Uranus and Neptune to have a bluish-green color?

   a. hydrogen
   b. methane
   c. helium
   d. carbon dioxide

💡 **Think it Over**

6. **Infer** Could Pluto support life?

   _____

   _____

   _____

   _____

⬤ After You Read

Mini Glossary

Great Red Spot: giant, high-pressure storm in Jupiter's atmosphere

Jupiter: largest planet, and fifth planet from the Sun; has an atmosphere made up mostly of hydrogen and helium

Neptune: usually the eighth planet from the Sun; is large, gaseous, and bluish-green in color

Pluto: dwarf planet, has a solid icy-rock surface and three single moons, Charon, Hydra, and Nix

Saturn: second-largest and sixth planet from the Sun; has a complex ring system, at least 31 moons, and a thick atmosphere made mostly of hydrogen and helium

Uranus (YOOR uh nus): seventh planet from the Sun; is large and gaseous, has a distinct bluish-green color.

1. Review the terms and their definitions in the Mini Glossary. Choose an outer planet and write a sentence that tells something you learned about it.

_____

_____

_____

2. Complete the table below to organize the information from this section.

THE OUTER PLANETS			
	ORDER FROM THE SUN	**ATMOSPHERE**	**MOONS**
Jupiter	5th	_____	_____, including _____
Saturn	_____	Thick; hydrogen and helium	At least 31, including Titan
Uranus	7th	_____	_____, including _____
Neptune	_____	Thick methane	_____, including _____

 Visit **glencoe.com** to access your textbook, interactive games, and projects to help you learn more about the outer planets.

 End of Section

The Solar System

section ④ Other Objects in the Solar System

 PS 1.1c The Sun and the planets that revolve around it are the major bodies in the solar system. Other members include comets, moons, and asteroids. **1.1e** Most objects in the solar system have a regular and predictable motion. **Also covered:** PS 2.1a

What You'll Learn

■ how comets change when they near the Sun
■ the differences among comets, meteoroids, and asteroids

● Before You Read

Look up into the sky on a clear night. There are many objects you can see in addition to the Moon. What do you think these objects are? What would you like to know about them?

_____

_____

_____

Mark the Text

Highlight Highlight the descriptions of comets, meteors, and asteroids as you read about them in this section.

FOLDABLES

Ⓓ Organize Information
Make the following three-tab Foldable to help you organize information about comets, meteoroids, and asteroids.

● Read to Learn

Comets

Planets and moons are not the only objects in the solar system. Comets, meteoroids, and asteroids are other important objects that orbit the Sun.

You may have heard of Halley's Comet. A **comet** is made up of dust and pieces of rock mixed with frozen water, methane, and ammonia. Halley's Comet was last seen from Earth in 1986. It takes Halley's Comet 76 years to orbit the Sun. Astronomer Jan Oort suggested that billions of comets surround the solar system. This cloud of comets, called the Oort Cloud, is located beyond the orbit of Pluto.

What is the structure of a comet?

A comet is a mass of frozen ice and rock similar to a large, dirty snowball. As a comet approaches the Sun, the Sun's heat turns the ice to gas. This releases dust and bits of rock which form a bright cloud, or coma, around the nucleus, or solid part, of the comet. The solar wind pushes on the gas and dust to form tails that point away from the Sun.

Meteoroids, Meteors, and Meteorites

After many trips around the Sun, most of the ice in a comet's nucleus has evaporated. The comet is now just rocks and dust, spread out within the original comet's orbit. These objects are called meteoroids. A meteoroid that enters Earth's atmosphere and burns up is called a **meteor**. Another term for a meteor is a shooting star.

Whenever Earth passes through the old orbit of a comet, small pieces of rock and dust enter Earth's atmosphere. The event is called a meteor shower. A **meteorite** is a large meteoroid that does not burn up completely in Earth's atmosphere and strikes Earth. Most meteorites are probably the remains from asteroid collisions or broken-up comets. Others come from the Moon and Mars. ☑

✔ **Reading Check**

1. **Define** What is a meteor shower?

_____

_____

Asteroids

An **asteroid** is a piece of rock made up of material like that which formed the planets. Most asteroids are located in an area between the orbits of Mars and Jupiter called the asteroid belt as shown in the figure. Other asteroids are scattered throughout the solar system.

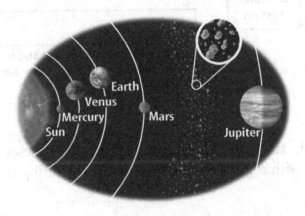

Picture This

2. **Interpret Scientific Illustrations** Between the orbits of which planets is the asteroid belt located?

_____

_____

What else do we know about asteroids?

Some asteroids are tiny. Others measure hundreds of kilometers. The first asteroid ever discovered, Ceres, is the largest. It measures 940 km in diameter.

Comets, asteroids, and most meteorites were formed early in the history of the solar system. Scientists study these space objects to learn what the solar system might have been like long ago. Understanding this could help scientists better understand how Earth formed.

Think it Over

3. **Explain** What is important about studying objects in space?

_____

_____

_____

⦿ After You Read

Mini Glossary

asteroid: a piece of rock made up of material similar to that which formed the planets

comet: space object made of dust and rock particles mixed with frozen water, methane, and ammonia

meteor: a meteoroid that burns up in Earth's atmosphere

meteorite: a meteoroid that strikes Earth's surface

1. Review the terms and their definitions in the Mini Glossary. Write a sentence to tell what the Oort cloud is.

   _____

   _____

2. Complete the concept chart with the correct words from the Mini Glossary.

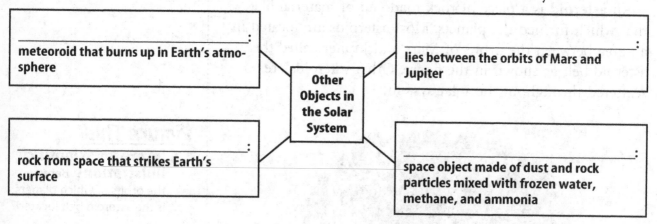

   _____: meteoroid that burns up in Earth's atmosphere

   _____: rock from space that strikes Earth's surface

   Other Objects in the Solar System

   _____: lies between the orbits of Mars and Jupiter

   _____: space object made of dust and rock particles mixed with frozen water, methane, and ammonia

3. Reread the sentences you highlighted in the text. Did this strategy help you describe comets, meteors, and asteroids? Work with a partner and take turns describing space objects to each other.

   _____

   _____

   _____

End of Section

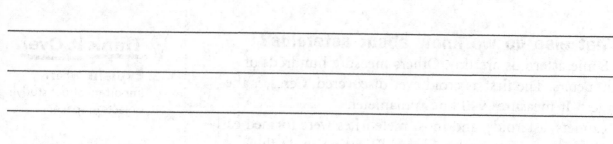

Science Online Visit **glencoe.com** to access your textbook, interactive games, and projects to help you learn more about other objects in the solar system.

Stars and Galaxies

section ❶ Stars

 PS 1.1b Other stars are like the Sun but are so far away that they look like points of light. Distances between stars are vast compared to distances within our solar system.

● Before You Read

Describe the sky on a cloudless, moonless night. What would you see? Write the names of any stars you know about.

_____

_____

_____

What You'll Learn

- about constellations
- the difference between absolute magnitude and apparent magnitude

● Read to Learn

Constellations

It's fun to look at clouds and find animals, faces, and objects. It takes more imagination to play this game with stars. Ancient Greeks, Romans, and other people who lived long ago found patterns, or shapes, made by stars in the night sky. These star patterns are called **constellations** (kahn stuh LAY shuns). In these star patterns, they saw characters, animals, and objects from stories they knew well.

From Earth, a constellation looks like spots of light arranged in a particular shape against the night sky. However, the stars in a constellation often have no relationship to each other in space.

What are some common constellations?

Modern astronomy divides the sky into 88 constellations. Many of these were named by early astronomers. The Big Dipper is part of the constellation Ursa Major. The two stars at the front of the Big Dipper point to the star Polaris. Polaris is often called the North Star. That is because Polaris is almost directly over Earth's north pole. Polaris is located at the end of the Little Dipper in the constellation Ursa Minor. See the figure on the next page for the locations of Polaris, the Big Dipper, and the Little Dipper.

Study Coach

Identify What You Know Create a K-W-L chart for this chapter. Write what you already know about stars, what you want to know, and what you learn as you read this section.

FOLDABLES

A Record Data For this section, create a Foldable to record important facts, notes, and new vocabulary about stars.

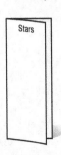

Stars

Copyright © Glencoe/McGraw-Hill, a division of The McGraw-Hill Companies, Inc.

1. **Interpret Diagram** Do the stars appear to rotate clockwise or counter-clockwise around Polaris?

_____

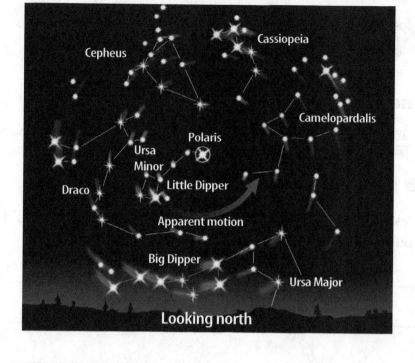

Looking north

Why do constellations appear to move?

You may have noticed that stars appear to move during the night. Constellations in the northern sky appear to circle around Polaris. Because of this, they are called circumpolar constellations. They appear to move because Earth is moving.

The figure above shows the circumpolar constellations rotating around Polaris. Because of their unique position, you can see the circumpolar constellations all year long. Other constellations, like Orion, can only be seen in certain seasons. In the summer, Orion can't be seen north of the equator because the northern hemisphere faces Orion during the day. ☑

Absolute and Apparent Magnitudes

When you look at constellations, you'll notice that some stars are brighter than others. Sometimes stars look brighter than others because they're closer to Earth.

There are two ways to describe a star's brightness. The **absolute magnitude** (MAG nuh tewd) of a star is the amount of light it gives off. The **apparent magnitude** is the amount of light that reaches Earth, or how bright it looks. A star that is dim can look bright in the sky if it's close to Earth. A star that is bright can appear dim if it's far away. For example, Rigel is a brighter star than Sirius, but Sirius appears brighter because it is 100 times closer to Earth than Rigel is.

2. **Identify** Which constellations can be seen all year?

_____

Measurement In Space

One way scientists measure the distance between Earth and a nearby star is to measure parallax (PER uh laks). Parallax is what makes an object seem to change its position when you look at it from two different positions. Stretch your arm out in front of you and look at your thumb with one eye closed. Now open your eye and close your other eye and look at your thumb. Your thumb looks like it has moved, even though it has not. That apparent shift is parallax. Try it again, but with your thumb closer to your face. What did you see? Your thumb appears to move when it is closer to your eyes. The nearer an object is, the greater its parallax. ☑

How is parallax measured?

Astronomers measure the parallax of a nearby star to see how far away it is from Earth. Astronomers observe the same star at two different times of the year. Astronomers look at how the star seems to change positions compared with stars that are farther away. Then they use the angle of the parallax and the size of Earth's orbit to calculate the distance of the star from Earth.

Space is so enormous that scientists need a special way to describe distances. Distances between stars and galaxies are measured in light-years. A **light-year** is the distance that light travels in one year. Light travels 300,000 km/s.

Properties of Stars

The color of a star indicates its temperature. For example, hot stars are a blue-white color. Stars that have a medium temperature, like the Sun, are yellow. A cooler star looks orange or red.

Astronomers use an instrument called a spectroscope to learn what a star is made of. The spectroscope spreads light out into a band of colors which might include dark lines. These dark lines stand for elements in a star's atmosphere. These patterns of lines help astronomers identify the elements in a star's atmosphere. ☑

✔ **Reading Check**

3. **Determine** Which would have a greater parallax—an object close to you or one that is far away?

_____

_____

✔ **Reading Check**

4. **Identify** What do the dark lines in the band of colors produced by a spectroscope represent?

_____

_____

● After You Read

Mini Glossary

absolute magnitude (MAG nuh tewd): the amount of light that a star gives off

apparent magnitude: the amount of a star's light that reaches Earth

constellation (kahn stuh LAY shun): a group of stars that forms a pattern in the night sky

light-year: the distance that light travels in one year

1. Review the terms and their definitions in the Mini Glossary. Write a sentence to explain why two stars can have the same absolute magnitude but may have different apparent magnitudes.

   _____

   _____

2. Complete the diagram to explain what you learned about stars.

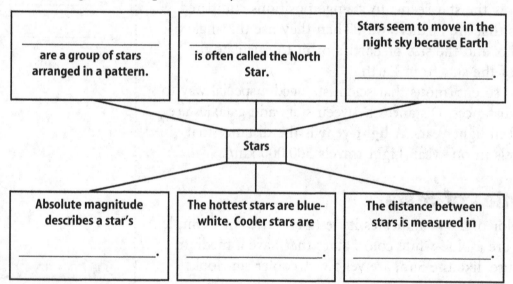

   _____ are a group of stars arranged in a pattern.

   _____ is often called the North Star.

   Stars seem to move in the night sky because Earth _____.

   Stars

   Absolute magnitude describes a star's _____.

   The hottest stars are blue-white. Cooler stars are _____.

   The distance between stars is measured in _____.

3. Look back at the K-W-L chart you made as you read this section. Did you add to what you already knew? Did you learn what you wanted to know? Did the K-W-L chart help you to understand what you read?

   _____

   _____

   _____

End of Section

Science Online Visit **glencoe.com** to access your textbook, interactive games, and projects to help you learn more about stars.

Stars and Galaxies

section ❷ The Sun

 PS 1.1a The Sun is more than a million times greater in volume than Earth. **1.1c** The Sun and the planets that revolve around it are the major bodies in the solar system. Other members include comets, moons, and asteroids. **Also covered:** PS 1.1d, 4.1a

● Before You Read

What comes to mind when you think about the Sun? Brainstorm some words and write them below.

_____

_____

What You'll Learn

- the Sun is the closest star to Earth
- the structure of the Sun
- the features of the Sun, such as sunspots and solar flares

● Read to Learn

The Sun's Layers

The Sun is an ordinary star and is the center of our solar system. It is also the closest star to Earth. Almost all life on Earth depends on energy from the Sun.

Like other stars, the Sun is an enormous ball of gas that produces energy in its core, or center. This energy is produced by fusing hydrogen into helium. This energy travels outward to the Sun's atmosphere. The energy is given off as light and heat.

The Sun's Atmosphere

The Sun is made up of different layers. The lowest layer of the Sun's atmosphere is the **photosphere** (FOH tuh sfihr). This is the layer that gives off the light we see from Earth. The photosphere is often called the surface of the Sun. Temperatures there are about 6,000 K. The layer above the photosphere is called the **chromosphere** (KROH muh sfihr). This layer is about 2,000 km thick. There is a change of zone between 2,000 km and 10,000 km above the photosphere. Above this zone is the outer layer of the Sun's atmosphere. This outer layer is called the **corona** (kuh ROH nuh). The corona is the largest layer of the Sun's atmosphere. It reaches millions of kilometers into space. The illustration on the next page shows the different layers of the Sun.

Mark the Text

Underline the different properties of the Sun as you read.

FOLDABLES

Ⓑ Take Notes Create a Foldable to record the main ideas about the Sun. Include information about the Sun's layers, atmosphere, and surface features.

1. **List** Number the parts of
the Sun's atmosphere
shown below, with 1 being
the innermost layer and 4
being the outermost layer.

_____ chromosphere

_____ corona

_____ core

_____ photosphere

The Sun's Atmosphere

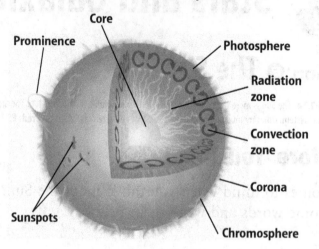

Core

Prominence

Photosphere

Radiation zone

Convection zone

Corona

Sunspots

Chromosphere

Surface Features

From our point of view on Earth, the Sun's surface looks smooth. But the Sun's surface has many features. Among them are sunspots, prominences, flares, and CMEs.

What is a sunspot?

<u>Sunspots</u> are areas of the Sun's surface that appear dark. Sunspots look this way because they are cooler than the area around them. Scientists have been studying sunspots for hundreds of years. They have observed the way that sunspots move. The fact that sunspots move has led scientists to determine that the Sun rotates. However, the Sun does not rotate like Earth does. The Sun rotates faster at its equator than at its poles. Sunspots near the equator take about 25 days to rotate once. Near the poles, sunspots take about 35 days.

Sunspots are not permanent features on the Sun. They appear and disappear over days, weeks, or months. The number of sunspots increases and decreases in a regular cycle of time. About every 10 or 11 years, there is a period of many large sunspots. In between those times, there are fewer sunspots.

What are prominences and solar flares?

Sunspots are related to other features on the Sun's surface. Sunspots and strong magnetic fields are found together on the Sun. The magnetic fields might cause prominences, which are huge arching columns of gas.

The gases near a sunspot may suddenly brighten and rapidly shoot outward. This is called a solar flare. ☑

Reading Check

2. **Describe** What happens in a solar flare?

_____

_____

_____

What is a CME?

When large amounts of electrically-charged gas shoot out from the Sun's corona, the event is called a CME. CME stands for coronal mass ejection.

CMEs present little danger to life on Earth, but they do affect our planet. CMEs can damage satellites. They can cause radio interference. Near the poles, they can produce a display of shifting colorful lights in the night sky. These displays tend to occur at Earth's poles. One such display of lights is called the Aurora borealis, or northern lights. The picture below shows the Aurora borealis.

Copyright © Glencoe/McGraw-Hill, a division of The McGraw-Hill Companies, Inc.

The Sun—An Average Star

The Sun is an average star. It is middle-aged and its absolute magnitude is about average. The Sun shines with a yellow light. Although the Sun is an average star, it is much closer to Earth than other stars. Light from the Sun reaches Earth in about eight minutes. Light from other stars takes many years to reach Earth. ☑

The Sun is unusual in one way. It is not close to any other stars. Most stars are found in groups of two or more stars that orbit each other. Stars can also be held together by each other's gravity. This kind of group is a star cluster. Most star clusters are far from the solar system. They might be visible as a fuzzy bright patch in the night sky.

💡 Think it Over

3. **Infer** Why do you think the Aurora borealis is also known as the northern lights?

_____

_____

☑ Reading Check

4. **Identify** How long does it take for the light from the Sun to reach Earth?

_____

● After You Read

Mini Glossary

chromosphere (KROH muh sfihr): one of the middle layers of the Sun's atmosphere

corona (kuh ROH nuh): the top, largest layer of the Sun's atmosphere

photosphere (FOH tuh sfirh): the lowest layer of the Sun's atmosphere; gives off light

sunspot: an area on the Sun's surface that is cooler and less bright than surrounding areas

1. Review the terms and their definitions in the Mini Glossary. Write a sentence using three terms to describe the Sun's atmosphere.

_____

_____

_____

2. Complete the chart to show how the Sun is like other stars and different from other stars.

The Sun vs. Other Stars	
Similarities	**Differences**
It is a huge ball of _____.	Its light reaches Earth in _____.
It produces energy in its _____.	Life on _____ depends on it.
It has an _____ that has different layers. One is the corona.	It is not close to other _____.

3. Look at the list of words you brainstormed to describe the Sun before you read this section. What words would you add to this list? Look at the text you underlined to describe the Sun. Now look at your new list. What was the most surprising thing you learned about the Sun?

_____

_____

_____

End of Section

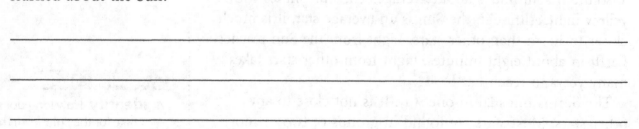
Science Online Visit **glencoe.com** to access your textbook, interactive games, and projects to help you learn more about the Sun.

Stars and Galaxies

section ❸ Evolution of Stars

PS 1.1b Other stars are like the Sun but are so far away that they look like points of light. Distances between stars are vast compared to distances within our solar system. **Also covered:** PS 4.4a

● Before You Read

What makes one star different from another? Do you think the Sun is the same as other stars? Write your ideas on the lines below.

_____

_____

_____

● Read to Learn

Classifying Stars

When you look at the night sky, all stars might look about the same. However, they're very different. They vary in age and size. They vary in temperature and brightness as well. These features led scientists to organize stars into categories, or groups.

How is a star's temperature related to its brightness?

In the early 1900s, two scientists named Ejnar Hertzsprung and Henry Russell noticed that hotter stars are usually brighter. In other words, stars with higher temperatures have brighter absolute magnitudes.

How do scientists show this relationship?

Hertzsprung and Russell developed a graph to show this relationship. You can see this graph on the next page. The temperatures are at the bottom. Absolute magnitude goes up the left side. A graph that shows this relationship between a star's temperature and its brightness is called a Hertzsprung-Russell diagram, or an H-R diagram.

What You'll Learn

- how stars are sorted into groups
- ways the Sun is the same as other types of stars
- ways the Sun is different from other types of stars
- how stars develop

Study Coach

Make Flash Cards to help you record new vocabulary words. Write the word on one side of the flash card and a brief definition on the other side.

FOLDABLES

C Create a Foldable as shown below about evolution of stars. Label the three columns Star Classification, Star Temperature and Color, and How a Star Evolves.

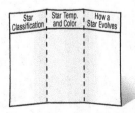

Star Classification	Star Temp. and Color	How a Star Evolves

Picture This

1. **Complete the Diagram** Color hot, bright stars blue. Color cool, dim stars red. Color in-between stars yellow. Read to find out how to color dwarfs and giants.

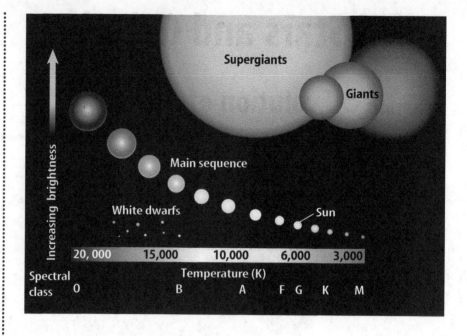

What is the main sequence?

The H-R diagram above shows the connection between a star's temperature and its brightness. As you can see, most stars seem to fit into a band that runs from the upper left to the lower right. This band is called the main sequence. Hot, blue, bright stars begin at 20,000 K and continue to about 15,000 K. Cool, red, dim stars range from 5,000 K to 3,000 K. Yellow stars, like the Sun, are in between.

What are dwarfs?

About 90 percent of all stars are main sequence stars. Most of these are small, red stars found in the lower right of the H-R diagram. Some of the stars that are not in the main sequence are hot, but they are not bright. These small stars are called white dwarfs, although they are usually blue in color. White dwarfs are found on the lower left of the H-R diagram. ☑

What are giants?

Other stars are very bright, but they are not hot. These large stars are called giants or red giants, because they are usually red in color. They're found on the upper right of the H-R diagram. The largest giants are called supergiants. These stars can be hundreds of times bigger than the Sun and thousands of times brighter.

Reading Check

2. **Identify** What are small stars that are hot but not bright called?

_____

_____

How do stars shine?

For centuries, people have wondered what stars were made of and what made them shine. Over time, people realized the Sun had been shining for billions of years. What material could burn for so long?

What process creates the light that reaches Earth?

In the 1930s, scientists made an important discovery about atoms. Scientists observed that the nuclei, or centers, of atoms reacted with one another. They hypothesized that the center of the Sun was hot enough to cause hydrogen atoms to fuse, or link together, and form another kind of atom—helium atoms. This reaction, called fusion, releases huge amounts of energy. Much of this energy is released as different kinds of light. A very small part of this light comes to Earth. ☑

Evolution of Stars

The H-R diagram explained a lot about stars. However, scientists wondered why some stars didn't fit in the main sequence. Scientists also wondered what happened when a star used up its hydrogen fuel. Now, there are theories about how stars evolve, or change over time. These theories also explain what makes stars different from one another, and what happens when a star "dies."

When a star uses up its hydrogen, that star is no longer in the main sequence. This can take less than 1 million years for the brightest stars. It can take billions of years for the dimmest stars. The Sun has a main sequence life span of about 10 billion years. Half of its life is still in the future.

How are stars formed?

Stars begin as a large cloud of gas and dust called a **nebula** (NEB yuh luh). The pull of gravity between the particles of gas and dust causes the nebula to contract, or shrink. The nebula can break apart into smaller and smaller pieces. Each piece eventually might collapse to form a star.

The particles in the smaller pieces of nebula move closer together. This causes temperatures in each piece to rise. When the temperature in the core of a piece of nebula reaches 10 million K, fusion begins. Energy is released from the core and travels outward. Now the object is a star.

☑ Reading Check

3. Identify What is the name of the process in which hydrogen is converted to helium?

_____

Applying Math

4. Calculate About how many years are left in the Sun's main sequence life span?

_____

What is a giant?

After a star is formed, the heat created by fusion creates outward pressure. Without this pressure, the star would collapse from its own gravity. The star becomes a main sequence star. It continues to use its hydrogen fuel. The different stages in the life of a star are shown in the illustration on this page and the next page.

When hydrogen in the core of the star runs out, the core contracts and temperatures inside the star increase. The outer layers of the star expand and cool. In this late stage in its life cycle, a star is called a **giant**.

As the core contracts, its temperature continues to rise. By the time it reaches 100 million K, the star is huge. Its outer layers are much cooler than when it was a main sequence star. In about 5 billion years, the Sun will become a giant.

What is a white dwarf?

The star's core contracts even more after it uses much of its helium and the outer layers escape into space. This leaves only the hot, dense core. At this stage in a star's life cycle, it is about the size of Earth. It is called a **white dwarf**. In time, the white dwarf will cool and stop giving off light.

What are supergiants and supernovas?

The length time it takes for a star to go through its stages of life depends on its mass. The stages happen more quickly and more violently in stars that are more than eight times more massive than the Sun. In massive stars, the core heats up to much higher temperatures. Heavier and heavier elements form in the core. The star expands into a **supergiant**. Finally, iron forms in the core. Iron can't release energy through fusion. The core collapses violently. This sends a shock wave outward through the star. The outer part of the star explodes. This produces a kind of star called a supernova. A supernova can be millions of times brighter than the original star was.

Think it Over

5. Infer What is the relationship between how much hydrogen a star has and the star's temperature?

_____

_____

What is a neutron star?

What happens next depends on the size of the supernova's collapsed core. If the collapsed core is between 1.4 and 3 times as massive as the Sun, the core shrinks until it is only about 20 km in diameter. In this dense core, there are only neutrons. This kind of star is called a **neutron star.** Because the star is so dense, one teaspoonful of a neutron star would weigh more than 600 million metric tons on Earth.

What is a black hole?

The core of some supernovas is more than three times more massive than the Sun. Nothing can stop the core's collapse in these supernovas. All of the core's mass collapses to a point. The gravity near this point is so strong that not even light can escape from it. Because light cannot escape from this region, it is called a **black hole.** If you could shine a light into a black hole, the light would disappear into it. However, a black hole is not like a vacuum cleaner. It does not pull in faraway objects. Stars and planets can orbit around a black hole, as long as they are far enough away.

Where does a nebula's matter come from?

You learned that a star begins as a nebula. Where does the matter, or gas and dust, come from to form the nebula? Some of it was once in other stars. A star ejects large amounts of matter during the course of its life. Some of this matter becomes part of a nebula. It can develop into new stars. The matter in stars is recycled many times.

The matter that is created in the cores of stars and during supernova explosions is also recycled. Elements such as carbon and iron can become parts of new stars. Spectrographs of the Sun show that it contains some carbon, iron, and other heavy elements. However, the Sun is too young to have formed these elements itself. The Sun condensed from material that was created in stars that died long ago.

Some elements condense to form planets and other objects. In fact, your body contains many atoms that were formed in the cores of ancient stars.

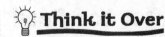

Think it Over

6. **Infer** If the collapsed core of a supernova is 2.4 times as massive as the Sun, what will it become next?

_____

● After You Read

Mini Glossary

black hole: the final stage in the evolution of a very massive star, where the core collapses to a point that its gravity is so strong that not even light can escape

giant: a late stage in the life of a low-mass star, when the core contracts but its outer layers expand and cool; a large, bright, cool star

nebula (NEB yuh luh): a large cloud of gas and dust where stars are formed

neutron star: a very dense core of a collapsed star that can shrink to about 20 km in diameter and contains only neutrons

supergiant: late stage in the life cycle of a massive star in which the core heats up and the star expands; a large, very bright star

white dwarf: a late stage in the life cycle of a low-mass star; formed when its outer layers escape into space, leaving behind a hot, dense core; a small, dim, hot star

1. Review the terms and their definitions in the Mini Glossary. Write a sentence to compare a white dwarf and a giant.

   _____

   _____

   _____

2. Fill in the blanks to review what you have learned about the life of a massive star.

   A massive star forms in a _____. The star burns hydrogen fuel as a main

   _____ star. The core heats up. The star expands and cools into a

   _____. The star then explodes as a _____. Depending on its

   mass, it will then become either a _____ or a _____.

3. Could you use the flash cards you created to describe how the Sun developed? What information was helpful? What other information should have been on the cards?

   _____

   _____

   _____

Copyright © Glencoe/McGraw-Hill, a division of The McGraw-Hill Companies, Inc.

End of Section

 Science Online Visit **glencoe.com** to access your textbook, interactive games, and projects to help you learn more about the evolution of stars.

 **Stars and Galaxies**

section ❹ **Galaxies and the Universe**

 PS 1.1d Gravity is the force that keeps planets in orbit around the Sun and the Moon in orbit around the Earth. **Also covered:** PS 1.1b, 4.4a

● Before You Read

Imagine that someone on the other side of the universe wanted to send you mail. How might you give someone an address for Earth?

_____

_____

● Read to Learn

Galaxies

How can you describe the location of Earth? We are in the solar system. The solar system is in a galaxy called the Milky Way. A **galaxy** is a large group of stars, gas, and dust held together by gravity.

There are many other galaxies. Every galaxy has the same elements, forces, and types of energy that are found in our solar system.

You learned that stars are grouped together in galaxies. In the same way, galaxies are grouped into clusters. The Milky Way is part of a cluster called the Local Group. The Local Group is made up of about 45 galaxies in different sizes and shapes. There are three major types of galaxies.

What are the three major types of galaxies?

Spiral galaxies have spiral arms that wind outward from the center. The arms are made up of bright stars, dust, and gas. The Milky Way galaxy is a spiral galaxy.

Elliptical (ih LIHP tih kul) galaxies are a common type of galaxy. They are shaped like large, three-dimensional ellipses.

Irregular galaxies include all the galaxies that don't fit into the other two groups. These galaxies have many different shapes.

What You'll Learn
- the Sun's position in the Milky Way Galaxy
- what forces affect our solar system
- what forces affect other galaxies

Mark the Text

Highlight the main point in each paragraph. Use a different color to highlight a detail or example that helps explain the main point.

FOLDABLES

D Summarize Create a three-tab Foldable to summarize the main ideas from the section.

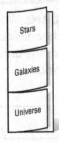

The Milky Way Galaxy

There might be one trillion stars in the Milky Way. It is about 100,000 light-years across. Find the Sun in the image of the Milky Way below. It is about 26,000 light-years from the galaxy's center in one of the spiral arms. In the galaxy, all stars orbit around a central region, or core. It takes about 225 million years for the Sun to orbit the center of the Milky Way.

Scientists put the Milky Way into the spiral galaxy group. However, it's difficult to know the exact shape because we can't look at the galaxy from the outside. You can't see the shape of the Milky Way because the location of our solar system is in one of its spiral arms. But you can see the Milky Way stretching across the sky. It looks like a dusty band of dim light. All the stars you can see in the night sky are part of the Milky Way. Like many other galaxies, the Milky Way has a black hole at its center.

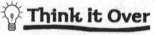

Sun | Side view

Overhead view

Sun

Origin of the Universe

Scientists have offered different models, or ideas, for how the universe began. One model is the steady state theory. It suggests that the universe always has been the same as it is now. The universe expands and new matter is created. This keeps the density of the universe in a steady state.

A second model is the oscillating (AH sih lay ting) model. This model states that the universe formed and then it expanded, or grew larger. Over time, the rate of growth slowed down. Then the universe began to contract, or shrink. Then the whole process began again. In other words, it oscillates back and forth in size.

A third model is called the big bang theory. This theory states that the universe began with a big bang and has been expanding ever since.

Copyright © Glencoe/McGraw-Hill, a division of The McGraw-Hill Companies, Inc.

Picture This

1. Explain Why can't you see the shape of the Milky Way?

_____

_____

_____

Think it Over

2. Compare What do the three theories about the origin of the universe have in common?

_____

_____

Expansion of the Universe

Think of the sound of a whistle on a passing train. The pitch of the whistle rises as the train moves closer. Then the pitch of the whistle drops as the train moves away. This happens because the sound waves coming from the whistle are compressed, or shortened, as the train gets closer. This effect is called the Doppler (DAH plur) shift. ☑

Does the Doppler shift affect light?

The Doppler shift happens with light too. Like sound, light moves in waves. If a star is moving toward Earth, the light waves are shortened. If a star is moving away from Earth, the light waves are stretched out. Blue-violet light waves are shorter than red light waves. Scientists can identify blue-violet light from stars moving toward Earth. When a star is moving away from Earth, the light shifts toward red. This is called a red shift.

How do we know the universe is expanding?

In 1929, Edwin Hubble noticed a red shift in the light from galaxies outside the Local Group. This meant the galaxies are moving away. If all galaxies outside the Local Group are moving away from Earth, then the entire universe must be expanding.

The Big Bang Theory

The **big bang theory** is the leading theory about how the universe formed. It states that the universe began about 13.7 billion years ago. There was a huge explosion. In less than a second, the universe grew from the size of a pinhead to 2,000 times the size of the Sun. Even today, galaxies are still moving away from this explosion.

Scientists don't know if the universe will expand forever or stop expanding. If there is enough matter in the universe, gravity might stop the expansion. Then the universe would contract until everything came back to a single point. But studies show the universe is expanding faster, not slower. Scientists are still trying to figure out what will happen to the universe.

✔ Reading Check

3. Apply You hear a police siren in the distance. If the siren's pitch is getting higher, is the police car coming closer or moving away?

_____

💡 Think it Over

4. Draw Conclusions Why do you think the leading theory about how the universe formed is called the big bang theory?

_____

_____

● After You Read

Mini Glossary

big bang theory: the theory that the universe began about 13.7 billion years ago with a huge explosion and has been expanding ever since

galaxy: a large group of stars, dust, and gas held together by gravity

1. Review the terms and their definitions in the Mini Glossary. Write a sentence using the terms *big bang theory* and *galaxy*.

_____

_____

_____

2. Complete the diagram to show how Earth fits into the Universe. Use the following terms: Milky Way, Solar System, and Local Group.

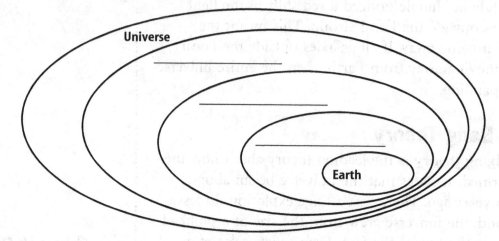

3. Look at your highlighted text about the Milky Way. Write a short description of the Milky Way that includes three details. Did highlighted text help you write your description? What other strategy could have helped you keep track of details about the Milky Way?

_____

_____

_____

End of Section

Science ●nline Visit **glencoe.com** to access your textbook, interactive games, and projects to help you learn more about galaxies and the universe.

216 Stars and Galaxies

Motion and Momentum

section ❶ What is motion?

 PS 5.1b The motion of an object can be described by its position, direction of motion, and speed. **Also covered:** PS 5.1a, 5.1c

● Before You Read

When you move from place to place, how do you know you have moved? Write what you think on the lines below.

_____

_____

● Read to Learn

Matter and Motion

When you are sitting quietly in a chair, are you in motion? It may surprise you to know that all matter in the universe is always in motion. Think about it. In the chair, your heart beats and you breathe. Your blood circulates through your veins. Electrons move around the nuclei of every atom in your body.

Changing Position

How do you know if something is in motion? Something is in motion if it is changing position. Changing position means moving from one place to another. Imagine runners in a 100-meter race. They sprint from the start line to the finish line. Their positions change, so they are in motion.

What is relative motion?

To find out if something changes position, you need a reference point to compare it to. An object changes position if it moves when compared to a reference point. Imagine you are competing in the 100-meter race. You begin just behind the start line. When you pass the finish line, you are 100 m from the start line. If you use the start line as your reference point, then your position has changed by 100 m when compared to the start line. You were in motion. ☑

What You'll Learn

■ what distance, speed, and velocity are
■ how to graph motion

Mark the Text

Underline As you read, underline material you do not understand the first time you read it. Reread the information until you understand it. Ask your teacher if you still do not understand it after rereading it.

☑ Reading Check

1. **Explain** What do you compare an object to when determining the object's motion?

_____

_____

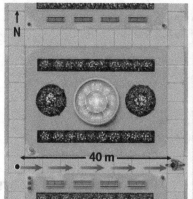
Distance: 40 m
Displacement: 40 m east

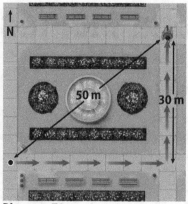
Distance: 70 m
Displacement: 50 m northeast

Distance: 140 m
Displacement: 0 m

Picture This

2. Explain Why is the displacement in the third figure zero?

_____

_____

What are distance and displacement?

Suppose you walk from your house to the park around the block. How far away is it? That depends on whether you are talking about distance or displacement. Distance is the length of the route you travel.

Suppose you travel 200 m from your house to the park. How would you describe your location now? You could say you are 200 m from your house. But where you are depends on both the distance you travel and direction. To describe exactly where you are, you need to tell the direction from your house. Displacement includes the distance between your starting and ending points and the direction in which you travel. The figure above shows the difference between distance and displacement.

Speed

When you describe motion, you usually want to say how fast something is moving. The faster something is moving, the less time it takes to travel a certain distance. The slower something is moving, the more time it takes to travel a certain distance. **Speed** is the distance traveled divided by the time it takes to travel that distance. Speed can be calculated with this equation:

$$\textbf{speed} \text{ (in meters/second)} = \frac{\textbf{distance} \text{ (in meters)}}{\textbf{time} \text{ (in seconds)}}$$

$$s = \frac{d}{t}$$

In SI units, distance is measured in m and time is measured in s. The SI measurement for speed is meters per second (m/s). This is the SI distance unit divided by the SI time unit.

What is average speed?

Suppose a sprinter ran the 100-m dash in 10 s. Did she run the whole race at a speed of 10 m/s? No, her speed could have been different at any instant during the race. You can describe her motion for the entire race by her average speed, 10 m/s. **Average speed** is the total distance traveled divided by the total time taken to travel the distance.

What is instantaneous speed?

Have you ever watched the speedometer when you are riding in a car? If the speedometer reads 50 km/h, the car is traveling at 50 km/h at that instant. **Instantaneous speed** is the speed of an object at one instant of time. ☑

How do average and instantaneous speed differ?

If it takes two hours to travel 200 km in a car, the average speed would be 100 km/h. But the car probably was not moving at this speed the whole time. It might have gone faster on the freeway and stopped at stoplights. There your speed was 0 km/h. If the car were able to travel 100 km/h the whole time, you would have moved at a constant speed.

For another example, see the diagram of the two balls below. Both balls have the same average speed because they both travel 3 m in 4 s. The top ball is moving at a constant speed. In each second, it moves the same distance. The bottom ball is moving at different speeds. Its instantaneous speed is fast between 0 s and 1 s, slower between 2 s and 3 s, and even slower between 3 s and 4 s.

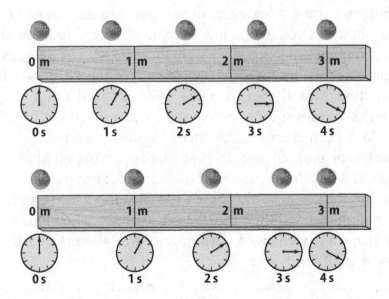

Copyright © Glencoe/McGraw-Hill, a division of The McGraw-Hill Companies, Inc.

✔ Reading Check

3. Identify What type of speed does the speedometer in a car show?

_____

_____

Picture This

4. Calculate What is the average speed of both balls in the diagram? Show all your work.

_____

_____

_____

Graphing Motion

You can show the motion of an object with a distance-time graph. In a distance-time graph, time is plotted on the horizontal axis. Distance is plotted on the vertical axis.

How do distance-time graphs compare speed?

The graph below is a distance-time graph that shows the motion of two students walking. According to the graph, after 1 s student A traveled 1 m. Her average speed is 1 m/1 s, or 1 m/s. Student B traveled only 0.5 m in 1 s. His average speed is 0.5 m/1 s, or 0.5 m/s. So student A traveled faster than student B. Now compare the steepness of the lines in the graph. The line for student A is steeper than the line for student B. A steeper line shows a faster speed. If the line is horizontal, no change in position happens. A horizontal line means a speed of zero.

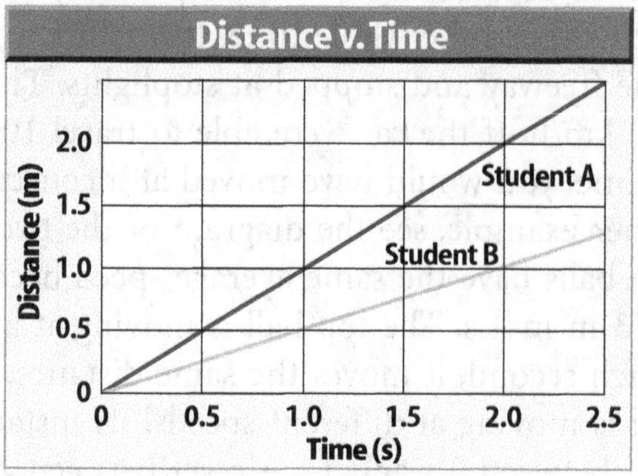

Copyright © Glencoe/McGraw-Hill, a division of The McGraw-Hill Companies, Inc.

Distance v. Time

Velocity

Suppose you are hiking in the woods. You may want to know how fast you are hiking. But you also need to know the direction you are going or you might get lost. The **velocity** of an object is the speed of the object and the direction of its motion. Velocity has the same units as speed and includes the direction of motion, for example 20 km/h east.

Velocity can change when speed changes, direction changes, or both change. If a car that is moving 60 km/h slows to 40 km/h, its velocity has changed. Suppose a car is traveling 40 km/h north. It then goes around a curve until it is heading east. All the time, the car's speed was 40 km/h. But the velocity changed. The velocity was 40 km/h north. Now it is 40 km/h east. ✔

● After You Read

Mini Glossary

average speed: equals the total distance traveled divided by the total time taken to travel the distance

instantaneous speed: the speed of an object at one instant of time

speed: equals the distance traveled divided by the time it takes to travel that distance

velocity: the speed of an object and the direction of its motion

1. Review the terms and their definitions in the Mini Glossary. Ramona divided the distance from her house to school by the time it took her to walk that distance. What quantity did Ramona find? Explain your answer in a complete sentence.

   _____

   _____

2. The distance-time graph below is for a bicyclist in a bicycle race.

   a. What was the bicyclist's average speed after two hours?

   _____

   b. What happened to her speed during the race?

   _____

   _____

   c. How can you tell?

   _____

   _____

   d. What was her average speed for the entire race?

   _____

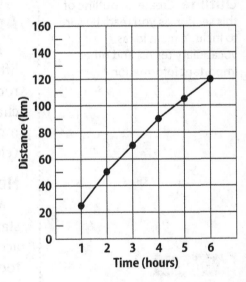

Science Online Visit **glencoe.com** to access your textbook, interactive games, and projects to help you learn more about motion.

End of Section

chapter 15

Motion and Momentum

section ❷ Acceleration

 PS 5.1c An object's motion is the result of the combined effect of all forces acting on the object. A moving object that is not subjected to a force will continue to move at a constant speed in a straight line. An object at rest will remain at rest. **Also covered:** PS 5.1d

What You'll Learn

- what acceleration is
- to predict how acceleration affects motion

> **Study Coach**
>
> **Outline** Create an outline of this section as you read. Be sure to include main ideas, vocabulary terms, and other important information.

FOLDABLES

B Classify Make the following three-tab Foldable to help you classify and understand the different types of acceleration.

Acceleration: Object Speeds Up

Acceleration: Object Slows Down

Acceleration: Object Turns, Changes Direction

● Before You Read

Have you ever been in a foot race? What kinds of things are measured in a foot race?

_____

_____

_____

● Read to Learn

Acceleration and Motion

Have you ever seen a rocket launch? When the rocket first lifts off, it seems to move very slowly. But very soon the rocket is moving at a fast speed. How can you describe the change in the rocket's motion? When an object changes its motion, it is accelerating. **Acceleration** is the change in velocity divided by the time it takes for the change to happen.

How is speeding up acceleration?

When you first get on a bike, it is not moving. When you start pedaling, the bike moves faster and faster. This is acceleration. An object that is already moving can accelerate too. Imagine you are biking along a level path. When you start to pedal harder, your speed increases. When the speed of an object increases, the object is accelerating.

How is slowing down acceleration?

Suppose you are biking at a speed of 4 m/s. If you brake, you will slow down. It might sound odd, but when you slow down you are accelerating. Any change in velocity is acceleration. Acceleration happens when an object speeds up or slows down.

When an object is speeding up, its acceleration is in the same direction as its motion. When an object is slowing down, its acceleration is in the opposite direction of its motion.

How is changing direction acceleration?

Remember that acceleration is a change in velocity. A change in velocity can be a change in speed, direction, or both. So, when an object changes direction, it accelerates. Think of yourself on a bicycle. If you lean to one side and turn the handlebars that direction, you turn. The direction of the bike's motion changes, so the bike accelerates. The acceleration is in the direction the bike turns.

Imagine throwing a ball straight up into the air. The ball starts out moving upward. After a while the ball stops moving upward and begins to come back down. The ball has changed its direction of motion. The ball is now accelerating downward.

Calculating Acceleration

If an object is moving in a straight line, its acceleration can be calculated with this equation.

$$\text{acceleration}\ (\text{m/s}^2) = \frac{\textbf{final speed}\ (\text{m/s}) - \textbf{initial speed}\ (\text{m/s})}{\textbf{time}\ (\text{seconds})}$$

$$a = \frac{(s_f - s_i)}{t}$$

In this equation, time is the length of time it takes for the motion to change. Initial speed is the starting speed. Acceleration has units of meters per second squared (m/s^2).

What are positive and negative acceleration?

Suppose you are riding your bike in a straight line. You speed up from 2 m/s to 8 m/s in 6 seconds.

$$a = \frac{(s_f - s_i)}{t}$$

$$= \frac{(8\ \text{m/s} - 2\ \text{m/s})}{6s} = \frac{6\ \text{m/s}}{6s} = +1\ \text{m/s}^2$$

So your acceleration is $+1\ \text{m/s}^2$. Now suppose you slow down from 8 m/s to 2 m/s in 6 s.

$$a = \frac{(s_f - s_i)}{t}$$

$$= \frac{(2\ \text{m/s} - 8\ \text{m/s})}{6s} = \frac{-6\ \text{m/s}}{6s} = -1\ \text{m/s}^2$$

Your acceleration is $-1\ \text{m/s}^2$.

Copyright © Glencoe/McGraw-Hill, a division of The McGraw-Hill Companies, Inc.

💡 Think it Over

1. **Explain** how an object accelerates when it changes direction.

_____

_____

_____

Applying Math

2. **Calculate** A sports car accelerates from zero to 28 m/s in 4 seconds. What is its acceleration?

_____

What does negative acceleration mean?

When you speed up, your acceleration is positive. When you slow down, your acceleration is negative. That is because when you slow down, your final speed is less than your initial speed. This gives you a negative value in the equation and a negative acceleration. ☑

How do you graph accelerated motion?

You can show the motion of an accelerating object on a graph. For this type of graph, speed is plotted on the vertical axis. Time is plotted on the horizontal axis. The graph below is an example.

Positive Acceleration In section A of the graph, speed increases from 0 m/s to 10 m/s during the first 2 seconds. Acceleration is 5 m/s². An object that is speeding up will have a line that slopes up on a speed-time graph.

Zero Acceleration In section B of the graph, the speed does not change. If speed does not change, the object is not accelerating. A horizontal line on a speed-time graph means zero acceleration.

Negative Acceleration In section C of the graph, the object goes from 10 m/s to 4 m/s in 2 s. Acceleration is −3 m/s². You can see that the line on the graph slopes downward as an object slows down.

✔ **Reading Check**

3. Identify What type of acceleration do you have if you are slowing down?

_____

Picture This

4. Interpret Data For how many seconds does the object in the speed-time graph have an acceleration of zero?

_____

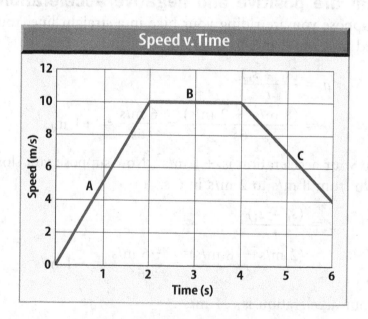

● After You Read

Mini Glossary

acceleration: the change in velocity divided by the time it takes for the change to happen; occurs when an object speeds up, slows down, or turns

1. Review the term and its definition in the Mini Glossary. Describe the term *acceleration* in your own words.

_____

_____

2. Fill in the chart with the different ways an object can accelerate.

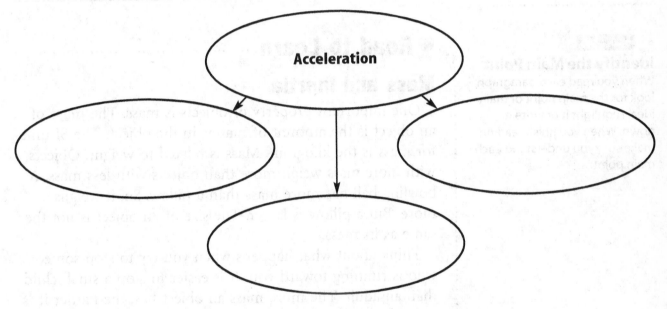

Acceleration

3. Why do you think that slowing down is sometimes called deceleration instead of acceleration?

_____

_____

 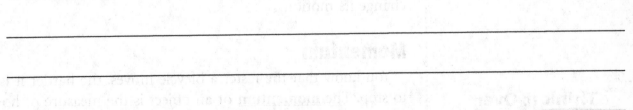 Visit **glencoe.com** to access your textbook, interactive games, and projects to help you learn more about acceleration.

End of Section

section ❸ Momentum

 PS 5.1c An object's motion is the result of the combined effect of all forces acting on the object. A moving object that is not subjected to a force will continue to move at a constant speed in a straight line. An object at rest will remain at rest. **Also covered:** PS 4.5a

What You'll Learn

- how mass and inertia are related
- what momentum is
- to use the law of conservation of momentum to predict motion

Study Coach

Identify the Main Point
When you read each paragraph, look for the main point or main idea. Highlight it or write it down. When you finish reading, make sure you understand each main point.

 **Think it Over**

1. **Determine** Which has more inertia, a soccer ball or a bowling ball?

_____

● Before You Read

What happens if you are riding in a car and the driver slams on the brakes? Explain on the lines below.

_____

_____

● Read to Learn

Mass and Inertia

One important property of objects is mass. The **mass** of an object is the amount of matter in the object. The SI unit for mass is the kilogram. Mass is related to weight. Objects with more mass weigh more than objects with less mass. A bowling ball has more mass than a pillow. So, it weighs more. But a pillow is larger. The size of an object is not the same as its mass.

Think about what happens when you try to stop someone who is running toward you. It is easier to stop a small child than an adult. The more mass an object has, the harder it is to start moving, stop moving, slow down, speed up, or turn. **Inertia** is the tendency of an object to resist a change in its motion. The more inertia an object has, the harder it is to change its motion.

Momentum

You know that the faster a bicycle moves, the harder it is to stop. The **momentum** of an object is the measure of how hard it is to stop the object. It depends on the object's mass and velocity. Momentum is usually symbolized by p.

momentum (in kg · m/s) = **mass** (in kg) × **velocity** (in m/s)

$$p = mv$$

Mass is measured in kilograms. Velocity is measured in meters per second. So, the unit of momentum is kilograms multiplied by meters per second (kg • m/s). Momentum has a direction that is the same as the direction of the velocity.

Conservation of Momentum

When you play billiards, you knock the cue ball into other balls. When a cue ball hits another ball, the motion of both balls changes. The cue ball slows down and may change direction. So its momentum decreases. The other ball starts moving. So its momentum increases.

What happens to lost momentum?

The momentum lost by the cue ball is moved to the other ball. It is gained by the other ball. This means that the total momentum of the two balls was the same just before and just after the collision. This is true for any collision, but only as long as no outside forces like friction act on the objects. The **law of conservation of momentum** states that the total momentum of objects that collide is the same before and after the collision. This is true for the collision of the billiard balls. It is also true for collisions of atoms, cars, football players, or any other matter. ☑

Using Momentum Conservation

Outside forces are almost always acting on objects that are colliding. These are forces like friction and gravity. But sometimes, these forces are very small and can be ignored. Then the law of conservation of mass can be used to predict how the motions of objects will change after a collision.

What happens after objects collide?

There are many ways that collisions can happen. Sometimes the objects that collide will bounce off each other. In another type of collision, objects stick to each other after they collide.

Bounce Off What happens when you knock down bowling pins with a bowling ball? Picture a bowling ball rolling down the alley and hitting some bowling pins. The bowling ball and pins bounce off each other. When the ball hits the pins, some of the ball's momentum is transferred to the pins. The ball slows down and the pins speed up. The speeds change, but the total momentum does not. Momentum is conserved.

2. Use Formulas
Calculate the momentum of a 14-kg bicycle traveling north at 2 m/s. Show all your work.

_____

_____

✔ **Reading Check**

3. **Identify** The law of conservation of momentum affects objects that

a. rotate.
b. turn.
c. collide.
d. roll.

FOLDABLES

C Organize Information
Make the following Foldable to help you organize information about how momentum is transferred and the law of conservation of momentum.

Stick together Suppose you're watching a football game when one player tackles another. The two players collide, but instead of bouncing apart, they stick together. The speeds of both players change, but the total momentum does not. In this type of collision, momentum also is conserved. In both of these types of collisions, you can use the law of conservation of momentum to find the speeds of the objects after they collide.

How do you calculate the momentum of two objects that stick together?

Imagine you are standing still on a pair of skates. You are not moving. Then someone standing in front of you throws you a backpack. You catch the backpack and begin to move backwards. You and the backpack move in the same direction that the backpack was moving before the collision.

You can use the law of conservation of momentum to find your velocity after you catch the backpack. Suppose the backpack has a mass of 2 kg and is tossed at a velocity of 5 m/s. Your mass is 48 kg and you have no velocity because you are standing still. So, your velocity before the collision is 0 m/s.

First, find the total momentum of you and the backpack. Remember, momentum equals mass times velocity.

$$
\begin{aligned}
\text{total momentum} &= \text{your momentum} + \text{backpack momentum} \\
&= (48 \text{ kg} \times 0 \text{ m/s}) + (2 \text{ kg} \times 5 \text{ m/s}) \\
&= 0 \text{ kg} \cdot \text{m/s} + 10 \text{ kg} \cdot \text{m/s} \\
&= 10 \text{ kg} \cdot \text{m/s}
\end{aligned}
$$

The law of conservation of momentum tells you that the total momentum before the collision is the same as the total momentum after the collision. After the collision, the total momentum does not change. You and the backpack have become one object and are moving at the same velocity. You can use the equation for momentum to find the final velocity.

$$
\begin{aligned}
\text{total momentum} &= (\text{mass of backpack} + \text{your mass}) \times \text{velocity} \\
10 \text{ kg} \cdot \text{m/s} &= (2 \text{ kg} + 48 \text{ kg}) \times \text{velocity} \\
10 \text{ kg} \cdot \text{m/s} &= (50 \text{ kg}) \times \text{velocity} \\
\frac{10 \text{ kg} \cdot \text{m/s}}{(50 \text{ kg})} &= \text{velocity} \\
0.2 \text{ m/s} &= \text{velocity}
\end{aligned}
$$

Your velocity right after you catch the backpack is 0.2 m/s.

Think it Over

4. Predict Will the velocity of the student and the backpack together be faster or slower than the velocity of the backpack by itself?

Applying Math

5. Calculate Find the velocity of the student and the backpack if the backpack's mass is 3 kg, it was tossed at a velocity of 4 m/s, and the mass of the student is 57 kg. Show all your work.

Stopping Friction between your skates and the ground will slow you down as you move on your skates. The momentum of you and the backpack will continue to decrease until you stop because of friction.

How can mass predict motion after collisions?

You can use the law of conservation of momentum to predict collisions between two objects. What happens when one marble hits another marble that is at rest? It depends on the masses of the marbles that collide. The figure shows a marble with a smaller mass hitting a marble with a larger mass. The larger marble is at rest. After the collision, the marble with a smaller mass bounces off in the opposite direction. The larger marble moves in the same direction that the small marble was moving.

What if the larger marble hits a smaller marble that is not moving? Both marbles will move in the same direction. But the marble with the smaller mass always moves faster than the marble with the greater mass.

How does bouncing affect momentum?

Two objects can also bounce off of each other. The two marbles in the figure have the same mass and are moving at the same speed. They bounce off each other when they collide. Before the collision, the momentum of each marble was the same but in opposite directions. So the total momentum was zero. That means that the total momentum after the collision has to be zero too. The two marbles must move in opposite directions with the same speed after the collision. Then the total momentum is zero again.

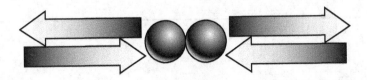

Picture This

6. **Describe** From which marble to which marble was momentum moved?

_____

_____

Applying Math

7. **Analyze** Would the total momentum still be zero if one marble had greater mass than the other marble?

_____

● After You Read

Mini Glossary

inertia: tendency of an object to resist a change in motion.

law of conservation of momentum: states that the total momentum of objects that collide is the same before and after the collision

mass: amount of matter in an object

momentum: the measure of how hard it is to stop an object

1. Review the terms and their definitions in the Mini Glossary. Explain in complete sentences what affects the inertia of an object.

_____

_____

2. The sketch below shows two marbles. The arrows show the size and the direction of the momentum of the two marbles. Draw arrows in the space below that show what will happen to these two marbles because of the law of conservation of momentum when they collide.

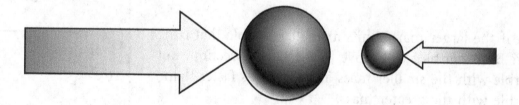

3. How can a football game be used to explain inertia and momentum?

_____

_____

_____

End of Section

 **Science Online** Visit **glencoe.com** to access your textbook, interactive games, and projects to help you learn more about momentum.

230 Motion and Momentum

Force and Newton's Laws

section ❶ Newton's First Law

 PS 5.1c An object's motion is the result of the combined effect of all forces acting on the object. An object at rest will remain at rest. **5.1d** Force is directly related to an object's mass and acceleration. **Also covered:** PS 5.1d

● Before You Read

What do you have to do to move an object like a shopping cart? What causes motion?

_____

_____

What You'll Learn

- the difference between balanced and net forces
- Newton's first law of motion
- how friction affects motion

● Read to Learn

Force

To make a soccer ball move, you kick it. You can pick up a book from your desk. If you hold the book in the air and then let it go, gravity pulls it to the floor. The motion of the soccer ball and the book was changed by something pushing or pulling on each of them.

A **force** is a push or a pull. When you throw a ball, your hand exerts, or puts, a force on the ball. Then, gravity puts another force on the ball. Gravity pulls it to the ground. When the ball hits the ground, the ground exerts a force on the ball to stop it from moving.

Forces can act on objects in different ways. For example, you can pick up a paper clip with a magnet. The magnet puts a force on the paper clip. Or, you can put a force on the paper clip with your hand to pick it up. If you let go of the paper clip, Earth's gravity exerts a force on the paper clip and it falls to the ground.

How can forces be combined?

More than one force can act on an object at the same time. Imagine holding a paper clip near a magnet. You, the magnet, and Earth's gravity are all putting forces on the paper clip. The **net force** is the combination of all forces acting on an object.

Study Coach

Make Flash Cards As you read, write main ideas and vocabulary terms on note cards. When you finish reading, use your flash cards to make sure you understand the main ideas and terms.

FOLDABLES

Ⓐ Compare and Contrast Make the following two-tab Foldable to organize important information about balanced and unbalanced forces.

Balanced Forces

Unbalanced Forces

How does net force determine motion?

When more than one force is acting on an object, the net force determines the motion of the object. If a paper clip near a magnet is not moving, then the net force on the paper clip is zero.

How do forces combine to form the net force? If the forces are in the same direction, they add together. If two forces are in opposite directions, the net force is the difference between the two forces. If one of the forces is greater than the other, the motion of the object is in the direction of the greater force.

What are balanced forces?

Suppose you and a friend push on opposite ends of a wagon. You both push with the same force, and the wagon does not move. Your forces cancel each other because they are equal and in opposite directions. **Balanced forces** are two or more forces acting on an object that cancel each other and do not change the object's motion. The net force is zero if the forces acting on an object are balanced. The figure below shows balanced forces.

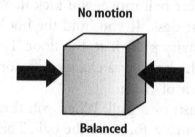

No motion

Balanced

What are unbalanced forces?

Unbalanced forces are forces that don't cancel each other. When unbalanced forces act on an object, the net force is not zero. The net force causes the motion of the object to change. The figure below shows how unbalanced forces change the motion of an object.

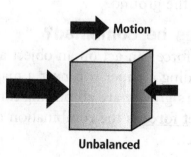

Motion

Unbalanced

Think it Over

1. Infer Imagine two people pushing on a door. One person pushes the door to close it. The other person pushes on the other side of the door to open it. If both people are pushing with the same force, what will happen to the door?

_____

_____

Picture This

2. Identify Look at the box with unbalanced forces. In which direction is the strongest force—to the right or to the left? In which direction is the box moving?

_____

_____

Newton's First Law of Motion

When you stand on a skateboard, you don't move. If someone gives you a push, you and the skateboard move. You and the skateboard were objects at rest until someone pushed you. An object at rest stays at rest unless an unbalanced force acts on it and causes it to move.

If someone pushes you on a skateboard, do you keep going? You probably would roll for a while, even after the person stops pushing you. An object can be moving without a net force acting on it.

One of the first to understand that objects could be moving without a force acting on them was Galileo Galilei. He was an Italian scientist who lived from 1564 to 1642. Galileo's ideas helped Isaac Newton understand motion better. Newton was able to explain the motion of objects in three rules. These rules are called Newton's laws of motion.

Newton's first law of motion describes how an object moves when the net force acting on it is zero. **Newton's first law of motion** states that if the net force acting on an object is zero, the object stays at rest or, if the object is already moving, it continues to move in a straight line with the same, or constant, speed.

Friction

Galileo knew that the motion of an object doesn't change unless an unbalanced force acts on it. So, why does a book stop sliding across a desktop just after you push it? There is a force acting on the sliding book. **Friction** is the force that resists sliding motion between two touching surfaces.

Friction also acts on objects moving through air or water. If two objects are touching each other, friction always will try to keep them from sliding past each other. Friction always will slow an object down.

What is static friction?

Have you ever tried to push something heavy, like a refrigerator or a sofa? At first heavy objects don't move. As you push harder and harder, the object will start to move. When you first push, the friction between the object and the floor is opposite to the force you are putting on it. So, the net force is zero. The object does not move. Static friction is the type of friction that prevents an object from moving when a force is applied.

FOLDABLES

B Classify Make the following table Foldable to help you organize Newton's laws of motion with examples from your own life. Write about Newton's first law as you read this section. You can complete your Foldable as you read Sections 2 and 3.

Force	Example in Your Life
First Law	

Think it Over

3. **Infer** Think about Newton's first law. What would happen to a moving object if there were no friction?

_____

_____

_____

What causes static friction?

Static friction is caused by the attraction between the atoms of two surfaces that are touching each other. This makes the two surfaces stick together. The force of static friction is greater when the object is heavy or if the surfaces are rough.

What is sliding friction?

Static friction keeps an object at rest. Sliding friction slows down an object that slides. If you push a box across a floor, you have to keep pushing to overcome the force of sliding friction. Sliding friction is caused by the roughness of the surfaces that are sliding. A force must be applied to move the rough areas of one surface past the rough areas of the other. Sliding friction slows down the sliding baseball player in the figure.

Picture This

4. Identify Draw an arrow below the sliding baseball player to show the direction of the force due to friction.

What is rolling friction?

Rolling friction is what makes a wheel turn. There is rolling friction between the ground and the part of the wheel touching the ground. Rolling friction keeps the wheel from slipping on the ground. If a wheel is rolling forward, rolling friction exerts a force on the wheel that pushes the wheel forward. ☑

It is usually easier to pull a load on a wagon that has wheels than it is to drag the load along the ground. This is because the rolling friction between the wheels and the ground is less than the sliding friction between the load and the ground.

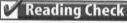

Reading Check

5. Explain If a wheel is rolling forward, what type of friction pushes the wheel forward?

_____

After You Read

Mini Glossary

balanced forces: two or more forces acting on an object that cancel each other and do not change the motion of the object

force: a push or a pull

friction: the force that resists sliding motion between two touching surfaces

net force: the combination of all forces acting on an object

Newton's first law of motion: if the net force acting on an object is zero, the object stays at rest; or, if the object is already moving, it continues to move in a straight line with constant speed

unbalanced forces: forces that don't cancel each other

1. Review the terms and their definitions in the Mini Glossary. When you push a skateboard on a flat surface, why does it stop after a while? Use at least one term in your answer.

_____

_____

2. Complete the table below to show how Newton's first law of motion affects objects at rest and objects that are moving. Name the types of friction that could affect objects at rest and moving objects.

	How is the object affected by Newton's first law?	Which type or types of friction affect it?
Object at rest		
Object in motion		

3. At the beginning of the section, you were asked to make flash cards. Did your flash cards help you learn about Newton's first law? Why or why not?

_____

_____

Science Online Visit **glencoe.com** to access your textbook, interactive games, and projects to help you learn more about Newton's first law of motion.

End of Section

section ❷ Newton's Second Law

 PS 5.1d Force is directly related to an object's mass and acceleration. The greater the force, the greater the change in motion.

What You'll Learn

- Newton's second law of motion
- why the direction of force is important

Mark the Text

Underline As you read, underline the main ideas under each heading. After you finish reading, review the main ideas that you have underlined.

FOLDABLES

B Classify As you read this section, use your table Foldable to write about Newton's second law.

Force	Example in Your Life
First Law	
Second Law	

Before You Read

If someone told you that a car was accelerating, what would that mean to you?

_____

_____

Read to Learn

Force and Acceleration

You know that it takes force to make a heavy shopping cart go faster. You must push harder and harder to make the cart speed up. When the heavy cart is moving, what do you have to do to slow it down? You have to use force to pull on the cart to make it slow down or stop. You also have to use force to turn a cart that is already moving. When the motion of an object changes, the object is accelerating. Speeding up, slowing down, and changing directions are all examples of acceleration.

Newton's second law of motion states that when a force acts on an object, the object accelerates in the direction of the force. You can calculate acceleration by using the equation below.

$$\text{acceleration (in meters/second}^2) = \frac{\text{net force (in newtons)}}{\text{mass (in kilograms)}}$$

$$a = \frac{F_{net}}{m}$$

In this equation, a is acceleration, m is the mass of the object, and F_{net} is the net force. You can multiply both sides of the equation by the mass, and write the equation this way:

$$F_{net} = ma$$

What are the units of force?

Force is measured in newtons (N). The newton is an SI measurement. So, if you are calculating force, the mass must be measured in kilograms (kg). The acceleration must be measured in meters per second squared (m/s^2). One N is equal to $1 \text{ kg} \cdot m/s^2$. ☑

Gravity

One force that you may already know about is gravity. Gravity is the force that pulls you downward when you jump into a pool or coast down a hill on a bike. Gravity also keeps Earth in orbit around the Sun and the Moon in orbit around Earth.

What is gravity?

Gravity is a force that exists between any two objects that have mass. It pulls two objects toward each other. Gravity depends on the mass of the objects and the distance between them. The force of gravity becomes weaker as objects move away from each other or as the mass of objects gets smaller. Large objects like Earth and the Sun have great gravitational forces. Objects with less mass like you or a pencil have weak gravitational forces.

There is a gravitational force between you and the Sun. There is also a gravitational force between you and Earth. Why doesn't the Sun's gravity pull you off of Earth? The gravitational force between you and the Sun is very weak because the Sun is so far away. Only Earth is close enough and massive enough to exert a noticeable gravitational force on you. Earth's gravitational force on you is 1,650 times greater than the Sun's gravitational force on you.

What is weight?

Earth's gravity causes all objects to fall toward Earth with an acceleration of 9.8 m/s^2. You can use the equation of Newton's second law to find the force of Earth's gravity on any object near Earth's surface:

$$F = ma = m \times (9.8 \text{ m/s}^2)$$

__Weight__ is the amount of gravitational force on an object. Your weight on another planet would be different from your weight on Earth. That's because the gravitational force on other planets is different. Other planets have masses different from Earth's. So, your weight would be different on other planets.

✔ **Reading Check**

1. **Explain** What units are used when force is measured?

_____

_____

Applying Math

2. **Calculate** Jamie has a mass of 35 kg. What is her weight on Earth, in newtons? Use the formula for gravitational force. Show your work.

_____

_____

How do weight and mass differ?

Weight and mass are different. Weight is the amount of gravitational force on an object. Your bathroom scale measures how much Earth's gravity pulls you down. Mass is the amount of matter in an object. Gravity doesn't affect the amount of matter in an object. Mass is always the same, even on different planets. A person with a mass of 60 kg has a mass of 60 kg on Earth or on Mars. But, the weight of the person on Earth and Mars would be different, as shown in the table. That's because the force of gravity on each planet is different. ☑

✔ **Reading Check**

3. Use Definitions If you were on Mars instead of on Earth, which would be different—your weight or your mass?

_____

_____

Applying Math

4. Explain By what number do you multiply 588 to get your weight in newtons on Pluto?

_____

_____

Weight of 60-kg Person on Different Planets

Place	Weight in Newtons If Your Mass Were 60 kg	Percent of Your Weight on Earth
Mars	223	38
Earth	588	100
Jupiter	1,388	236
Pluto	4	0.7

Using Newton's Second Law

Newton's second law tells how to calculate the acceleration of an object. You must know the object's mass and the forces acting on the object. Remember that velocity is how fast an object is moving and in what direction. Acceleration tells how velocity changes.

How is speeding up acceleration?

When an object speeds up, it accelerates. Think about a soccer ball sitting on the ground. If you kick the ball, it starts moving. You exert a force on the ball. The ball accelerates only while your foot is in contact with the ball. While something is speeding up, something is pushing or pulling the object in the direction it is moving. The direction of the push or pull is the direction of the force. It is also the direction of the acceleration.

How is slowing down acceleration?

Slowing down also is acceleration. If you wanted to slow down an object, you would have to push or pull it against the direction it is moving.

Suppose you push a book across a tabletop. When you start pushing, the book speeds up. Sliding friction also acts on the book. After you stop pushing, sliding friction makes the book slow down and stop. In the figure, the boy is slowing down because the force exerted by his feet is in the opposite direction of his motion.

Picture This

5. **Label** In the figure, label one arrow "Force due to friction" and the other arrow "Direction of motion."

How do you calculate acceleration?

Calculate acceleration using the equation from Newton's second law of motion. For example, suppose you pull a 10-kg sled with a net force of 5 N. You can find the acceleration as follows:

$$a = \frac{F_{net}}{m} = \frac{5 \text{ N}}{10 \text{ kg}} = 0.5 \text{ m/s}^2$$

The sled keeps accelerating as long as you keep pulling on it. The acceleration does not depend on how fast the sled is moving. It depends only on the net force and the mass of the sled.

Applying Math

6. **Calculate** Suppose you kick a 2-kg ball with a force of 14 N. What is the acceleration of the ball? Show your work.

_____

_____

_____

7. Draw Imagine that you throw a basketball and it goes through a basketball hoop. In the space below, sketch the path that the ball would follow.

[ ]

How do objects turn?

Forces and motion don't always happen in a straight line. If a net force acts at an angle to the direction an object is moving, the object will follow a curved path. Imagine shooting a basketball. When the ball leaves your hands, it doesn't continue to move in a straight line. Instead, it starts to curve downward due to gravity. The curved path of the ball is a combination of its original motion and the downward motion caused by gravity.

Circular Motion

You move in a circle when you ride on a merry-go-round. This motion is called circular motion. In circular motion, your direction of motion is constantly changing. This means you are constantly accelerating. There is a force acting on you the whole time. That's why you have to hold on tightly—to keep the force from causing you to fall off.

Imagine a ball on a string moving in a circle. The string pulls on the ball and keeps it moving in a circle. The force exerted by the string is called centripetal (cen TRIP eh tal) force. The centripetal force points to the center of the circle. Centripetal force is always perpendicular to the motion. The figure shows the direction of motion, centripetal force, and acceleration of a ball traveling in a circle on a string.

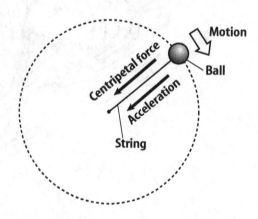

Picture This

8. Evaluate Look at the figure. Suppose the ball was traveling in the opposite direction around the circle. What would be the direction of the centripetal force? Why?

_____

_____

_____

How do satellites stay in orbit?

Satellites are objects that orbit Earth. They go around Earth in nearly circular orbits. The centripetal force acting on a satellite is gravity. But why doesn't a satellite fall to Earth like a baseball? Actually, satellites do fall toward Earth.

When you throw a baseball, its path curves until it hits Earth. If you throw the baseball faster, it goes a little farther before it hits Earth. If you could throw the ball fast enough, its curved path would follow the curve of Earth's surface. The baseball would never hit the ground. It would keep traveling around Earth.

How fast must a satellite travel?

The speed at which a satellite must travel to stay in orbit near Earth's surface is 8 km/s, or about 29,000 km/h. To place satellites into orbit, rockets carry satellites to the proper height. Then the rockets give the satellites a push in a forward direction to get them moving fast enough to orbit around the Earth.

Air Resistance

Have you ever run against the wind? If so, you have felt the force of air resistance. When an object moves through air, there is friction between the object and the air. This friction, or air resistance, slows down the object. Air resistance is a force that gets larger as an object moves faster. Air resistance also depends on the shape of an object. Think about two pieces of paper. One piece is crumpled into a ball and the other piece is flat. The paper that is crumpled into a ball will fall faster than the flat piece of paper falls.

When an object falls it speeds up as gravity pulls it downward. At the same time, the force of air resistance pushing up on the object is increasing as the object moves faster. Finally, the upward force of air resistance becomes large enough to equal the downward force of gravity.

When the air resistance force equals the weight of an object, the net force on the object is zero. Newton's second law explains that the object's acceleration then is zero. Its speed no longer increases. When air resistance balances the force of gravity, the object falls at a constant speed. This constant speed is called the terminal velocity.

Center of Mass

Imagine throwing a stick. The stick spins while it flies through the air. Even though the stick spins, there is one point on the stick, the center of mass, that moves in a smooth path. The **center of mass** is the point in an object that moves as if all the object's mass was concentrated at that point. For a symmetrical object, such as a ball, the center of mass is the center of the object. ☑

9. **Infer** Imagine that you could throw a baseball at a speed of 29,000 km/h. What would happen to the ball if you threw it that fast?

_____

_____

_____

☑ **Reading Check**

10. **Identify** Where is the center of mass of a ball?

_____

_____

After You Read

Mini Glossary

center of mass: the point in an object that moves as if all the object's mass was concentrated at that point

Newton's second law of motion: when a force acts on an object, the object accelerates in the direction of the force

weight: the amount of gravitational force on an object

1. Review the terms and their definitions in the Mini Glossary. What are three ways an object can accelerate? Answer in complete sentences.

   _____

   _____

2. Look at the figures below. For each object, draw and label an arrow to show the direction of the motion. Then draw and label an arrow to show the direction of acceleration.

3. You were asked to underline the main ideas as you read this section, then review what you underlined. Why do you think you were asked to review what you underlined?

   _____

   _____

   _____

End of Section

Science nline Visit **glencoe.com** to access your textbook, interactive games, and projects to help you learn more about Newton's second law of motion.

Force and Newton's Laws

section ❸ Newton's Third Law

 PS 5.1e For every action there is an equal and opposite reaction.

● Before You Read

Imagine stepping out of a canoe onto the shore of a lake. What happens to the canoe when you step out?

_____

_____

● Read to Learn

Action and Reaction

Newton's first two laws of motion explain how the motion of one object changes. You have learned that if balanced forces act on an object, the object will remain at rest or stay in motion with constant velocity. If the forces are unbalanced, the object will accelerate in the direction of the net force.

Another of Newton's laws describes something else that happens when one object exerts a force on another object. When you push on a wall, did you know that the wall also pushes on you? **Newton's third law of motion** states that forces always act in equal but opposite pairs. When you push on a wall, you apply a force to the wall. But, the wall also applies a force equal in strength to you. When one object applies a force on another object, the second object exerts the same size force on the first object.

Why don't action and reaction forces cancel?

The forces that two objects put on each other are called an action-reaction force pair. The forces in a force pair are equal in strength, but opposite in direction. The forces in a force pair don't cancel each other out because they act on different objects. Forces can cancel each other only if they act on the same object.

What You'll Learn

■ about forces that objects exert on each other

Study Coach

Outline As you read the section, create an outline using each heading from the text. Under each heading, write the main points or ideas that you read.

FOLDABLES

❸ **Classify** As you read this section, use your table Foldable to write about Newton's third law.

Force	Example in Your Life
First Law	
Second Law	
Third Law	

Action and Reaction Forces Imagine a bowling ball hitting a bowling pin. The action force from the bowling ball acts on the pin. The pin flies in the direction of the force. The reaction force from the pin acts on the ball. It causes the ball to slow down.

How do action-reaction force pairs work on large and small objects?

When you walk forward, your shoe pushes Earth backward. Earth pushes your shoe forward. So why do you move when Earth does not? Earth has so much mass compared to you that it does not appear to move when you push on it. If you step on a skateboard, the force from your shoe makes the skateboard roll backward. This is because you have more mass than the skateboard. ☑

How do rockets take off?

The launching of a space shuttle is a good example of Newton's third law. When the fuel in the shuttle's engines is ignited, a hot gas is produced. The gas molecules collide with the inside walls of the engines. The walls exert an action force that pushes the gas out of the bottom of the engine. The gas molecules put reaction forces on the walls of the engine. These reaction forces are what push the engine and the rocket forward. The force of the rocket engines is called thrust.

Weightlessness

You may have seen pictures of astronauts floating inside a space shuttle. The astronauts are said to be weightless—as if Earth's gravity were not pulling on them. But, Earth's gravity is what keeps a shuttle in orbit. Newton's laws of motion can explain why the astronauts float as if there weren't any forces acting on them.

How is weight measured?

Think about how you measure your weight. When you stand on a bathroom scale, your weight pushes down on the scale. This causes the scale pointer to show your weight. Newton's third law tells you that the scale pushes back up on you with a force equal to your weight. This force balances the downward pull of gravity on you, as shown in the figure on the left on the next page. ☑

☑ **Reading Check**

1. Describe Why doesn't Earth appear to move when you push down on it with your foot?

_____

_____

_____

☑ **Reading Check**

2. Explain When you stand on a scale, which force balances the downward pull of gravity on you?

_____

_____

_____

How does free fall cause weightlessness?

Imagine standing on a scale in an elevator that is falling, as shown in the figure on the right below. An object is in free fall when the only force acting on it is gravity. The elevator, you, and the scale are all in free fall. In free fall, the scale doesn't push back up on you. That's because the only force acting on you is gravity. According to Newton's third law, you are also not pushing down on the scale. So, the scale pointer stays at zero. You seem to be weightless. However, you are not really weightless. Earth's gravity is still pulling down on you. But, because nothing is pushing up on you, you have no sensation of weight.

3. Explain Why isn't an object in free fall really weightless?

_____

_____

_____

Force exerted by scale

— Weight of student

— Weight of student

Picture This

4. Describe Look at the figure. What is the only force acting on the girl in the elevator on the right?

_____

Why are spacecraft in orbit weightless?

Remember that an object will orbit Earth when its path follows the curve of Earth's surface. Gravity keeps pulling the object down. But, the forward motion keeps it from falling straight downward. Objects that orbit the Earth, like satellites and the space shuttle, are in free fall.

Objects inside the shuttle are also in free fall. This makes the shuttle and everything inside it seem weightless, even though gravity is acting on them.

Suppose an astronaut in the shuttle is holding a ball. When she lets go of the ball, it will not move unless she pushes it. The ball does not move because the ball, the astronaut, and the shuttle are all falling at the same speed. If the astronaut pushes the ball forward, it accelerates to a speed that is faster than the shuttle and astronaut. The ball moves forward inside the shuttle.

● After You Read

Mini Glossary

Newton's third law of motion: forces always act in equal
but opposite pairs

1. Review the term and its definition in the Mini Glossary. What are the action and
reaction forces that make a rocket move forward? Answer in complete sentences.

_____

_____

_____

2. On the figure below, draw arrows and label the action and reaction forces that are on the
objects as the bat hits the baseball.

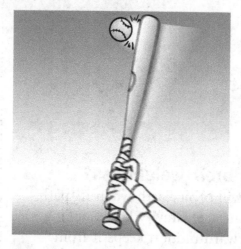

3. How could you use a skateboard to show Newton's third law of motion to a group of
elementary school students?

_____

_____

_____

End of Section

Science nline Visit **glencoe.com** to access your textbook, interactive games,
and projects to help you learn more about Newton's third law
of motion.

Forces and Fluids

section ❶ Pressure

 PS 2.1b As altitude increases, air pressure decreases. **3.1d** Gases assume the shape and volume of a closed container. **3.1e** A liquid has definite volume, but takes the shape of a container. **Also covered:** PS 2.2l, 5.1d

⬤ Before You Read

When people say that they are under a lot of pressure, what do they usually mean?

_____

_____

_____

⬤ Read to Learn

Pressure

Have you ever walked in deep, soft snow? Your feet sink. It can be difficult to walk. The same thing happens when you walk on dry sand. If you ride a bicycle in deep snow or dry sand, the tires would sink even deeper than your feet.

How deep you sink depends on your weight. It also depends on the area over which your weight is spread. When you stand on two feet, your weight is spread out over the area covered by your feet. If you are wearing snowshoes, the snowshoes spread your weight out over a larger area of snow. You do not sink as far. The area of contact between you and the snow changes.

What is pressure?

When you stand on snow, or any surface, your feet and your weight put, or exert, a downward force on the surface. This force is called pressure. **Pressure** is the force that is applied on a surface per unit area. When you put snowshoes on your feet, the force of your weight is spread out over a larger area. This decreases the pressure you put on the snow. When you change the area of contact, you also change the amount of pressure.

What You'll Learn

- what pressure is and how to calculate it
- to model pressure changes in a fluid

Study Coach

Create a Quiz When you read, write down questions that will help you remember the main ideas and vocabulary words. When you finish reading, make the questions into a quiz. See how many of the questions you can answer correctly.

FOLDABLES

Ⓐ Organize Information Make the following four-tab notebook paper Foldable to help you organize information about pressure.

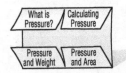

How do you calculate pressure?

What would happen to the pressure exerted by your feet if your weight increased? You would sink deeper into the snow, so pressure also would increase. Pressure increases if the force exerted increases. Pressure also increases if the area of contact decreases. You can calculate pressure using this formula. ☑

$$\text{Pressure (pascals)} = \frac{\text{force (newtons)}}{\text{area (meters squared)}}$$

$$P = \frac{F}{A}$$

The SI unit for pressure is the pascal (Pa). One pascal equals the force of 1 N applied over an area of 1 m^2, or 1 Pa = 1 N/m^2. The weight of a dollar bill lying flat on a table exerts a pressure of about 1 Pa on the table. Since 1 Pa is such a small unit, you often see pressure given in units of kPa, which is 1,000 Pa.

How are pressure and weight related?

To calculate the pressure that is exerted on a surface, you need to know the force and the area over which it is applied. Often, the force is the weight of an object. For example, you might want to know the pressure that is exerted on your hand when you hold a 2-kg book. Remember, 2 kg is the mass of the book. You first need to find the force that the book is exerting on your hand, or its weight. Use the following equation to find the weight of the book.

$$\text{Weight} = \text{mass} \times \text{acceleration due to gravity}$$
$$W = (2 \text{ kg}) \times (9.8 \text{ m/s}^2)$$
$$W = 19.6 \text{ N}$$

Now, suppose that the contact area between the book and your hand is 0.003 m^2. Calculate the pressure exerted on your hand by the book.

$$P = \frac{F}{A}$$
$$P = \frac{(19.6 \text{ N})}{(0.003 \text{ m}^2)}$$
$$P = 6,533 \text{ Pa} = 6.53 \text{ kPa}$$

✔ Reading Check

1. **Explain** What happens to pressure if the area of contact decreases?

_____

_____

Applying Math

2. **Calculate** the pressure exerted on your hand if the book had a mass of 3 kg. Show your work.

_____

_____

_____

_____

How are pressure and area related?

You already know that wearing showshoes will keep you from sinking deeply into snow. Why? Changing the area over which a force is applied changes the pressure. Increasing the area with snowshoes decreases the pressure. The opposite is also true. Think of driving a nail into a piece of wood, as shown in the figure below. The end of the nail is pointed. All of the force of the hammer is exerted on the wood by the tiny area covered by the point. Because the area is so small, the pressure is large. It is so large that the nail pushes the wood fibers apart. This lets the nail go into the wood.

Picture This

3. **Identify** Circle the place on the nail where there is more pressure when a hammer strikes it—on the head or the point of the nail.

Fluids

A **fluid** is any substance that has no definite shape and is able to flow. You probably think of fluids as being liquids, but gases are also fluids. When you are outside on a windy day, you can feel the air flowing around you. Air can flow and has no definite shape. So air is a fluid. Gases, liquids, and plasma are fluids and can flow. Plasma is a state of matter found in the Sun and other stars.

Pressure in a Fluid

Suppose you placed an empty glass on a table. The weight of the glass exerts pressure on the table. If you pour water into the glass, the weight of both the water and the glass exert pressure on the table. So the pressure exerted on the table increases. The water has weight. So it also exerts pressure on the bottom of the glass. The pressure is the weight of the water divided by the area of the bottom of the glass. If you pour more water into the glass, the height of the water increases. The weight also increases, so the pressure exerted by the water increases.

FOLDABLES

B **Compare and Contrast**
Use half-sheets of notebook paper to compare and contrast pressure in fluids and atmospheric pressure.

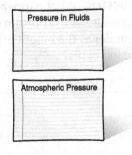

Pressure in Fluids

Atmospheric Pressure

Copyright © Glencoe/McGraw-Hill, a division of The McGraw-Hill Companies, Inc.

Can the same volume have different pressures?

In the figure below, the graduated cylinders both have the same amount of water. Since the cylinder on the right is narrower, the height of the water in it is greater.

Is the pressure the same at the bottom of each cylinder? You know the weight of the water is the same in each cylinder. But the contact area between the water and the bottom of the narrower cylinder is smaller than the contact area at the bottom of the wider cylinder. You already know that when contact area decreases, the pressure increases. So the pressure at the bottom of the narrower cylinder is greater than at the bottom of the wider cylinder.

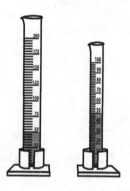

The pressure a fluid exerts on the bottom of a container depends on the height of the fluid. This is always true for any fluid or any container. The greater a fluid's height, the greater the pressure exerted by the fluid. The shape of the container does not matter.

Why does pressure increase with depth?

When you swim, you might feel pressure in your ears when you are underwater. The pressure increases as you swim deeper. The pressure you feel is from the weight of the water above you. As you swim deeper, the height of the water above you increases. When the height of the water increases, so does the weight. The pressure exerted by a fluid increases as the fluid gets deeper. ☑

How is pressure exerted by fluids?

The pressure exerted by a fluid is due to the weight of the fluid. Is the pressure exerted only downward? No. The pressure applied by a fluid on an object is perpendicular to all of the surfaces of the object. So when you dive to the bottom of a swimming pool, the pressure on you is the same on your back as it is on your stomach.

Picture This

4. **Interpret Data** How many milliliters of water are in each graduated cylinder?

_____

_____

5. **Describe** What happens to pressure at the bottom of a cylinder as the height of a fluid increases?

_____

_____

Atmospheric Pressure

You may not feel it, but you are surrounded by a fluid. It is the atmosphere and it exerts pressure on you all the time. The atmosphere at Earth's surface is about 1,000 times less dense than water. But the thickness of the atmosphere is large enough to exert a large pressure on objects at Earth's surface. The atmospheric pressure at sea level is about 100,000 Pa. The weight of Earth's atmosphere exerts about 100,000 N of force over every square meter on Earth. When you sit down, the force pushing down on your body from the atmospheric pressure can be equal to the weight of several small cars. ☑

Why doesn't atmospheric pressure crush you? Your body is filled with fluids such as blood. The pressure exerted outward by the fluids inside your body balances the pressure applied by the atmosphere. Therefore, atmospheric pressure does not crush you.

How does atmospheric pressure change?

When you go higher in the atmosphere, atmospheric pressure decreases as the amount of air above you decreases. The same thing happens in water. Water pressure is highest at the ocean floor and decreases as you go upward.

What is a barometer?

A barometer, like in the figure below, is an instrument used to measure atmospheric pressure. A barometer is made of a tube that is closed at the top and open at the bottom. The space at the top of the tube is a vacuum. Atmospheric pressure pushes liquid up the tube. When the pressure at the bottom of the column of liquid equals the atmospheric pressure, the liquid stops going up the tube. The force pushing on the surface of the liquid changes as the atmospheric pressure changes. So the height of the liquid in the tube increases as the atmospheric pressure increases.

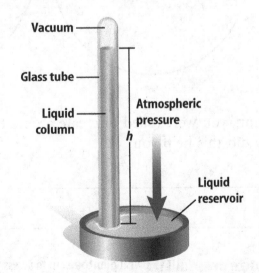

Vacuum

Glass tube

Liquid column

Atmospheric pressure

h

Liquid reservoir

☑ **Reading Check**

6. Identify What surrounds you and constantly exerts pressure on you?

_____

_____

Picture This

7. Apply What happens to the height of the liquid in the tube when atmospheric pressure decreases?

_____

_____

● After You Read

Mini Glossary

fluid: any substance that has no definite shape and is able to flow

pressure: the force that is applied on a surface per unit area

1. Review the terms and their definitions in the Mini Glossary. How does a fluid exert pressure on an object that is in the fluid?

_____

_____

2. Fill in the graphic organizer below to explain pressure, how to calculate pressure, and how the height of a fluid affects pressure.

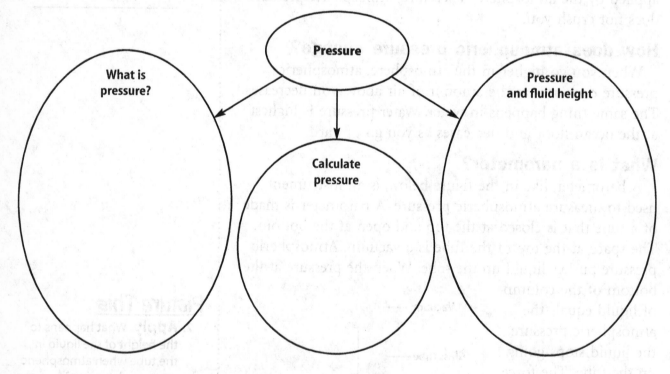

Pressure

What is pressure?

Calculate pressure

Pressure and fluid height

3. At the beginning of the section, you were asked to create a quiz to help you learn the material in the section. How did this help you?

_____

_____

End of Section

Science Online Visit **glencoe.com** to access your textbook, interactive games, and projects to help you learn more about pressure.

252 Forces and Fluids

Forces and Fluids

section ❷ Why do objects float?

 PS 3.1h Density can be described as the amount of matter that is in a given amount of space. **3.1i** Buoyancy is determined by comparative densities. **5.1d** Force is directly related to an object's mass and acceleration. **Also covered:** PS 5.1c

● Before You Read

What happens when you jump into a pool? Describe on the lines below how your body moves through the water.

_____

_____

_____

● Read to Learn

The Buoyant Force

Can you float? Think about the forces that act on you when you float in a pool. You are not moving when you float. So, according to Newton's second law of motion, the forces acting on you must be balanced. You know that Earth's gravity is pulling you downward. So what balances gravity? It is a force called the buoyant force. The **buoyant force** is an upward force that is exerted by a fluid on any object in the fluid. A balance between gravity and the buoyant force is shown in the figure below.

Ryan McVay/PhotoDisc

What You'll Learn

- how the pressure in a fluid makes a buoyant force
- what density is
- to explain floating and sinking using Archimedes' principle.

Mark the Text

Highlight Highlight words or sentences that you do not understand. When you finish reading, ask your teacher to help you understand the things that you highlighted.

Picture This

1. **Identify** Label the arrows in the figure as *Buoyant force* and *Gravity*.

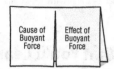
Picture This

2. Explain In the figure, why is the pressure pushing up on the bottom of the cube greater than the pressure pushing down on the top of the cube?

_____

_____

What causes the buoyant force?

The buoyant force is caused by the pressure exerted by a fluid on an object in the fluid. The figure below shows a cube-shaped object in a fluid. The fluid exerts a pressure everywhere on the surface of the cube. Remember that the direction of the pressure on a surface in a fluid is always perpendicular to the surface. Recall also that pressure exerted by a fluid increases as you go deeper into the fluid.

How does pressure affect buoyant force?

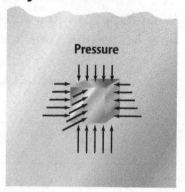

The pressure exerted by the water on the cube in the figure is greater toward the bottom of the cube. This is because the bottom of the cube is deeper in the water. The pressure exerted on the cube from the bottom is greater than the pressure pushing down on the top of the cube. Since these forces are not balanced, there is a net force pushing upward on the cube. This upward force is the buoyant force. A buoyant force acts on all objects that are in a fluid. It does not matter whether the objects float or sink.

Sinking and Floating

When you toss a stone into a pond, it sinks. If you toss a stick into a pond, it floats. A buoyant force acts on both the stone and the stick. Why does one sink and the other float?

Remember, gravity always pulls objects downward. If the weight of an object is greater than the buoyant force pushing upward, the object sinks. If the buoyant force is equal to the weight of an object, it floats.

Changing the Buoyant Force

Whether an object floats or sinks depends on whether the buoyant force is less than its weight. The weight of an object depends only on the mass of the object. Remember, mass is the amount of matter in an object. The weight of an object does not change if its shape changes. Think about a ball of clay. The clay has the same amount of matter whether it is in a ball or pressed flat.

How does shape affect buoyant force?

Buoyant force does depend on the shape of an object. Remember, fluid exerts upward pressure on the entire lower surface of an object that is in contact with the fluid. If the surface is made larger, more upward pressure is exerted on the object. This increases the buoyant force. If a piece of aluminum foil is folded, the buoyant force is less than the weight, so it sinks. If the aluminum is flattened into a thin sheet, the area of the bottom of the aluminum increases. On this piece, the buoyant force is large enough that the sheet floats.

Shape is why large metal ships float. If the metal of a ship were crushed into a cube, it is heavy enough to sink. But ships are made with curved bottoms called hulls. A ship's hull has a large area in contact with the water. This increases the buoyant force enough so the ship floats. ☑

Why doesn't buoyant force change with depth?

You know that the pressure exerted on an object by a fluid increases with depth. You might think that a rock will only sink to a depth where the buoyant force on the rock balances its weight. But this does not happen. As a rock sinks in a pond, the pressure pushing up on the bottom surface does increase. But so does the pressure pushing down on the top surface. The difference between these pressures is always the same. So the buoyant force acting on the rock is always the same, no matter how deep it goes.

Archimedes' Principle

The Greek mathematician Archimedes (ar kuh MEE deez) figured out how to find buoyant force more than 2,200 years ago. **Archimedes' principle** states that the buoyant force on an object is equal to the weight of the fluid it displaces, or moves.

Think about dropping an ice cube in a glass that is full to the top with water. When you drop the ice cube in, it takes the place of some of the water and causes this water to overflow. Suppose you catch the water that spills out of the glass. If you weighed this water, its weight would be equal to the buoyant force on the ice cube. Because the ice cube is floating, you know the buoyant force is balanced by the weight of the ice cube. So the water that is displaced by the ice cube, or the buoyant force, is equal to the weight of the ice cube. ☑

Copyright © Glencoe/McGraw-Hill, a division of The McGraw-Hill Companies, Inc.

☑ **Reading Check**

3. **Explain** why a ship's hull is curved.

_____

_____

_____

☑ **Reading Check**

4. **Describe** According to Archimedes' principle, what is the weight of the displaced fluid equal to?

_____

What is density?

Whether an object floats or sinks depends on the density of the fluid and the density of the object. **<u>Density</u>** is the mass of an object divided by the volume it takes up. You can find density with the following formula:

$$\text{density (in g/cm}^3) = \frac{\text{mass (in g)}}{\text{volume (in cm}^3)}$$

$$D = \frac{m}{V}$$

For example, water has a density of 1.0 g/cm³. If you multiply both sides of the equation above by the volume, you can find the mass for any volume of a substance. This gives you the equation mass = density × volume. If you know the density and volume of a material, you can find its mass.

How does density affect sinking and floating?

Suppose you place a solid plastic block in a container of fluid. Whether the block sinks or floats depends on the density of the plastic and the density of the fluid. Suppose the density of the block is less than the density of the fluid. In this case, the block will float. Now suppose the density of the block is greater than the density of the fluid. In this case, the block will sink.

Boats

Suppose you have a steel boat and a steel cube, like those in the figure. Both have the same mass. The boat is shaped so it takes up a large volume—much larger than the cube. So the boat displaces more water than the cube. The boat displaces so much water that the water it displaces weighs more than the boat. According to Archimedes' principle, increasing the weight of the water that is displaced increases the buoyant force. By making the volume of the boat large enough, enough water can be displaced to balance the weight of the boat. So the boat floats.

The cube and the boat have the same mass, but the boat has a greater volume. So the boat is less dense. The boat floats because its density is less than the density of water.

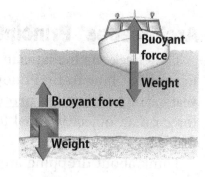

Applying Math

5. **Calculate** What is the density of an object that has a mass of 42 g and a volume of 7 cm³? Show your work.

_____

_____

_____

Picture This

6. **Identify** Circle the object in the figure that is less dense. Explain how you know.

_____

_____

_____

● After You Read

Mini Glossary

Archimedes' principle: the buoyant force on an object is equal to the weight of the fluid it displaces, or moves

buoyant force: an upward force that is exerted by a fluid on any object in the fluid

density: the mass of an object divided by the volume it takes up

1. Review the terms and their definitions in the Mini Glossary. Use the word density in a sentence to explain why an object floats or sinks.

_____

_____

2. Fill in the table below by describing how each concept affects whether objects will float or sink.

Concept	Floating	Sinking
Buoyant force	The buoyant force is greater than the weight of the object.	
Archimedes' principle		The fluid moved weighs less than the object.

3. Why do you think that you go deeper into a pool when you dive than when you do a belly flop?

_____

_____

Science Online Visit **glencoe.com** to access your textbook, interactive games, and projects to help you learn more about why objects float.

End of Section

Reading Essentials **257**

section ❸ Doing Work with Fluids

 PS 5.1d Force is directly related to an object's mass and acceleration. The greater the force, the greater the change in motion. **Also covered:** PS 5.1c

What You'll Learn

- how forces are moved through fluids
- how a hydraulic system increases force
- about Bernoulli's principle

● Before You Read

Have you ever jumped on one side of an air mattress when someone was lying on the other side? On the lines below, explain what happens.

_____

_____

Study Coach

Make Flash Cards Make a flash card for each question heading in this section. On the back of each flash card, write the answer to the question. When you're finished reading, review your flash cards.

Picture This

1. **Identify** Circle the area of the figure where the most force is.

● Read to Learn

Using Fluid Forces

Fluids can be made to exert forces that do work, such as making cars stop, making airplanes fly, and pumping water. How are these forces made by fluids?

What happens when you push on a fluid?

The pressure in a fluid can be increased by pushing on the fluid. The figure shows a container of fluid with a movable cover. The cover is called a piston. If you push down on the piston, the fluid cannot escape around the piston. The fluid does not move because it cannot go anywhere. The force on the bottom of the container is the weight of the fluid plus the downward force on the piston. The force exerted by the fluid at the bottom of the container has increased. The pressure exerted by the fluid also has increased. When you push on the brake pedal of a car, a rod pushes a piston into a fluid, as in the figure.

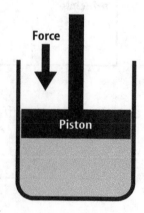

Force

Piston

Pascal's Principle

Have you ever had a drink that comes in a box? You have to poke a hole in the box with a straw to drink the liquid inside. What happens if you squeeze the container? The drink comes squirting out through the straw. When you squeeze the container, you apply a force on the fluid. This increases the pressure in the fluid. The increased pressure pushes the fluid out of the straw.

Suppose you poke the straw in the container on the side instead of the top. Would the liquid still squirt out when you squeeze the container? Yes, it would. When you squeeze, the force you exert on the fluid by squeezing is moved to all parts of the container. This is an example of Pascal's principle. **Pascal's principle** states that when a force is applied to a fluid in a closed container, the pressure in the fluid increases everywhere by the same amount.

Hydraulic Systems

Pascal's principle is used in hydraulic systems like the ones used to lift cars. A **hydraulic system** uses a fluid to increase an input force. The fluid in a hydraulic system transfers pressure from one piston to another.

Pressure Transfer An example of a hydraulic system is shown in the figure below. An input force pushes down on the small piston. This increases the pressure in the fluid. The pressure increase moves through the fluid and acts on the large piston. The force the fluid exerts on the large piston is the pressure in the fluid times the area of the piston. The area of the large piston is greater than the area of the small piston. So the output force exerted on the large piston is greater than the input force exerted on the small piston.

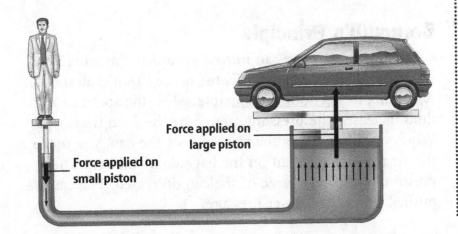

Force applied on large piston

Force applied on small piston

FOLDABLES™

D Organize Information
Make the following Foldable to help you organize information about doing work with fluids.

Pressure in Fluids

Atmospheric Pressure

Picture This

2. **Infer** How would the force on the large piston change if its area decreased?

_____

_____

How do hydraulic systems increase force?

How do you find the amount of force pushing up on the large piston in a hydraulic system? Suppose that the area of the small piston is 1 m² and the area of the large piston is 2 m². If you push on the small piston with a force of 10 N, the increase in pressure at the bottom of the small piston is

$$P = F/A$$
$$= (10 \text{ N})/(1 \text{ m}^2)$$
$$= 10 \text{ Pa}$$

Pascal's principle states that the increase in pressure happens throughout the fluid. This means the pressure exerted by the fluid on the large piston is 10 Pa. The increase in force on the large piston can be found by multiplying both sides of the formula by A.

$$F = P \times A$$
$$= 10 \text{ Pa} \times 2 \text{ m}^2$$
$$= 20 \text{ N}$$

The force pushing on the larger piston is twice as large as the force pushing on the smaller piston. If the area of the large piston increases, the force pushing up on the piston increases. So a small force can lift a very heavy object.

Pressure in a Moving Fluid

What happens to the pressure in a fluid if the fluid is moving? If you place an empty soda can on your desktop and blow to the right of the can, the can moves to the right. It moves toward the moving air. The moving air lowers the air pressure on the right side of the can. This makes the force exerted on the left side of the can by air pressure greater. The can is pushed to the right by this greater pressure.

Bernoulli's Principle

The reason why the can moved toward the moving air was discovered by a Swiss scientist named Daniel Bernoulli. According to **Bernoulli's principle**, when the speed of a fluid increases, the pressure exerted by the fluid decreases. When you blew across the right side of the can, you made the air move faster than on the left side of the can. The pressure on the right side of the can decreased. The can was pushed toward the lower pressure. ☑

Copyright © Glencoe/McGraw-Hill, a division of The McGraw-Hill Companies, Inc.

Applying Math

3. **Calculate** What would be the force pushing on the larger piston if the area of the larger piston was 5 m² instead of 2m²? Show your work.

_____

_____

☑ Reading Check

4. **Describe** According to Bernoulli's principle, what happens to the pressure exerted by a fluid when its speed increases?
   a. The pressure increases.
   b. The pressure decreases.
   c. The pressure stays the same.
   d. The pressure moves objects.

How are chimneys affected by Bernoulli's principle?

Hot air is less dense than cold air. Hot air above a fire is pushed up a chimney by the cooler, denser air in the room. Wind outside increases the rate at which smoke rises. Look at the figure below. Air moving across the top of the chimney decreases the air pressure above the chimney. This follows Bernoulli's principle. The decreased pressure causes more smoke to be pushed up by the higher pressure of the air in the room.

Picture This

5. Identify On the figure, label the areas where the air pressure is low, and where the air pressure is high.

How do high winds cause damage?

Bernoulli's principle also applies to high winds. Hurricanes are storms that cause very high winds. High winds from a hurricane blowing across a house cause the pressure outside of the house to be less than the pressure inside. The difference in pressure between outside and inside can be large enough to cause windows to be pushed out and to shatter. High winds sometimes can blow roofs off of houses. When winds blow across a roof, the pressure above the roof decreases. If the winds are blowing fast enough, the outside pressure can become so low that the higher pressure inside the house can push the roof off of the house. ☑

✔ **Reading Check**

6. Explain What principle explains why high winds can cause windows to blow out and roofs to blow off of houses?

_____

_____

Wings and Flight

Have you ever stuck your hand out the window of a moving car? If so, you have felt a push on your hand from the air moving by. If you angle your hand upward, what happens? You feel your hand being pushed upward. If you angle your hand up even more, the upward push is stronger. Did you know that your hand was behaving like an airplane wing? The force that lifts your hand is made by a fluid—the air. Remember that fluids are liquids, gases, and plasma.

How do wings produce lift?

Air Flow A jet airplane's engine pushes the plane forward through the air. A propeller airplane's engine pulls the plane forward through the air. Air flows over the wings as the plane moves. The wings are tilted upward into the airflow. This is just like your hand that was tilted outside the car window. The figure below shows how the tilt of a wing causes air flowing around the wing's upper and lower surfaces to be directed downward.

Lift Making the air flow downward creates lift. Remember that air is made of molecules. The wing exerts a force on the molecules, pushing them downward. Recall Newton's third law of motion: for every action force there is an equal but opposite reaction force. When the wing exerts a downward action force on the air molecules, the air molecules exert an upward reaction force on the wing. This reaction force pushes the wing upward. This upward force is called lift. ☑

Copyright © Glencoe/McGraw-Hill, a division of The McGraw-Hill Companies, Inc.

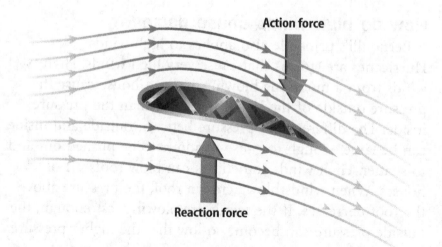

Action force

Reaction force

✔ **Reading Check**

7. Explain what happens when a wing pushes down on air molecules.

_____

_____

_____

_____

Picture This

8. Identify What provides the action force and what provides the reaction force shown in the figure?

_____

_____

_____

Why are there different types of wings?

Not all wings look the same. The wing shape of an airplane depends on how the airplane is used. Lift depends on the amount of air the wing pushes downward and how fast that air is moving. Lift can be increased by increasing the surface area of a wing. A larger wing is able to push more air downward. The amount of lift also depends on how fast the plane moves. Fast planes, such as jet fighters, can have small wings. Large planes, such as cargo planes, that are heavy and fly at slow speeds need large wings with more surface area to provide more lift. ☑

How do bird wings work?

A bird's wing provides lift the same way an airplane's wing does. But birds wings have two functions. Not only do they provide lift, but they also act as propellers. When a bird flaps its wings, they pull the bird forward.

Why do bird wings have different shapes?

Bird wings have different shapes, depending on the way the bird usually flies. Seabirds have long, narrow wings, like the wings of a glider. These wings help seabirds glide long distances. Forest and field birds, like pheasants, have short, rounded wings. These wings help the birds take off quickly. They also allow the birds to make sharp turns. Some birds, like swallows, swifts, and falcons fly at high speeds. These birds have small, narrow, tapered wings. Their wings look somewhat like those of a jet fighter. The figure below shows some examples of different types of bird wings.

Seagull   **Sparrow**   **Swift**

✔ **Reading Check**

9. Describe What happens to lift as the area of a wing increases?

_____

_____

Picture This

10. Identify Which of these birds has wings that are designed for fast flight? How can you tell?

_____

_____

_____

● After You Read

Mini Glossary

Bernoulli's principle: when the speed of a fluid increases, the pressure exerted by the fluid decreases

hydraulic system: uses a fluid to increase an input force

Pascal's principle: when a force is applied to a fluid in a closed container, the pressure in the fluid increases everywhere by the same amount

1. Review the terms and their definitions in the Mini Glossary. Explain which principle allows a hydraulic system to work and how it works.

   _____

   _____

   _____

2. Write the name of the principle that explains each example on the line next to the example.

   a. A roof is blown off of a house in a hurricane. _____

   b. A hydraulic system is used to lift a car. _____

   c. A soda can moves when you blow air past it. _____

   d. Juice squirts out of a plastic bottle when you poke a hole in it

   and squeeze. _____

3. You were asked to make a flash card for each heading as you read the section. How could you use your flashcards to study for a test?

   _____

   _____

   _____

End of Section

 **Science** nline Visit **glencoe.com** to access your textbook, interactive games, and projects to help you learn more about doing work with fluids.

Electricity

section ❶ Electric Charge

 **PS 4.4f** Without touching them, material that has been electrically charged attracts uncharged material, and may either attract or repel other charged material. **Also covered:** PS 3.3a

⬤ Before You Read

You use electricity every day. What would be different in your life if you didn't have electricity?

_____

_____

⬤ Read to Learn

Electricity

To understand electricity, first you must think small—very small. Remember that all solids, liquids, and gases are made of tiny particles called atoms. Atoms are made of even smaller particles called protons, neutrons, and electrons. Look

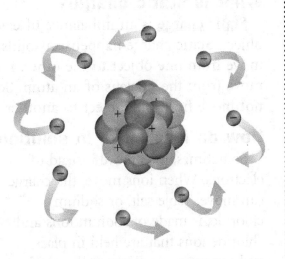

at the figure. Protons and neutrons are held together tightly in the nucleus at the center of an atom. Electrons swarm around the nucleus in all directions. Protons and electrons have electric charge. Neutrons have no electric charge.

What are positive and negative charges?

There are two kinds of electric charge—positive and negative. A proton has a positive charge. An electron has a negative charge. Atoms have an equal number of protons and electrons. So, atoms are electrically neutral. They have no overall electric charge.

What You'll Learn

■ how objects become electrically charged
■ about electric charges
■ about conductors and insulators
■ about electric discharge

Mark the Text

Find the Main Idea As you read, highlight the main idea of each paragraph.

Picture This

1. **Label** Use three different colored highlighters, crayons, or pencils to mark the protons, neutrons, and electrons. Use a different color for each.

2. **Explain** Does an object that is positively charged have more electrons than protons or fewer electrons than protons?

_____

_____

FOLDABLES™

A **Compare and Contrast**
Use two quarter sheets of notebook paper to compare and contrast information about gaining and losing electrons.

Picture This

3. **Describe** Look at the figure. How would you describe the chloride and sodium ions in the water? Circle your answer.

a. tightly held together
b. all the ions are negative
c. spread out evenly
d. all the ions are positive

Ions An atom can gain electrons. When it does, it becomes negatively charged. An atom also can lose electrons and become positively charged. A positively or negatively charged atom is an **ion** (I ahn).

How can electrons move in solids?

Electrons can move from atom to atom. They also can move from object to object. Rubbing is one way that electrons can move. Have you ever had clinging clothes when you took them out of the dryer? If so, you have seen what happens when electrons move from one object to another.

Imagine rubbing a balloon on your hair. The atoms in your hair hold their electrons more loosely than the atoms in the balloon. The electrons from the atoms in your hair move to the atoms on the surface of the balloon. So, your hair loses electrons and becomes positively charged. The balloon gains electrons and becomes negatively charged. Your hair and the balloon become attracted to one another. Your hair stands on end because of the static charge.

What is static charge?

Static charge is an imbalance of electric charge on an object. Static charge happens in solids because electrons move from one object to the other. Protons cannot easily move from the nucleus of an atom. So, protons usually do not move from one object to another.

How do ions move in solutions?

Sometimes, ions move instead of electrons. When ions move, the charge can move. Table salt, or sodium chloride, is made of sodium ions and chloride ions that are held in place and cannot move through the solid. Ions cannot move through solids, but they can move through solutions. Look at the figure. When salt is dissolved in water, the sodium and chloride ions break apart. The ions spread out evenly in the water and form a solution. In the solution, the positive and negative ions are free to move. Solutions that have ions make parts of your body able to communicate with each other. Nerve cells use ions to send signals to other cells. These signals move throughout your body so that you can see, touch, taste, smell, move, and even think.

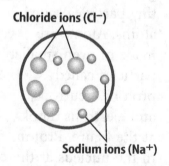

Chloride ions (Cl⁻)

Sodium ions (Na⁺)

Electric Forces

Remember that electrons in an atom swarm around the nucleus. What keeps the electrons close to the nucleus? The positively charged protons in the nucleus exert an attractive electric force on the negatively charged electrons. **Electric force** is the force between charged objects. All charged objects exert an electric force on each other. The electric force can attract or it can repel, or push away.

Look at the figure below. Objects with unlike charges, like positive protons and negative electrons, attract each other. Objects with like charges repel each other. Two positive objects repel each other. Two negative objects repel each other.

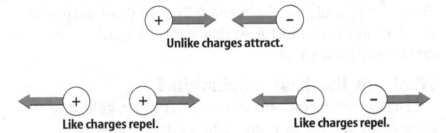

The electric force between two charged objects depends on the distance between them. Electric force also depends on the amount of charge on each object. The electric force between two charges gets stronger as the charges get closer together. As positive and negative charges come closer together, the attraction gets stronger. When two like charges come closer together, they repel each other more strongly. If the amount of charge on at least one object increases, then the electric force between the two objects increases. ☑

What are electric fields?

Charged objects don't have to touch each other to exert an electric force on each other. Imagine two charged balloons. They push each other apart even though they do not touch. Why does this happen?

Every electric charge has a space, or a field, around it. An **electric field** is the space in which charges exert a force on each other. If an object with a positive charge is placed in the electric field of another positive object, the objects repel each other. If an object with a negative charge is placed in the electric field of an object with a positive charge, the objects attract each other. Also the closer the objects are, the stronger the electric fields.

FOLDABLES

● **Contrast** Make the following Foldable to show the differences between like charges and unlike charges.

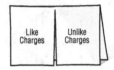

Picture This

4. Apply Circle the part of the figure that shows the force between two electrons.

✔ Reading Check

5. Explain What happens as a positively charged object comes closer to a negatively charged object?

_____

_____

_____

Conductors

Insulators

✔ Reading Check

6. Determine Give an example of each.

Conductor: _____

Insulator: _____

🔆 Think it Over

7. Explain How do the extra electrons get on your hand?

_____

_____

_____

Insulators and Conductors

When you rub a balloon on your hair, the electrons from your hair move to the balloon. But, only the part of the balloon that is rubbed on your hair gains the electrons. Electrons cannot move easily through rubber. So, the electrons that move from your hair to the balloon stay in one place on the balloon. The balloon is an insulator. An **insulator** is a material in which electrons cannot move easily from place to place. Plastic, wood, glass, and rubber are examples of insulators.

A **conductor** is a material in which electrons can move easily from place to place. An electric cable is made from a conductor coated with an insulator, like plastic. The electrons move easily in the conductor (the wire), but do not move easily in the insulator (the plastic). The insulator keeps the electrons in the conductor so that someone touching the cable won't get a shock.

What are the best conductors?

The best conductors are metals, like copper, gold, and aluminum. In a metal atom, some electrons are not attracted as strongly to the nucleus as others. When metal atoms form a solid, the atoms cannot move far. But, the electrons inside the atoms that are not strongly attracted to each nucleus can move easily in a solid piece of metal. Insulators are different. In an insulator, the electrons of an atom are strongly attracted to the nucleus. The electrons in an insulator cannot move easily. ✔

Induced Charge

Have you ever walked on carpet and then touched a doorknob? Maybe you felt an electric shock or saw a spark. Look at the figure on the next page to see what happened.

As you walk, electrons rub off the carpet onto your shoes. The electrons spread over the surface of your skin. As your hand gets near the doorknob, the electric field around the extra electrons on your hand repels the electrons in the doorknob. The doorknob is metal, so it is a good conductor. The electrons on the doorknob move easily away from your hand. The part of the doorknob closest to your hand becomes positively charged. This separation of positive and negative charges because of an electric field is called an induced charge. The word induce means "to cause". You induced, or caused, a positive charge on the doorknob.

A As you walk across the floor, you rub electrons from the carpet onto the bottom of your shoes. These electrons then spread out all over your skin, including your hands.

B As you bring your hand close to the metal doorknob, electrons on the doorknob move as far away from your hand as possible. The part of the doorknob closest to your hand is left with a positive charge.

C The attraction between the electrons on your hand and the induced positive charge on the doorknob might be strong enough to pull electrons from your hand to the doorknob. You might see a spark or feel a mild electric shock.

If the electric field between your hand and the doorknob is strong enough, charge can be pulled quickly from your hand to the doorknob. The quick movement of extra charge from one place to another place is an **electric discharge**. Lightning is an example of an electric discharge. Imagine a storm cloud. The movement of air causes the bottom of the cloud to become negatively charged. The negative charge induces a positive charge on the ground below the cloud. Cloud-to-ground lightning strikes when electric charge moves between the cloud and the ground.

Grounding

Lightning is an electric discharge that can cause damage and hurt people. A lightning bolt releases a large amount of electric energy. Even electric discharges that release small amounts of electric energy can cause damage to electrical objects, like computers. One way to avoid damage caused by electric discharges is to make the extra charges flow into Earth's surface. Earth is a good conductor. Since it is so large, it can absorb, or take in, a large amount of extra charge. You may have seen a lightning rod at the top of a building. The rods are metal and are connected to metal cables. These cables conduct the electric charge into Earth if the rod is struck by lightning. So, the extra charge goes to Earth and the building is protected. ☑

Picture This

8. **Describe** Look at the figure. When do the electrons on the doorknob first begin to move away from your hand? Circle your answer.
   a. when you walk across the floor
   b. when your hand gets close to the doorknob
   c. when you induce a positive charge
   d. when you touch the doorknob

☑ Reading Check

9. **Determine** Is Earth an insulator or conductor?

● After You Read

Mini Glossary

conductor: a material in which electrons can move easily from place to place

electric discharge: the quick movement of extra charge from one place to another place

electric field: the field, or space, in which charges exert a force on each other

electric force: the attraction or repulsion between charged objects

insulator: a material in which electrons cannot move easily from place to place.

ion: a positively or negatively charged atom

static charge: an imbalance of electric charge on an object

1. Read the key terms and definitions in the Mini Glossary above. What would cause the electric force between two objects to increase? Explain.

_____

_____

_____

2. The table below lists the charges of two objects. Use the words *attract* and *repel* to describe the electric force between the objects.

Charges of Two Objects	Electric Force
Positive and positive	
Positive and negative	
Negative and negative	

3. You were asked to highlight the main idea of each paragraph. Did this strategy help you learn about electric charge? Why or why not?

_____

_____

_____

End of Section

Science Online Visit **glencoe.com** to access your textbook, interactive games, and projects to help you learn more about electric charge.

Electricity

section ❷ Electric Current

 **PS 4.4e** Electrical circuits provide a means of transferring electrical energy. **5.2b** Electric currents and magnets can exert a force on each other.
Also covered: PS 4.4d

● Before You Read

You can turn on the light in a room any time you wish. Where does the electricity come from?

_____

_____

Copyright © Glencoe/McGraw-Hill, a division of The McGraw-Hill Companies, Inc.

● Read to Learn

Flow of Charge

Lights, refrigerators, TV's and other things need a steady source of electrical energy that can be controlled. Electric currents are used for steady and controlled electricity. An **electric current** is the flow of electric charge. In solids, the flowing charges are electrons. In liquids, the flowing charges are ions. Remember that ions can be positive or negative. Electric currents are measured in amperes (A). A model of an electric current is flowing water. Water flows downhill because a gravitational force acts on it. Electrons flow because an electric force acts on them.

What is a simple circuit?

The flow of water can create energy. Look at the figure. Water that is pumped high above the ground has potential energy because gravity acts on it. As water falls, it loses potential energy. When the water falls on a waterwheel and turns it, the waterwheel gains kinetic energy. The water flows through a continuous loop. A closed, conducting loop that electric charges flow continuously through is a **circuit**.

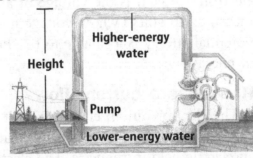

Height

Higher-energy water

Pump

Lower-energy water

What You'll Learn

- about electric currents and voltage
- how batteries make electric currents
- what electrical resistance is

> Study Coach

Outline As you read the section, make an outline using each heading. Under each heading, write the main ideas that you read.

Picture This

1. **Highlight** Use a highlighter to mark the flow of water through the continuous loop.

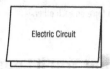

FOLDABLES™

ⓓ Organize Information
Make the following Foldable to write down information about electric circuits.

Electric Circuit

Picture This

2. Identify Circle the source of electric energy in the figure.

3. Identify In a circuit (like the one in the figure above), what increases the electrical potential energy of the electrons?

_____

What are electric circuits?

The simplest electric circuit has a source of electric energy and an electric conductor. In the figure below, the source of electric energy is the battery. The electric conductor is the wire. The wires connect the lightbulb to the battery in a closed path. Electric current flows in the circuit as long as the wires, including the filament wire in the lightbulb, stay connected.

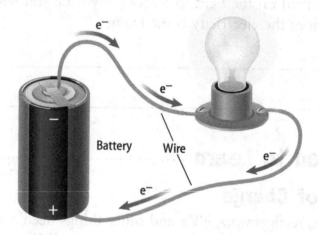

Battery   Wire

What is voltage?

Think of the example of the waterwheel. The pump increases the gravitational potential energy of the water by raising it from a lower level to a higher level. In an electric circuit, the battery increases the electrical potential energy of electrons. This electrical potential energy can be changed into other forms of energy. ☑

The measure of how much electrical potential energy each electron can gain is the **voltage** of a battery. Voltage is measured in volts (V). As voltage increases, more electrical potential energy is available to be changed into other forms of energy.

How does a current flow?

The electrons in an electric circuit move slowly. When the ends of a wire are connected to a battery, the battery makes an electric field in the wire. The electric field forces electrons to move toward the positive end of the battery.

Look at the plus sign on the battery in the figure on the previous page. As electrons move, they bump into other electric charges in the wire. Then, they bounce off in different directions. Electrons start to move again toward the positive end of the battery. An electron can have more than ten trillion of these bumps each second. So, it can take several minutes for an electron to travel even one centimeter.

How do batteries work?

Battery Terminals Batteries have a negative terminal, or end, and a positive terminal. You have learned that the battery in a circuit makes an electric field that forces electrons to move toward the positive terminal of the battery. When the positive and negative terminals of a battery are connected in a circuit, the electric potential energy of electrons in the circuit increases. As electrons move toward the positive terminal, the electric potential energy turns into other forms of energy. This also happens with water. The gravitational potential energy of the water turns into kinetic energy as the water turns the waterwheel.

Electrical Potential Energy The battery changes chemical energy into electric potential energy. In the figure on the previous page, the battery shown is an alkaline battery. Between the positive terminal and negative terminal is a moist paste. Chemical reactions in the moist paste move electrons from the positive terminal to the negative terminal. So, the negative terminal becomes negatively charged and the positive terminal becomes positively charged. This makes the electric field in the circuit that causes the electrons to move away from the negative terminal to the positive terminal. The chemical energy is now electrical potential energy.

How long can batteries last?

Batteries cannot supply energy forever. Do you know what happens if the lights on a car are left on for a long time? The car battery runs down and the car won't start. Why do batteries run down? Batteries have only a certain amount of chemicals in them that react to make chemical energy. As long as the battery is used, these chemical reactions happen. The chemicals change into other compounds. When the chemicals are used up, the chemical reactions stop. The battery is then "dead." ☑

Think it Over

4. **Explain** How does the negative terminal of a battery become negatively charged?

_____

_____

_____

Reading Check

5. **Explain** Why does a battery "die"?

_____

_____

_____

Resistance

Remember that electrons move more easily through conductors than through insulators. But, even in conductors, the flow of electrons can be slowed down. The measure of how difficult it is for electrons to flow through a material is **resistance**. The unit of resistance is the ohm (Ω). Insulators have a higher resistance than conductors.

You learned that, in a circuit, electrons bump into other electric charges. When this happens some of the electrical energy in the electrons turns into thermal energy in the form of heat or light. The amount of electrical energy that turns into heat and light depends on the resistance of the materials in the circuit.

Why are copper wires used in buildings?

The amount of electrical energy that turns into thermal energy increases when the resistance of the wire increases. Copper is one of the best conductors of electric energy. It also has a low resistance. So, less heat is made when an electric current flows through copper wire. Copper wire is used in houses and other buildings because copper wire usually will not become hot enough to cause fires.

How are length and thickness of a wire related to resistance?

A wire can have high or low electric resistance depending on what the wire is made of. The electric resistance of a wire also depends on the wire's length and thickness. The electric resistance of a wire increases as the wire becomes longer. The electric resistance also increases as the wire becomes narrower. ☑

How do lightbulbs work?

Lightbulbs have a tiny wire inside called a filament. The filament wire is so narrow that it has a high resistance. Remember that a material that has high resistance can turn electric energy into thermal energy in the form of heat or light. When electric current flows in the filament, the wire becomes hot enough to make light. Why doesn't the filament melt? The filament is made of tungsten metal. Tungsten has a much higher melting point than most other metals. So, the tungsten metal filament will not melt at the high temperature needed to make light.

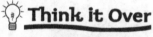

Reading Check

6. Recognize Cause and Effect What increases when a wire is made longer or thinner?

_____

_____

Think it Over

7. Explain Why is tungsten used for lightbulb filaments?

_____

_____

_____

● After You Read

Mini Glossary

circuit: a closed, conducting loop that electric charges flow continuously through

electric current: the flow of electric charge

resistance: the measure of how difficult it is for electrons to flow through a material

voltage: the measure of how much electrical potential energy each electron can gain.

1. Review the terms and their definitions in the Mini Glossary. Write one or two sentences to compare resistance in a conductor and an insulator.

   _____

   _____

2. Complete the graphic organizer to compare and contrast copper wire and tungsten wire using the information below.

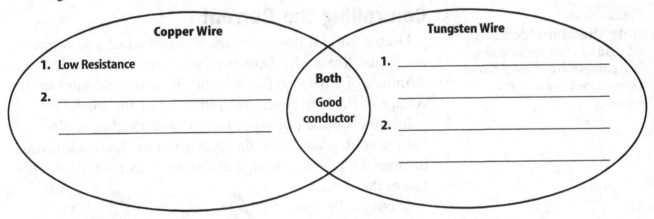

   Copper Wire

   1. Low Resistance

   2. _____

   _____

   Both

   Good conductor

   Tungsten Wire

   1. _____

   _____

   2. _____

   _____

3. At the beginning of the section, you were asked to create an outline of the section. How did the outline help you learn about electric current?

   _____

   _____

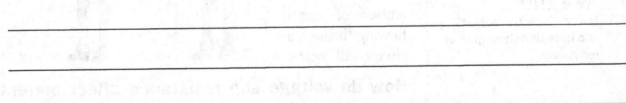 **Science Online** Visit **glencoe.com** to access your textbook, interactive games, and projects to help you learn more about electric current.

End of Section

Electricity

section ❸ Electric Circuits

PS 4.4e Electrical circuits provide a means of transferring electrical energy. **Also covered:** PS 4.4d, 5.2b

What You'll Learn

- how voltage, current, and resistance are related
- about series and parallel circuits
- how to avoid dangerous electric shock

> **Study Coach**
>
> **State the Main Ideas** As you read this section, stop after each paragraph and write down the main idea in your own words.

Picture This

1. **Infer** Circle the bucket and hose that show greater resistance.

● Before You Read

You use circuits every day. Name some circuits you have used.

_____

_____

● Read to Learn

Controlling the Current

Electric current flows through a circuit when you connect a conductor, like a wire, between the positive and negative terminals of a battery. The amount of current depends on the voltage of the battery and the resistance of the conductor.

Imagine a bucket of water with a hose attached in the bottom of it. Look at the figure. If you raise the bucket, you increase the potential energy of the water in the bucket. This causes the water to flow out of the hose faster. This happens with electric current, too. If the amount of voltage increases, the amount of current flowing through a circuit will increase.

How do voltage and resistance affect current?

As the figure shows, the higher the bucket is raised, the more energy the water has. Increasing the voltage in a battery is like increasing the height of the water. The electric current in a circuit increases if the voltage increases. If the resistance in an electric circuit is greater, less current can flow through the circuit.

What is Ohm's law?

In the nineteenth century, a German scientist named Georg Simon Ohm measured how changing the voltage in a circuit affects the current. He found a relationship among voltage, current, and resistance in a circuit, know as Ohm's law. <u>Ohm's law</u> states that when voltage in a circuit increases, the current increases. The equation below shows this relationship.

Voltage (in volts) = **current** (in amperes) × **resistance** (in ohms)

$$V = IR$$

If the voltage in a circuit stays the same, but the resistance changes, the current will change, too. If the resistance increases, the current in the circuit will decrease.

Series and Parallel Circuits

Circuits control the movement of electric current by providing paths for electrons to follow. In order for a current to flow, the circuit must be an unbroken path. Imagine a string of lights with tiny light bulbs. In some strings of lights, if only one bulb is burned out, the whole string of lights won't work. This is an example of a series circuit. Some strings of lights will stay lit no matter how many bulbs burn out. This is an example of a parallel circuit.

What is a series circuit?

A <u>series circuit</u> is a circuit that has only one path for the electric current to follow. Look at the figure. If the path is broken, current cannot flow. The bulbs in the circuit will not light. The path could be broken if a wire comes off or if a bulb burns out. The filament in the lightbulb is also part of the circuit. So, if the filament breaks, then the flow of current stops.

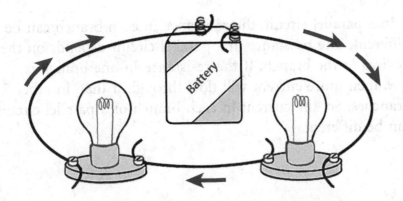

2. Calculate An iron is plugged in a wall socket. The current in the iron is 5 A. The resistance is 20 Ω. What is the voltage provided by the wall socket? Show your work.

_____

_____

_____

FOLDABLES

E Organize Information
Use two half-sheets of notebook paper to write information about series and parallel circuits.

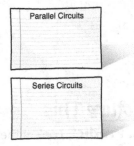

Picture This

3. Predict Look at the figure. What would happen if you remove a wire from one of the lightbulbs?

_____

_____

_____

What happens when resistance increases?

In a series circuit, electrical devices are connected along the same path. So, the current is the same through every device. But, if a new device is added to the circuit, the current will decrease throughout the circuit. Why? Each device has its own electrical resistance. In a series circuit, the total resistance increases as each new device is added. Ohm's law tells us that if resistance increases and the voltage doesn't change, the current will decrease. ☑

What is branched wiring?

What would it be like if all the electrical devices in your house were on a series circuit? You would have to turn on all the appliances in your house just so you could watch TV.

Parallel Circuits Your house, school, and other buildings are wired using parallel circuits. A **parallel circuit** is a circuit that has more than one path for the electric current to follow. The figure shows a parallel circuit. The circuit branches so that the electrons flow through each of the paths. If one of the paths is broken, electrons will still flow through the other paths. So, you can add or remove a device in one branch and the current will still flow.

Parallel Circuit

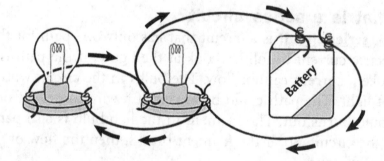

In a parallel circuit, the resistance in each branch can be different. The resistance in a parallel circuit depends on the devices in the branch. If the resistance in one branch is low, then more current will flow through it than in other branches. So, the current in each branch of a parallel circuit can be different.

Copyright © Glencoe/McGraw-Hill, a division of The McGraw-Hill Companies, Inc.

---

4. Recognize Cause and Effect A series circuit has 2 lightbulbs on it. What happens to the resistance if you add another lightbulb to the circuit?

_____

_____

Picture This

5. Predict Look at the figure. What would happen to the lightbulb on the right if you remove the lightbulb on the left?

_____

_____

_____

Protecting Electric Circuits

In a parallel circuit, electric current that flows out of a battery or electric outlet increases as more devices are added to the circuit. As the current through the circuit increases, the wires heat up.

What are fuses and circuit breakers?

If wires get too hot, they can cause a fire. To make sure that wires don't get too hot, the circuits in your house and other buildings have fuses or circuit breakers. Fuses and circuit breakers limit the amount of current in the wiring. If the current becomes greater than 15 A or 20 A, a piece of metal in the fuse melts or a switch in the circuit breaker opens, stopping the current. The device that caused the problem can be removed. Then, the fuse can be replaced or the circuit breaker can be reset.

Electric Power

When you use a toaster or a hair dryer, electrical energy changes into other kinds of energy. The rate, or speed, at which electrical energy is changed into other kinds of energy is **electric power**. In any electric device or electric circuit, the electric power that is used can be found by using the equation below.

Power (in watts) = **current** (in amperes) × **voltage** (in volts)

$$P = IV$$

The electric power is equal to voltage provided to the electrical device multiplied by the current that flows into the device. The SI unit of power is the watt. The table lists the electric power used by some common devices.

Power Used by Common Devices	
Device	**Power (in watts)**
Computer	350
Color TV	200
Stereo	250
Refrigerator	450
Microwave	700–1,500
Hair dryer	1,000

Think it Over

6. Explain What do fuses and circuit breakers do?

_____

_____

_____

Applying Math

7. Calculate A toaster is plugged into a wall outlet. The current in the toaster is 10 A. The voltage of the wall outlet is 110 V. How much power in watts does the toaster use? Show your work.

_____

_____

_____

Applying Math

8. Interpret Data How many more watts does a hair dryer use than a color TV?

_____

How do electric companies measure power?

Power is the amount of energy that is used per second. When you use a hair dryer, the amount of electrical energy you use depends on the power of the hair dryer. It also depends on how long you use it. Suppose you used the hair dryer for 10 minutes today and 5 minutes yesterday. You used twice as much energy today than you did yesterday.

How much does electrical energy cost?

Electric companies make electrical energy and sell it in units of kilowatt-hours. One kilowatt-hour (kWh) is equal to using one kilowatt of power continuously for one hour. This is about the amount of energy needed to light ten 100-W lightbulbs for one hour or just one 100-W lightbulb for 10 hours.

An electric company charges customers for the number of kilowatt-hours they use every month. An electric meter on the outside of each building measures the number of kilowatt-hours used in that building.

Electrical Safety

Electricity can be very dangerous. In 1997, electric shocks killed about 490 people in the United States. Here are some tips that will help prevent electrical accidents.

Preventing Electric Shock
Never use a device with frayed or damaged electric cords.
Unplug appliances before you work on them. For example, if a piece of toast gets stuck in a toaster, unplug the toaster before you take the toast out.
Never use an electric device near water.
Never touch power lines with anything, including a kite string or ladder.
Always pay attention to warning signs and labels.

How do electric shocks happen?

If an electric current enters your body, you feel an electric shock. Your body is like a piece of insulated wire. The fluids inside your body are good conductors of electric current. The electrical resistance of dry skin is much higher than the fluids in your body. Skin insulates the body in the same way that plastic insulates a copper wire. Remember that electrons cannot move easily in an insulator like plastic. Your skin works in the same way. ☑

Copyright © Glencoe/McGraw-Hill, a division of The McGraw-Hill Companies, Inc.

Picture This

9. Infer Why should you not use an electric device near water?

_____

_____

_____

☑ **Reading Check**

10. Identify Is skin a conductor or an insulator?

_____

You actually become part of an electric circuit when current enters your body. The shock you feel can be mild or deadly, depending on the amount of current that flows into your body.

How much is too much?

The amount of current that can light a 60-W lightbulb is about 0.5 A. If this amount of current enters your body, it could be deadly. Even a current as low as 0.001 A can be painful. The table shows what you would feel when a certain amount of electric current flows through your body.

Current's Effects	
Amount of Current (in amperes)	What You Feel
0.0005 A	Tingle
0.001 A	Pain
0.01 A	Can't let go
0.025 A	
0.05 A	Difficult to breathe
0.10 A	
0.25 A	
0.50 A	Heart failure
1.00 A	

Copyright © Glencoe/McGraw-Hill, a division of The McGraw-Hill Companies, Inc.

How do you keep safe from lightning?

Electricity in lightning can be very dangerous. Lightning can harm people, plants, and animals. In the United States, more people are killed every year by lightning than by hurricanes or tornadoes. Most of these lightning deaths happened outdoors. If you are outside and can see lightning or hear thunder, you need to go indoors right away. If you cannot go indoors, you need to take the following steps:

- Stay away from open fields and high places

- Stay away from tall objects like trees, flagpoles, or light towers

- Stay away from objects that conduct current such as water, metal fences, picnic shelters, and bleachers. ☑

Picture This

11. Interpret Data Describe how you would feel if you were shocked by a current of 0.10 A.

_____

_____

_____

✔ Reading Check

12. Explain Why should you stay away from metal fences when you see lightning or hear thunder?

_____

_____

_____

● After You Read

Mini Glossary

electric power: the rate, or speed, at which electrical energy is changed into other kinds of energy

Ohm's law: the relationship among voltage, current, and resistance; when the voltage in a circuit increases, the current increases

parallel circuit: a circuit that has more than one path for the electric current to follow

series circuit: a circuit that has only one path for the electric current to follow

1. Review the terms and their definitions in the Mini Glossary. Explain why it is better to have a parallel circuit in your home than a series circuit.

_____

_____

_____

2. Explain the main ideas of Ohm's law in the cause-and-effect map below. Write *increases* or *decreases* in the blanks.

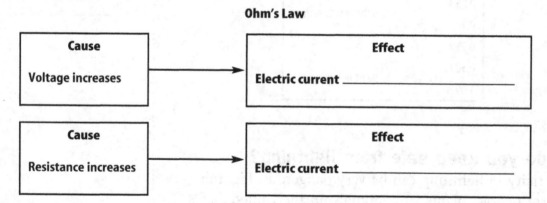

Ohm's Law

Cause		Effect
Voltage increases	→	Electric current _____
Resistance increases	→	Electric current _____

3. You were asked to write the main idea of each paragraph as you read this section. How did you decide which is the main idea for each paragraph?

_____

_____

_____

End of Section

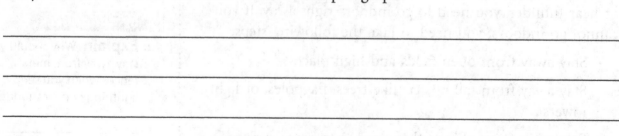

Science Online Visit **glencoe.com** to access your textbook, interactive games, and projects to help you learn more about electric circuits.

Magnetism

section ❶ What is magnetism?

 PS 4.4g Without direct contact, a magnet attracts certain materials and either attracts or repels other magnets. The attractive force of a magnet is greatest at its poles. **Also covered:** PS 5.2b

● Before You Read

Do you have magnets on your refrigerator? Why do magnets stick to a refrigerator and other things?

Copyright © Glencoe/McGraw-Hill, a division of The McGraw-Hill Companies, Inc.

● Read to Learn

Early Uses

Thousands of years ago, people found that a mineral called magnetite attracted other pieces of magnetite. It also attracted bits of iron. When they rubbed small pieces of iron with magnetite, the iron began to act like magnetite. If they let the pieces turn freely, one end pointed north. These might have been the first compasses. Compasses helped sailors and explorers know which direction they were going. Before compasses, sailors and explorers had to look at the Sun and stars to know which direction they were going.

Magnets

A piece of magnetite is a magnet. Magnets attract objects made of iron or steel, like nails and paper clips. Magnets also attract or repel other magnets. To repel means "to push away." Every magnet has two ends. The two ends are called poles. One end is called the north pole. The other end is called the south pole. The figure on the next page shows what happens when you put two magnetic poles together. Two north poles will repel each other. Two south poles also repel each other. But a north pole and a south pole are attracted to each other. ☑

What You'll Learn

■ how magnets behave
■ how the behavior of magnets and magnetic fields are related
■ why some materials are magnetic

◀ **Study Coach**

Create an Outline Use the headings to make an outline of the information in this section.

☑ **Reading Check**

1. **Determine** Do the north poles of two magnets attract or repel each other?

_____

Picture This

2. Highlight Use one color to circle the poles that are attracted to each other. Then use another color to circle the poles that repel each other.

Poles That Repel or Attract

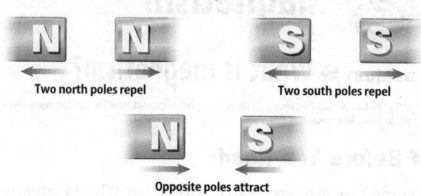

Two north poles repel   **Two south poles repel**

Opposite poles attract

What is a magnetic field?

Remember that a force is a push or a pull that can make an object move. Gravitational and electric forces can act on an object even when objects are not touching. Magnetic force also can act on objects when they are not touching. Notice that the magnets in the figure above are not touching and a magnetic force is acting on them. A magnet can even make an object move without touching it. The magnetic force gets weaker when the magnets move farther apart.

A **magnetic field** is the space around a magnet where the magnetic force is. Magnetic fields are around all magnets. If you sprinkle iron fillings near a magnet, the iron filings will show the magnetic field lines of the magnet. The figure below shows these curved lines. The lines start on one pole and end on the other.

Picture This

3. Highlight Trace the magnetic field lines as they leave the magnet. Which pole of the magnet did you always start at?

_____

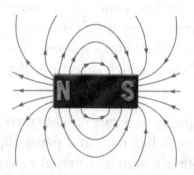

Magnetic field lines begin at a magnet's north pole and end at the south pole. The lines are close together where the field is strong. The lines get farther apart as the field gets weaker. The magnetic field is strongest close to the magnetic poles. It gets weaker farther away from the poles. Field lines that curve toward each other show attraction. Field lines that curve away from each other show repulsion.

How are magnetic fields made?

A moving electric charge produces a magnetic field. All atoms have negatively charged particles called electrons. These electrons spin around the nucleus of an atom. Each electron produces a magnetic field because of how it moves. The electrons in atoms that make up magnets are like even smaller magnets. The magnetic fields of many of the atoms in iron and other materials point in the same direction. A group of atoms with their magnetic fields pointing in the same direction is called a **magnetic domain**. ☑

How can some materials become magnetized?

A material, like iron or steel, that can become magnetized has many magnetic domains. When the material is not magnetized, these magnetic domains point in all directions as shown in the figure below. The material does not act like a magnet. This is because the magnetic fields made by the domains cancel each other out.

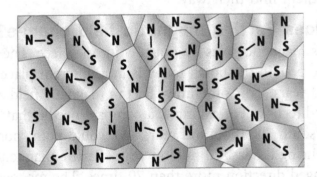

A magnet has a large number of magnetic domains that are lined up and pointing in the same direction. Suppose you hold a strong magnet next to a piece of iron. The magnet causes the magnetic field in many of the magnetic domains in the iron to line up with the magnet's field, as in the figure below. The magnetic fields of the iron's magnetic domains are added together. This magnetizes the iron.

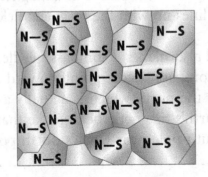 

4. Identify Do the magnetic fields in a magnetic domain all point in the same direction or in different directions?

_____

_____

Picture This

5. Explain How do you know that the material in this picture is not magnetized?

_____

_____

_____

Picture This

6. Label Which pole of the bar magnet on the right should be closest to the figure on the left? Label this pole of the bar magnet N for north or S for south.

Earth's Magnetic Field

Bar magnets are not the only objects that have magnetism. Earth has a magnetic field, too. The space affected by Earth's magnetic field is the **magnetosphere** (mag NEE tuh sfihr). The magnetosphere repels most of the charged particles from the Sun. Earth's magnetic field probably comes from deep within Earth's core. Moving melted iron in the outer core might produce the magnetic field. The shape of Earth's magnetic field is like the magnetic field of a huge bar magnet. ☑

What are magnets found in nature?

Some animals, including honeybees, rainbow trout, and homing pigeons, use magnetism to find their way. They have tiny pieces of magnetite in their bodies. These pieces are so small that they might contain only one magnetic domain. Scientists have shown that some animals use these natural magnets to find Earth's magnetic field. They use Earth's magnetic field and the position of the Sun or stars to help them find their way.

How does Earth's magnetic field change?

Earth's magnetic poles do not stay in one place. The magnetic pole in the north today is in a different place than it was 20 years ago. Sometimes, Earth's magnetic field also changes direction. For example, a compass needle that pointed south 700 thousand years ago would point north today. During the last 20 million years, Earth's magnetic field has changed direction more than 70 times. The magnetism of old rocks shows these changes in the magnetic field. When some kinds of molten rock cool, magnetic domains of iron in the rock line up with Earth's magnetic field. After the rock cools, the domains are frozen in place. So, the old rocks show the direction of Earth's magnetic field as it was long ago.

What is a compass needle?

A compass needle is a small bar magnet. It has a north and a south magnetic pole. When a compass is in a magnetic field, the needle turns until it lines up with the magnetic field line at its location.

Earth's magnetic field also makes a compass needle turn. The north pole of the compass needle points toward Earth's magnetic pole that is in the north which is actually a magnetic south pole. Earth's magnetic field is like that of a bar magnet with the south pole near Earth's north pole.

✔ **Reading Check**

7. Explain How does Earth's magnetosphere protect Earth from charged particles from the Sun?

_____

_____

_____

💡 **Think it Over**

8. Infer If Earth's magnetic field is like a bar magnet, where is the north pole of the bar magnet?

_____

_____

● After You Read

Mini Glossary

magnetic domain: a group of atoms with their magnetic fields pointing in the same direction

magnetic field: the space around a magnet where the magnetic force is

magnetosphere: the space affected by Earth's magnetic field

1. Review the terms and their definitions in the Mini Glossary above. Circle two of the terms. On the lines below, tell how these two terms are related.

_____

_____

_____

2. Complete the flowchart below to describe how the magnetic domains of a paper clip change as it becomes magnetized.

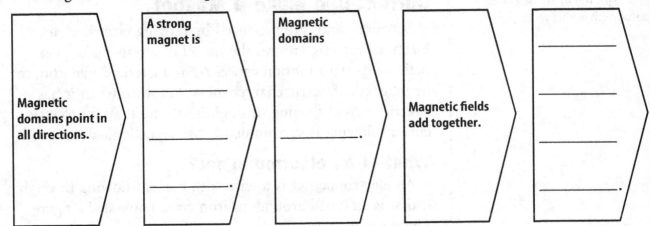

3. You were asked to make an outline of the section. How can you use the outline to help you study for a quiz?

_____

_____

End of Section

Copyright © Glencoe/McGraw-Hill, a division of The McGraw-Hill Companies, Inc.

Magnetism

section 2 Electricity and Magnetism

PS 4.4d Electrical energy can be produced from a variety of energy sources and can be transformed into almost any other form of energy. **4.4f** Without touching them, material that has been electrically charged attracts uncharged material, and may either attract or repel other charged material. **Also covered:** PS 4.4g, 5.2b

What You'll Learn

- how electricity can make motion
- how motion can make electricity

Mark the Text

Identify Main Ideas
Highlight the main idea of each paragraph in this section.

Before You Read

Electricity makes your radio and other things work. Where does electricity come from?

_____

_____

Read to Learn

Current Can Make a Magnet

Magnetic fields are produced by moving electric charges. Electrons moving around the nuclei of atoms make magnetic fields. This motion causes some materials, like iron, to be magnetic. Electric charges move in a wire when it has electric current flowing through it. A wire that has electric current flowing is surrounded by a magnetic field, too.

What is an electromagnet?

An **electromagnet** is a wire with current flowing through it that is wrapped around an iron core. Look at the figure. There is a magnetic field around each coil of wire. The magnetic fields add together to make a stronger magnetic field inside the coil. When the coils are wrapped around an iron core, the magnetic field of the coils makes the iron core magnetic. This makes the magnetic field inside the coils even stronger.

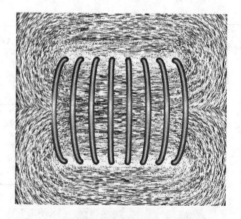

When a wire is wrapped in a coil, the field inside the coil is made stronger.

Picture This

1. **Draw** a line that shows the magnetic field inside the coils.

How do electromagnets work?

When an electric current is turned on, the magnetic field of an electromagnet is turned on. When the electric current is turned off, the magnetic field turns off, too. By changing the current, the strength and direction of the magnetic field of an electromagnet can be changed. This makes electromagnets useful.

How are electromagnets used?

The figure shows a doorbell that uses an electromagnet. When a button is pressed, a switch in a circuit that includes an electromagnet is closed. The magnet attracts an iron bar. There is a hammer attached to the iron bar. The hammer hits the bell. When it hits the bell, it has moved far enough to open the circuit again. The electromagnet loses its magnetic field. A spring pulls the iron bar and hammer back into place. This closes the circuit. This happens again and again as long as the button is pushed.

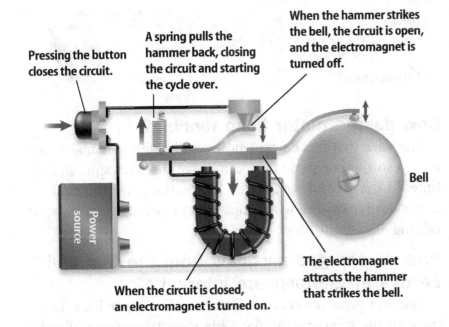

Pressing the button closes the circuit.

A spring pulls the hammer back, closing the circuit and starting the cycle over.

When the hammer strikes the bell, the circuit is open, and the electromagnet is turned off.

Power source

Bell

When the circuit is closed, an electromagnet is turned on.

The electromagnet attracts the hammer that strikes the bell.

Magnets Push and Pull Currents

Think of an electric device that produces motion, like a fan. How does the electric energy going into the fan change into kinetic energy? Remember that wires with electric current flowing through them produce a magnetic field. This magnetic field acts the same way as a magnetic field made by a magnet. Two wires that are carrying current in the same direction can attract each other as if they were two magnets.

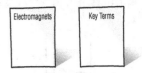

A Identify Terms Use quarter-sheets of paper to write examples of electromagnets and key terms from the chapter.

| Electromagnets | Key Terms |

Picture This

2. Identify Circle the electromagnet in the figure.

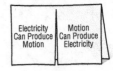

B Organize Information Make the following Foldable to help you organize information about how electricity can produce motion and how motion can produce electricity.

| Electricity Can Produce Motion | Motion Can Produce Electricity |

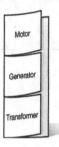
Picture This

3. **Analyze** Look at the figure on the right. What would happen to the loop if there were no current running through it?

What is an electric motor?

Two magnets exert a force on each other. So do two wires that have current flowing through them. The magnetic field around a wire that has current flowing through it causes it to be pushed or pulled by a magnet.

Look at the first part of the figure below. The magnetic field will be pushed or pulled, depending on the direction the current is flowing through the wire. A magnetic field like the one shown will push a current-carrying wire upward. So, some of the electric energy carried by a current is changed into kinetic energy of the moving wire. Any machine that changes electric energy into kinetic energy is a **motor**.

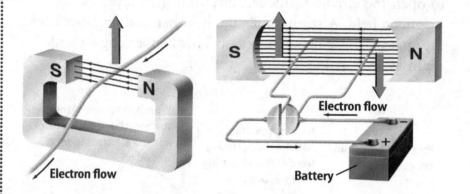

Electron flow

Electron flow

Battery

How does a motor keep running?

The wire that has current flowing through it is made into a loop so the magnetic field can make the wire spin all the time. In the second part of the figure, the magnetic field exerts a force on the wire loop. This causes the loop to spin as long as current flows in the loop.

How do charged particles from the Sun and Earth's magnetosphere interact?

The Sun gives off charged particles. These particles flow through the solar system like a huge electric current. Earth's magnetic field pushes and pulls on the electric current made by the Sun. This is just like how a magnetic field pushes and pulls on a wire that is carrying current. This pushing and pulling causes most of the charged particles from the Sun to be repelled. The charged particles do not hit Earth. This protects living things on Earth from damage that might be caused by the charged particles. The solar current also pushes on Earth's magnetosphere. It stretches the magnetosphere away from the Sun.

What is the aurora?

Sometimes the Sun gives off a great number of charged particles all at once. Earth's magnetosphere repels most of these charges. But some of the particles from the Sun produce other charged particles in Earth's outer atmosphere. These charged particles move along Earth's magnetic field lines. They move toward Earth's magnetic poles. At the poles, they crash into atoms in the atmosphere. These crashes cause the atoms to give off light. The light given off from the Sun's charged particles crashing into atoms in Earth's atmosphere is the **aurora** (uh ROR uh). In northern parts of the world, the aurora is called the northern lights.

Using Magnets to Create Current

In an electric motor, a magnetic field turns electricity into motion. A machine that uses a magnetic field to turn motion into electricity is a **generator.** In a motor, electric energy is changed into kinetic energy. In a generator, kinetic energy is changed into electric energy.

The figures below show how current can be produced in a wire that moves in a magnetic field. As the wire moves, the electrons in the wire also move in the same direction. If a wire is pulled downward through a magnetic field, the electrons in the wire also move downward. This is shown in the figure on the left.

The magnetic field exerts a force on the moving electrons. This force pushes the electrons along the wire in the figure on the right. This produces an electric current.

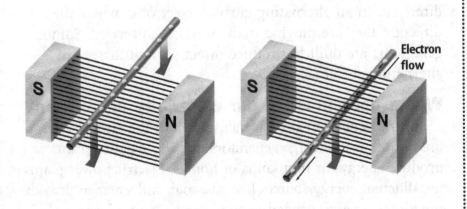

Think it Over

4. Explain Would there be an aurora if Earth's magnetosphere repelled all of the electric charges from the Sun? Why or why not?

_____

_____

_____

Picture This

5. Highlight Arrows In the figure on the right, highlight the arrows that show the direction of electric current flow in the wire.

How does an electric generator work?

To produce electric current, the wire is made into a loop. Look at the figure below. A power source provides the kinetic energy to spin the wire loop. Every time the loop makes a half turn, the current in the loop changes direction. This makes the current change from positive to negative.

A current that changes direction is an **alternating current** (AC). To alternate means to switch back and forth. In the United States, electric currents change from positive to negative to positive 60 times each second.

Picture This

6. Analyze Will the lightbulb be on or off if the wire loop is not spinning?

_____

Electric Generator

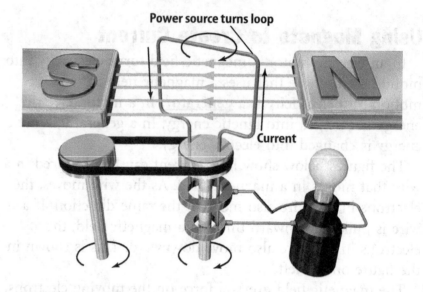

Power source turns loop

Current

What is a direct current?

A battery produces direct current instead of alternating current. In a **direct current** (DC), electrons flow in only one direction. In an alternating current, electrons change the direction they are moving many times each second. Some generators are built to produce direct current instead of alternating current.

Where does most of our electricity come from?

Electric generators produce almost all of the electric energy used in the world. Large generators in electric power plants can produce energy for thousands of homes. Electric power plants use different energy sources like gas, coal, and water to provide the kinetic energy needed to turn the coils of wire in a magnetic field. Coal-burning power plants are the most common. In the United States, coal-burning plants produce more than half of the electric energy made by power plants. ☑

✔ **Reading Check**

7. Describe Where do power plants get kinetic energy?

_____

_____

_____

What voltage do power plants transmit?

Electric energy made in power plants is carried to your home in wires. Remember that voltage is how much energy the electric charges in a current are carrying. Power lines from power plants send out electric energy at a high voltage of about 700,000 V. At a high voltage, less energy is changed into heat in the wires. But, high voltage is not safe to use in homes and businesses. So, the voltage must be reduced. ✔

Changing Voltage

A machine that changes the voltage of an alternating current without losing much energy is a **transformer**. Some transformers increase the voltage before sending out an electric current through the power lines. Other transformers decrease the voltage so the energy can be used in homes and businesses. Transformers also are used in power adaptors. Adaptors are used with devices that can be plugged into a wall outlet or can run on batteries. The adaptor changes the 120 V from the wall outlet to the same voltage that the batteries produce.

A transformer usually has two coils of wire wrapped around an iron core. One wire coil is connected to an alternating current source. The current produces a magnetic field in the iron core, just like in an electromagnet. The magnetic field it produces switches direction because the current is alternating. This alternating magnetic field causes an alternating current in the other wire coil.

How does a transformer change voltage?

A transformer increases or decreases the input voltage depending on the number of coils it has on each side. The number of coils on the output side divided by the number of coils on the input side equals the output voltage divided by the input voltage.

Look at the figure of a transformer. There are three coils on the input side. There are nine coils on the output side. 9 ÷ 3 = 3. The answer 3 can be used to find the output voltage of the transformer. If the voltage going into the transformer is 60 V, the output would be found by multiplying 60 × 3. The output voltage would be 180 V. If the input side has more coils, the transformer decreases the voltage. If the output side has more coils, the transformer increases the voltage.

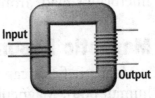

Input

Output

✔ **Reading Check**

8. **Explain** Why are transformers needed to decrease the voltage of electricity before it gets to homes and businesses?

_____

_____

_____

Picture This

9. **Analyze** Is the transformer in the figure increasing or decreasing voltage?

_____

Superconductors

Electric current can flow easily through materials, like metals, that are electrical conductors. But even in conductors there is some resistance to the flow of current. Some of the electric current is changed into heat. This happens when electrons bump into atoms in the material.

A superconductor is a material that has no resistance to the flow of electrons. Superconductors are made when certain materials are cooled to low temperatures. For example, aluminum becomes a superconductor at about −272°C. No electric energy is changed into heat when electric current flows through a superconductor. So, no heat is made.

How does a superconductor affect a magnet?

Superconductors have other properties. For example, a superconductor repels a magnet. When a magnet gets close to a superconductor, the superconductor produces a magnetic field that is opposite to the field of the magnet. The field produced by a superconductor can cause a magnet to float above the superconductor.

How are superconductors used?

Superconductor materials can be used to produce very strong magnetic fields. If you make the wire of an electromagnet from superconductor material, the electromagnet will produce a very strong magnetic field. A particle accelerator is a machine that uses more than 1,000 superconducting electromagnets. A particle accelerator is used to speed up subatomic particles to nearly the speed of light.

Other uses for superconductors are being studied. If power lines were made from superconductors, they could carry electric current over long distances and not change electric energy into heat. Very fast computers could be built with microchips made from superconductor materials. ☑

Magnetic Resonance Imaging

Magnetic fields can be used to look at the inside of the human body. Magnetic resonance imaging, or MRI, uses magnetic fields to make images of the inside of a human body. MRI images can show if tissue is damaged. It also can show if there are tumors growing in the body.

Inside an MRI machine is an electromagnet made of a superconductor. The magnetic field is more than 20,000 times stronger than Earth's magnetic field.

Copyright © Glencoe/McGraw-Hill, a division of The McGraw-Hill Companies, Inc.

Think it Over

10. **Compare and Contrast** How is a superconductor different from a conductor?

_____

_____

Reading Check

11. **Describe** one possible use for superconductors.

_____

_____

_____

How does an MRI make pictures?

About 63 percent of all the atoms in your body are hydrogen atoms. The nucleus of a hydrogen atom is a proton. The proton acts like a tiny magnet. The strong magnetic field inside the MRI tube makes all the hydrogen protons line up in the direction of the magnetic field. Then radio waves are applied to the part of the body being looked at. The protons absorb some of the energy in the radio waves. When this happens, the protons change the direction in which they are lined up.

When the radio waves are turned off, the protons go back to where they were. They line up with the magnetic field again and give off the energy they took in. How much energy they give off depends on the kind of tissue in the body. A computer uses the energy to make an image, like the one below. ☑

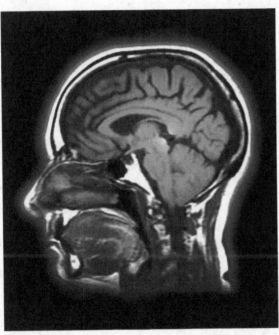

PhotoDisc

How are electric charges and magnets related?

Moving electric charges produce magnetic fields. Magnetic fields exert forces on moving electric charges. Together, these make electric motors and generators work.

Copyright © Glencoe/McGraw-Hill, a division of The McGraw-Hill Companies, Inc.

✔ **Reading Check**

12. Explain What does the computer use to make an MRI image?

_____

_____

_____

Picture This

13. Identify What part of the body is shown in the upper part of the MRI image?

_____

● After You Read

Mini Glossary

alternating current: a current that changes direction

aurora: the light given off from the Sun's charged particles crashing into atoms in Earth's atmosphere

direct current: a current in which electrons flow in only one direction

electromagnet: a wire with current flowing through it that is wrapped around an iron core

generator: a machine that uses a magnetic field to turn motion into electricity

motor: any machine that changes electric energy into kinetic energy

transformer: a machine that changes the voltage of an alternating current without losing much energy

1. Review the terms and their definitions in the Mini Glossary. Describe how a generator and a motor can be used together to make kinetic energy from a magnetic field.

_____

_____

_____

2. Match each machine with the description of what the machine does. Write the letter of each machine in Column 2 on the line in front of the description in Column 1.

Column 1	Column 2
_____ 1. turns motion into electricity	a. particle accelerator
_____ 2. uses magnetic fields to make images of the body	b. generator
_____ 3. moves electricity without making heat	c. motor
_____ 4. speeds up subatomic particles	d. MRI
_____ 5. changes the voltage of an alternating current	e. transformer
_____ 6. makes kinetic energy	f. superconductor

3. You were asked to highlight the main idea of each paragraph. How did you decide what the main ideas were?

_____

_____

_____

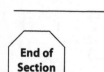

End of Section

Science Online Visit **glencoe.com** to access your textbook, interactive games, and projects to help you learn more about electricity and magnetism.

PERIODIC TABLE OF THE ELEMENTS

Columns of elements are called groups. Elements in the same group have similar chemical properties.

Gas

Liquid

Solid

Synthetic

Element — Hydrogen
Atomic number — 1
Symbol — H
Atomic mass — 1.008

State of matter

The first three symbols tell you the state of matter of the element at room temperature. The fourth symbol identifies elements that are not present in significant amounts on Earth. Useful amounts are made synthetically.

Group	1	2	3	4	5	6	7	8	9
1	Hydrogen 1 **H** 1.008								
2	Lithium 3 **Li** 6.941	Beryllium 4 **Be** 9.012							
3	Sodium 11 **Na** 22.990	Magnesium 12 **Mg** 24.305							
4	Potassium 19 **K** 39.098	Calcium 20 **Ca** 40.078	Scandium 21 **Sc** 44.956	Titanium 22 **Ti** 47.867	Vanadium 23 **V** 50.942	Chromium 24 **Cr** 51.996	Manganese 25 **Mn** 54.938	Iron 26 **Fe** 55.845	Cobalt 27 **Co** 58.933
5	Rubidium 37 **Rb** 85.468	Strontium 38 **Sr** 87.62	Yttrium 39 **Y** 88.906	Zirconium 40 **Zr** 91.224	Niobium 41 **Nb** 92.906	Molybdenum 42 **Mo** 95.94	Technetium 43 **Tc** (98)	Ruthenium 44 **Ru** 101.07	Rhodium 45 **Rh** 102.906
6	Cesium 55 **Cs** 132.905	Barium 56 **Ba** 137.327	Lanthanum 57 **La** 138.906	Hafnium 72 **Hf** 178.49	Tantalum 73 **Ta** 180.948	Tungsten 74 **W** 183.84	Rhenium 75 **Re** 186.207	Osmium 76 **Os** 190.23	Iridium 77 **Ir** 192.217
7	Francium 87 **Fr** (223)	Radium 88 **Ra** (226)	Actinium 89 **Ac** (227)	Rutherfordium 104 **Rf** (261)	Dubnium 105 **Db** (262)	Seaborgium 106 **Sg** (266)	Bohrium 107 **Bh** (264)	Hassium 108 **Hs** (277)	Meitnerium 109 **Mt** (268)

The number in parentheses is the mass number of the longest-lived isotope for that element.

Rows of elements are called periods. Atomic number increases across a period.

The arrow shows where these elements would fit into the periodic table. They are moved to the bottom of the table to save space.

Lanthanide series	Cerium 58 **Ce** 140.116	Praseodymium 59 **Pr** 140.908	Neodymium 60 **Nd** 144.24	Promethium 61 **Pm** (145)	Samarium 62 **Sm** 150.36
Actinide series	Thorium 90 **Th** 232.038	Protactinium 91 **Pa** 231.036	Uranium 92 **U** 238.029	Neptunium 93 **Np** (237)	Plutonium 94 **Pu** (244)